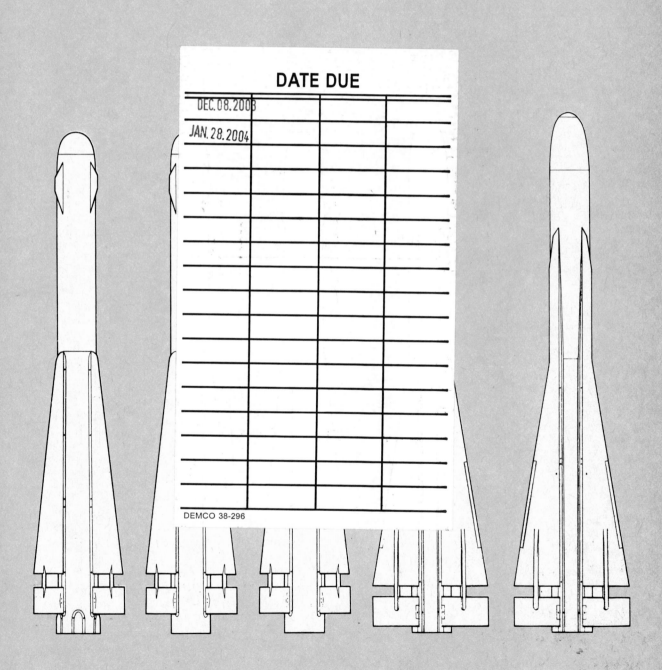

DATE DUE

DEC. 08. 2003			
JAN. 28. 2004			

DEMCO 38-296

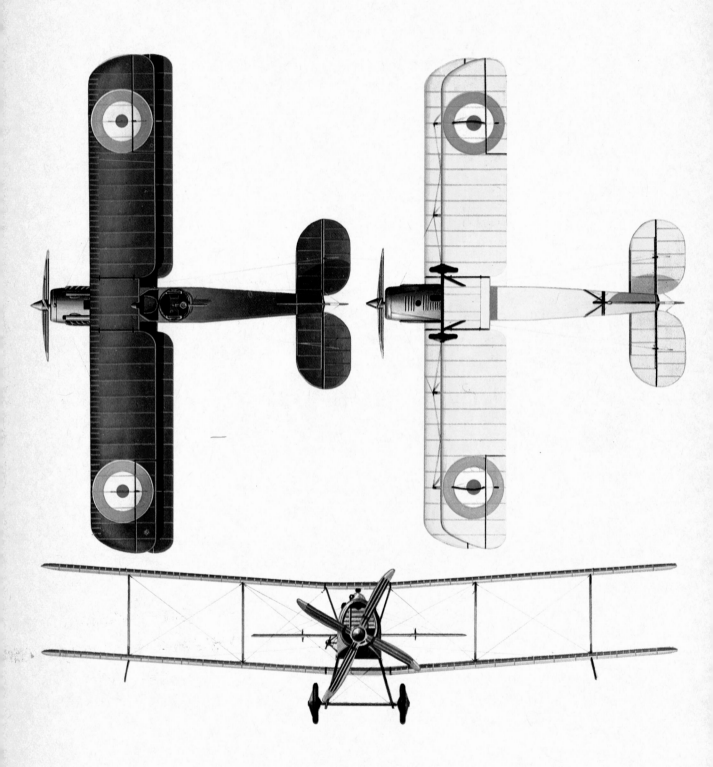

The Illustrated Encyclopedia of 20th Century

WEAPONS AND WARFARE

COLUMBIA HOUSE/New York

Editor: Bernard Fitzsimons
Consultant Editors: Bill Gunston (Aviation)
Ian V. Hogg (Land Weapons)
Antony Preston (Naval)
Deputy Editor: Suzanne Walker
Copy Editor: Michael Maddison
Assistant Editors: Will Fowler, Richard Green,
Corinne Benicka, John
Liebmann, Michael de Luca
Editorial Assistant: Julie Leitch
Art Editor: David Harper
Assistant Art Editor: John Bickerton
Design Assistants: Jeff Gurney, John Voce
Production: Sheila Biddlecombe
Picture Research: Jonathan Moore
Contributors: Chaz Bowyer, Bill Gunston,
Mark Hewish, Ian V. Hogg,
Kenneth Munson,
Antony Preston,
John A. Roberts,
Anthony J. Watts
Illustrator: John Batchelor

Cover Design: Harry W. Fass
Production Manager: Stephen Charkow

"To be prepared for war is one of the most effectual means of preserving peace."—George Washington

INTRODUCTION

The **Felix** heat-seeking glide bomb arrived too late to see action during the Second World War, and by comparison with such modern homing missiles as the **Falcon** series it was an extremely crude weapon. Yet only five years before its appearance it would have been inconceivable as a practical proposition. However, Felix was only one of a vast number of projects initiated under the supervision of the Office of Scientific Research and Development, the organization established in 1941 to oversee and coordinate America's scientific war effort.

This organization was in direct contrast to the haphazard approach of Germany and Japan. In Germany, expectations of a swift and decisive victory using the weapons produced prior to 1945 meant that little research was carried out in the early years of the war, and what there was took place under the control of the armed forces' own research departments. Consequently, there was a great deal of duplication of effort, promising programs were axed and resources poured into hopeless undertakings. In Japan, rivalry between the army and navy, both responsible only to the emperor, and various civilian agencies, whose heads reported to the prime minister, was the main problem. The result was a complete lack of coordination, to the extent that the army and navy used different frequencies for radar identification of their aircraft, which resulted in neither service being able to distinguish between the other's aircraft and hostile machines. The OSRD made sure that such wasteful and unnecessary mistakes were avoided.

Among the fruits of the US scientists' labors were contributions to submarine detection and destruction, the application of radar to almost every conceivable task, an enormous variety of rockets and guided weapons, and the development of such unspectacular but vital pieces of equipment as proximity fuzes and fire control systems. Yet some of their most significant work was done in areas which might be less obviously significant to the war effort—for example, the research on aviation medicine carried out by the CMR.

In the era of such complex and sophisticated aircraft as the General Dynamics **F-111**, operating a bomber like the B-17 **Flying Fortress** would appear to have been a comparatively simple task. Yet even such a primitive aircraft —by today's standards—raised problems.

The B-17G had an operational ceiling of 35,000 ft. But at such altitudes the atmosphere contains too little oxygen to support the human body. The obvious answer is to carry supplies of oxygen. However, every pound of extra weight in the form of oxygen cylinders means a pound less of fuel, or bombs, or ammunition for the defensive machine guns. The solution was a regulator which would add sufficient oxygen to the crew's air supply at high altitudes while conserving it at lower altitudes.

Even then the problem was not solved: a method had to be found of inhaling the correctly mixed air and oxygen. This may appear a simple problem. But no standard mask would ever fit two men in the same way, and a badly fitting mask gave rise to leaks; water vapour tended to freeze in the air passages; a communications microphone had to be incorporated; and the crew members were going to find it difficult to move around inside the bomber while attached by a rubber hose to an oxygen cylinder.

The ultimate answer, and the standard practice in modern high-altitude aircraft, was, of course, pressurization of the whole cabin. In the meantime, though, the Committee on Medical Research went so far as to have facial dimensions of more than 1,000 cadets analyzed by a team of anthropologists, and from these measurements to design five standard types of mask, while other research was carried out into the precise effects of leakage and the findings applied to the design of the masks.

Such attention to detail, and such a thorough approach to the problem, was typical of the efficiency achieved by the OSRD.

The FB-111 has an internal bomb bay capable of carrying two B61 nuclear bombs, but for most missions the eight hardpoints on the wings are used to hang loads such as 24 'iron' bombs in clusters of three with a nominal weight of 226 kg (500 lb) each. The FB-111 can also carry cluster bombs, dispensers, ALQ-119V ECM pods and other stores on the hardpoints

F-111, General Dynamics

US tactical or strategic bomber. During the 1950s, the general development of tactical aircraft moved in the direction of greater performance, at the expense of long field length, high cost and inflexibility. By 1959, USAF Tactical Air Command was ready to plan a new aircraft, in the first instance to replace the F-105, which would combine many new features and offer outstanding capability and versatility. In particular, it would be the first combat aircraft to have a variable-sweep (so-called 'swing wing') aerofoil to match the conflicting needs of high lift at takeoff or landing, low-speed efficiency in subsonic cruise or loiter, and minimum-area minimum-span shape for low-level attack at the highest possible speed.

What caused great difficulty was that, in the first place, the TAC planners set their sights too high in drafting Specific Operational Requirement 183, so that the figures could not be met. Second, the US Navy in 1959 also wanted an important new aircraft, a Fleet Air Defense Fighter, carrying a powerful radar and long-range missiles. In 1960, the new Secretary for Defense, Robert S McNamara, studied the two requirements and, in his words, 'was struck by the high

degree of similarity'. After discussion with his civilian aides, he decided to urge that the USAF and Navy work towards a common aircraft design. His advisors suggested that such a move, called 'commonality', would save a billion dollars.

After the longest and most hard-fought procurement battle in history, General Dynamics Fort Worth won over Boeing-Wichita, the choice being announced on November 24, 1962. There had been an unprecedented four rounds of detailed technical and cost bidding, and in each round the consensus of customer opinion had, it was claimed, favoured Boeing. The Wichita team had not only offered what was in some respects a superior product, but they had consistently quoted a lower price. After Pentagon adjustments, the quotation for research, development and production of a total of 1726 aircraft (231 of them to be of the navy version) by Boeing was $5387 million and that from GD was $5803 million. As soon as the decision was announced, there was a storm of protest in Washington. It grew, as there was a prolonged public enquiry, and the position was later exacerbated by trouble with the winning aircraft and consistent failure to meet the impossible specification.

GD flew the first F-111A on December 21,

1965, and on the second flight operated the wings through the whole range of sweep, from 16° to 72·5°, ahead of schedule. An attempt to win a further bonus by exceeding Mach 1 was thwarted by severe engine compressor stall. The chosen engine, the Pratt & Whitney JTF10A-20, later given the military designation TF30-P-1, had been selected because it was a typically conservative Pratt & Whitney product. It was likely to deliver the modest specified performance—maximum thrust with full afterburner was only 8390 kg (18 500 lb)—and give little trouble. It was the world's first afterburning turbofan, calculated to combine high performance in the supersonic dash mode with excellent fuel economy in the subsonic cruise regime. The new feature of afterburning in both the core and fan streams gave little difficulty, but the installed powerplant was a disaster. Part of the problem was that, to save weight, General Dynamics had cut the inlet ducts back under the wings, and turbulent air was hitting the aerodynamically tricky compressor. It took considerable redesign of the engine and a total redesign of the inlet system, with a so-called triple flow 3 inlet, before the installation would work properly in all flight regimes.

Further extremely severe trouble was met with aircraft weight and drag, so that at first

The General Dynamics/Convair FB-111 variable geometry bomber. Dogged by development troubles this futuristic design had wings which could be adjusted according to the bomber's attack role. In a high speed run the wings were folded back against the fuselage, while for strategic high-altitude attacks they could be aligned for maximum lift

General Dynamics

F-111, General Dynamics

the specified range was not even approached. During 1965-66, using 18 development aircraft, the Fort Worth team restored some of the lost range by increasing the internal fuel capacity. This naturally raised the gross weight sharply, and accentuated the already marginally acceptable large size and weight of the F-111B Navy fighter version, co-producer of which was Grumman. After years of heartbreaking toil the F-111B came to an end in 1968 simply by the refusal of Congress to vote any further funds.

This removed the captivating goal of commonality, leaving the F-111A not quite the way it would have been designed for the USAF alone. A further fundamental point is that, partly owing to confusion over the concept of a 'fighter', the F-111 had been planned to replace all the tactical aircraft of the USAF, including fighters, and attack bombers and fighters of the navy. In fact, the resulting aircraft was in no way a fighter, though with different radar and missiles it might have been a long-range intercepter. It had neither the capability nor equipment for close air combat, and though it had been given an internal gun, a 20-mm (0.79-in) M61 Vulcan, with its ammunition drum occupying the internal weapon bay instead of bombs, this gun had no air-combat role and was removed from most of the delivered aircraft. The F-111A was instead a bomber, and by far the most lethal and useful tactical bomber in the world. Had this been understood from the start, there would have been no fruitless search for commonality, many millions of dollars would have been saved, and the USAF would have received a better aircraft about two years sooner.

Though the internal bay had been included to carry two B61 nuclear bombs at supersonic speed in a low-level or high-altitude attack, the main weapon load has always been hung externally. There are eight hardpoints on the wings, and all are on the swinging part; curiously, there are no pylons on the fixed gloves or fuselage. The outer pylons are seldom fitted, and a normal weapon load is 24 bombs (eight triplets) of a nominal 226 kg (500 lb) on the four inners, a true weight of 6314 kg (13 920 lb). The F-111A can also carry a wide range of cluster bombs, dispensers, ALQ-119V ECM pods and other stores. Guided missiles are usually reserved for the other, less-accurate aircraft. In Thailand an

F-111A pilot, asked if he carried smart (laser-guided) bombs, replied: "No, but we've got smart aircraft."

This is precisely true. The F-111A was the first tactical aircraft to go into service with blind first-pass strike capability, which means the ability to hit a target accurately in any weather, without seeing it, in a single full-throttle run straight overhead. The equipment needed includes a large multi-mode nose radar (in most versions, by General Electric), with two small dishes serving a terrain-following radar (TFR). The latter feeds via the autopilot to the powered flight-control system to enable the F-111, when so instructed, to adopt a terrain-following mode at any selected height above ground (above a safe minimum) and with soft, medium or hard ride, selected by the pilot. In the most dangerous environment of radars and SAMs the choice would be hard ride at the lowest altitude, generally 61 m (200 ft). The pilot sits on the left and has no view to the rear or right side. The right-seater is an observer or weapons-system officer, with comprehensive navigation and radar displays, and in the terrain-following mode it is his job to keep the pilot constantly informed about obstructions or other objects coming up ahead.

The F-111A entered service with the 4881 Tactical Fighter Squadron at Nellis AFB in July 1967, for intensive-trials evaluation. Even at that time no two aircraft were exactly alike, but the F-111A was so much better than earlier TAC equipment that it soon won the affection and respect of air and ground crews, and the required 30 hours' flying per aircraft per month was doubled. With four tandem-triplets of bombs, the maximum speed proved to be about 925 km/h (575 mph) at typical attack height; with two bombs in the weapon bay and nothing external it was Mach 1·1, roughly according with SOR-183. At height the attainable speed in the clean condition was about Mach 2, but the One-Eleven, as it is called, hardly ever goes there except for long-range subsonic cruise. Ferry range with six 2271-litre (500 Imperial gallons) drop tanks is about 6400 km (3980 miles). Lightly loaded a 1000-m (3280-ft) strip can be used for takeoff, but—contrary to the spirit of SOR-183, and the obvious needs of modern tac-air operations—virtually all F-111 missions have been from long paved runways.

GD delivered 141 of the A-model with TF30-3 engines, including two YF-111A aircraft rebuilt from a cancelled British order for 50 F-111K. The Royal Australian Air Force bought 24 F-111C with long-span wings and stronger landing gears, these suffering a nine-year delay due to structural problems and contract uncertainties. The F-111D, of which 96 were built, has the slightly more powerful 8891-kg (19 600-lb) TF30-9 engine and the totally different 'Mk II' avionics, with mainly solid-state digital circuits. This advanced avionic fit was late and costly. The F-111E (94) had only improved engine inlets, otherwise resembling an A. The final F-111F version (106) has the vastly improved TF30-100 engine, rated at 11 385-kg (25 100-lb) thrust, and a simpler and cheaper version of the F-111D avionics. In 1967 some $118 million was spent in the development of a multi-sensor reconnaissance pallet which was test-flown in the eleventh F-111A. It included a computer and promised to result in the most effective tac-recon aircraft in the world. Nothing more was heard of it, though there remains an intention to rebuild some or all D-models as RF-111Ds. Since 1976 the RAAF has been paying significant sums to buy a reconnaissance capability for four of its 22 surviving aircraft. The present users of these tactical versions are: A, 366 TFW, Mountain Home AFB, and 57 FWW, McClellan AFB; C, RAAF 1 and 6 Sqn, Amberley; D, 27 TFW, Cannon AFB; E, 20 TFW, RAF Upper Heyford; F, 48 TFW, RAF Lakenheath.

Since 1976 much further development has been in progress to update this vital and powerful tactical attack force. Grumman has been developing the EF-111A electronic-warfare aircraft by transferring the ALQ-99 tac-jamming system of the EA-6B Prowler to rebuilt F-111A airframes. Results are encouraging, and there is an expectation that 40 aircraft will be thus converted and put into the inventory. Unlike the EA-6B, the EF-111A remains a two-seater, and has advanced computers and displays to enable one operator to manage the system. The Pave Tack pod with laser designator/ranger and FLIR (forward-looking infrared) is being flown on an F-111F and is likely to be fitted to all E and F models, enabling them to launch various Mavericks and other homing weapons. Several ECM pods, including ALQ-131, are being issued to the F-111D, E

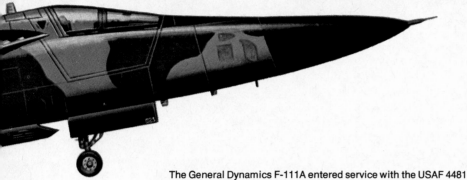

would have a longer fuselage, much greater fuel capacity, long and redesigned inlets and ducts feeding two GE F101 (B-1 type) engines in the 13 600 kg (29 980 lb) thrust class, and markedly improved capability in all respects. New tandem-wheel landing gears would leave the belly free for six SRAM pylons; more could be carried under the wings and on a new four-round SRAM launcher or five B61 bombs in the larger bomb bay.

Span: 72.5° sweep (A, D, E, F) 9.74 m (31 ft 11½ in); (C, FB) 10.34 m (33 ft 11 in); 16° sweep (A, D, E, F) 19.2 m (63 ft); (C, FB) 21.34 m (70 ft) *Length:* (with probe) 23.1 m (75 ft 9½ in) *Gross weight:* (A, D and E) 41 958 kg (92 500 lb); (C) 51 846 kg (114 300 lb); (F) 45 360 kg (100 000 lb); (FB after in-flight refuelling) 55 747 kg (122 900 lb) *Maximum speed:* (Sea level, clean, most versions) 1346 km/h (836 mph, Mach 1.1); (high altitude, clean) 2335 km/h (1450 mph, Mach 2.2) (F-111F, about Mach 2.5)

F 221 and F 222, Farman

French heavy bomber aircraft. In May 1929, the Service Technique Aéronautique issued a requirement for a BN5 aircraft (Bombardement de Nuit, 5-seat) to replace the ageing LeO 20 series then in service with the Aviation Militaire. The result was the rather ugly prototype Farman 220-01, which flew for the first time on May 26, 1932. It was powered by four Hispano-Suiza 12-Lbr, V-type engines, mounted in tandem pairs in nacelles beneath the wings, each pair driving one

The General Dynamics F-111A entered service with the USAF 4481 Tactical Fighter Squadron at Nellis AFB in July 1967. It proved a popular aircraft with flight and weapon responsibilities divided between a pilot who sits on the left and a weapons-system officer who sits on the right. The weapons officer controls the navigation and radar displays which facilitate contour flying and the delivery of an accurate first-pass attack

and (in part) A force, while the F has the internal ALQ-137.

In 1965 McNamara, before leaving the Pentagon, announced that 210 strategic bomber versions designated FB-111A would be bought to replace Strategic Air Command's B-58 and older B-52 bombers. Increased costs caused the eventual force to be terminated at only 76, and these equip two small (30-aircraft) wings, styled Bomb Wing (Medium), the 380th at Plattsburgh and 509th at Pease. The FB-111A has a modest engine, the 9230 kg (20 350 lb) TF30-7, a so-called 'Mk 2B' avionics system, and the long-span wing and strong landing gear. It can carry a theoretical bombload of 50 free-fall bombs of

nominal 340 kg (750 lb), actually weighing a total of 18 710 kg (41 250 lb), but the usual load is four SRAM missiles, which can be individually targeted; sometimes two more are carried in the internal bay, but this is usually occupied by an extra fuel tank.

When the B-1 was cancelled in 1977, General Dynamics published one of the 'stretched' FB-111 versions which they had been discussing with SAC since 1974. While the B-1 lived, SAC scorned these still rather limited aircraft, but the situation today is so serious that money may be found to build at least some flight development aircraft. Designated FB-111H (a stupid designation, B-2 would be logical), these proposed aircraft

An F-111A with its wings deployed for maximum lift. This arrangement can be used at takeoff, during high-altitude flight or during low-speed runs

F221 and F222, Farman

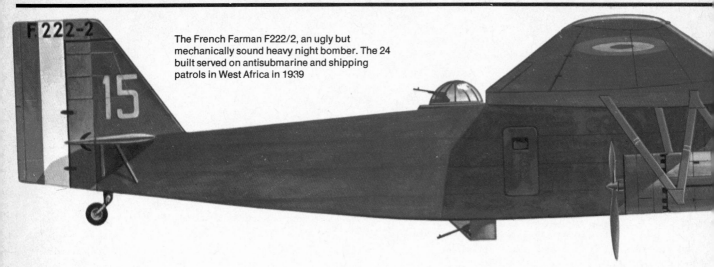

The French Farman F222/2, an ugly but mechanically sound heavy night bomber. The 24 built served on antisubmarine and shipping patrols in West Africa in 1939

tractor and one pusher three-blade propeller.

This prototype later flew for many years as F-ANLG Centaure with Air France on air mail services to South America. In the summer of 1933, a second bomber prototype, the F221-01, was flown with 800-hp Gnome-Rhône 14K radial engines and a more extensively-glazed nose—permitting a better field of view for the pilots. The number of crew members in the F221 was increased to seven. Ten examples of the F221 were built at Billancourt from 1934. On June 16 of that year, the prototype set up a new international payload-to-height record by lifting 5000 kg (11 025 lb) to an altitude of 7000 m (22 970 ft). The first five production F221s were delivered to the 15e Escadre de Bombardement

of the Armée de l'Air (as the Aviation Militaire had by then been retitled) in April 1936.

Meanwhile, the prototype F221-01 had been further developed, with a main undercarriage that retracted forward into redesigned engine nacelles (the F221 had a non-retractable gear). Thus modified, it became the F222-01, prototype for a new BN5 bomber. Eleven production F222s were ordered initially, designated F222/1; seven were delivered in April 1937 to GB I/15, and the other four to the 4e Escadre at Tong, French Indo-China. Improvement of the basic design continued, and the F222/2 appeared with a lengthened and redesigned nose section, dihedral on the outer wing

panels, and the step beneath the bomb-aimer's position removed. Of the production order for 24 of this type, the first eight (with Gnome-Rhône 14-Kirs engines) were manufactured by Farman factories and the other 16 by the SNCA du Centre, the new organization formed in 1937 by the amalgamation of the Farman and Hanriot companies under the French nationalization programme. These latter aircraft had 860-hp Gnome-Rhône 14N 11/15 powerplants, and the first official trials began in November 1937. The aircraft were of all-metal construction, with a rectangular-section fuselage. A manually-operated turret, fitted with a single 7.5-mm (0.29-in) MAC 1934 machine-gun, was positioned in the extreme nose, and single guns of the same calibre were installed in the manually-operated dorsal turret and in a ventral housing. The bomb bay, in the undersides of the wings, comprised four compartments for up to 4200 kg (9260 lb) of bombs of varying sizes.

About two dozen Farman 221s and 222s remained in service in September 1939. During the early stages of the Second World War, they flew on antisubmarine and shipping patrols along the West African coast. Night sorties were made to Germany and Czechoslovakia in late 1939, but mainly on reconnaissance or leaflet-dropping missions. Two were allocated to the Aéronavale for maritime reconnaissance in November 1939, and were subsequently transferred with their unit to Casablanca in January 1940. Fitted with two 1000-litre (220-Imperial gallons) auxiliary fuel tanks occupying half of the bomb bay, they were used for Atlantic patrol duties. On May 14, 1940, Groupement 15 utilized F222s on night bombing raids over the Rhine, Württemburg and Bavaria; this unit moved to North Africa a month later.

The Vichy authorities disbanded most Groupes de Bombardement after the French armistice in 1940, but F221s and 222s formed part of a transport and communications unit which was based in Morocco in late 1942. Although Allied attacks destroyed many aircraft, operations continued in the Mediterranean and North Africa and the type was still in use as late as January 1944, but by September of that year the few survivors had been withdrawn from service and scrapped.

Above: A French Farman F222 heavy bomber. *Below:* The Farman F223, successor to the F222. It was the last bomber designed by Farman before it was nationalized and became SNCAC

(F 222/2) *Span:* 36 m (118 ft 1¼ in) *Length:* 21.45 m (70 ft 4½ in) *Gross weight:* 18 700 kg (41 230 lb) *Maximum speed:* 325 km/h (202 mph)

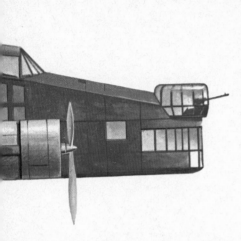

Fabrica de Avione Romanian aircraft
See **S.E.T. XV**

Fagot, Mikoyan MiG-15

Soviet jet fighter. The MiG-15 is one of the classic jet fighters, more than 15000 having been built in four countries. The type caused consternation among the United Nations forces when it made its combat debut over Korea in November 1950, although it had already been in service for more than two years. The MiG-15 was developed to meet a requirement, formulated in March 1946, for a high-altitude clear-weather bomber intercepter which could double as a close-support fighter. The Mikoyan/Gurevich, Lavochkin and Yakovlev design bureaux competed for the production contract, striving to meet the specification of a Mach 0.9 top speed, high rate of climb to 10000 m (32800 ft), good manoeuvrability at this height and above, a minimum of one hour's duration and cannon armament, combined with simplicity of design and operation.

The need for a near-sonic speed demanded the adoption of wing sweep, and the design team was able to draw on the expertise of Gurevich himself, in addition to other work carried out by Russian and German engineers. A swept-forward wing layout was examined but discarded in favour of the sweptback solution which was rapidly becoming the standard for jet fighters. A swift development programme was initiated, the aircraft being designed around the RD-10A turbojet of 1000 kg (2205 lb) thrust, which was based on the German Jumo 004. A Russian-designed powerplant with twice the thrust was in the pipeline and was expected to become available within a year, but the Anglo-Soviet trade agreement of 1946 offered a more attractive possibility.

The trade pact included the supply of 25 Rolls-Royce Nene turbojets, most of which were allocated to the Klimov engine design bureau or to research establishments. However, one found its way to the Mikoyan/Gurevich team. The embryo MiG-15 was redesigned to accommodate the fatter Nene, which had a centrifugal compressor compared with the axial unit or the Russian engine under development, and which also produced greater thrust.

It seems likely that the first prototype, designated I-310, made its maiden flight in July 1947, but crashed during low-speed

trials. Several design changes were introduced as a result, including the adoption of 2° of wing anhedral in place of the dihedral layout, installation of wing fences and several changes to the back end. The rear fuselage was shortened and the jet pipe cut back to reduce the amount of engine power being lost, the tailplane was removed from the top of the fin and repositioned two-thirds of the way up, and the fin itself was swept back by 56°. The replacement prototype, S-01, first flew on December 30, 1947, and the type was ordered into production only three months later.

The revised design was far from perfect—it tended to enter a spin from a tight turn, necessitating the fitting of recovery rockets—but it was apparent that the layout was basically sound. The Mikoyan/Gurevich team had six months' headway over their competitors, and this proved decisive, although both the La-168 and Yak-30 proceeded to the flight-test stage and the former entered limited production. Early production MiG-15s powered by the RD-45, copied from the Nene, reached the squadrons before the end of 1948. The RD-45F (*Forsirovanny,* meaning boosted), uprated from 2200 kg (4850 lb) to 2270 kg (5000 lb) thrust for takeoff, soon replaced the earlier powerplant.

The layout of the MiG-15 closely resembled that of many contemporaries. Air was fed from a bifurcated nose intake via four ducts which passed either side of the cockpit and then over and under the unbroken wing centre section. The wing, of almost parallel chord, was swept back by 35° at the leading edge and was built up from two main spars skinned with light alloy. The upper surfaces carried two full-chord fences on each side and large Fowler flaps, set at 20° for takeoff and 55° for landing, were attached to the wing, just forward of the trailing edge. The ailerons were the only power-operated aerodynamic controls.

The circular-section fuselage was constructed in two halves which could be separated by means of quick-release bolts at the attachment point for the rear wing spar, exposing the complete engine for maintenance. Air brakes were fitted on either side of the rear fuselage. The tailplane was swept back by 40° and its incidence could be adjusted manually before takeoff. Two fuel tanks in the rear fuselage carried 90 litres (19.8 Imp gal) each, but the majority was contained in a 1225-litre (269-Imp gal) tank fitted between the wing spars. The undercarriage had a wide track—4 m (13 ft 1½ in)—to allow operation from rough fields; the levered-suspension mainwheels retracted inwards to lie within the fork of the front main spar.

Navigation, communication and fire-control equipment was extremely simple but this solution, combined with formidable firepower, proved to be the correct solution when the type was blooded in combat. A gyro gunsight with a maximum range of 800 m (875 yards) was used to aim the two 23-mm (0.90-in) NS-23 cannon mounted in a pack under the nose. This arrangement was later replaced by a lopsided installation comprising a single 37-mm (1.46-in) N-37 cannon with 40 rounds on the right-hand side and a pair of NS-23s with 80 rounds each on the left. The wing hardpoints were stressed to carry up to

500 kg (1102 lb) of bombs, although two weapons of 100 kg (220 lb) each were more usual, and rockets were also fitted. Alternatively, auxiliary fuel tanks could be carried to increase endurance.

The uprated MiG-15SD, more often referred to as the MiG-15bis, first flew in 1949 under the power of the Klimov VK-1 (originally designated RD-45FA). This latest development of the Nene provided 2700 kg (5950 lb) of thrust for takeoff, or 3000 kg (6615 lb) with water injection. The engine's external dimensions remained the same, but the mass flow was increased and the larger diameter hot end resulted in dry weight rising from 870 kg (1918 lb) in the RD-45 to 875 kg (1930 lb) in the VK-1. Fuel capacity—which had suffered when the Nene was adopted in place of the Russian engine planned originally—was increased by 160 litres (35 Imp gal) and improved equipment was fitted. Perforated flaps were therefore adopted to save airframe weight, offsetting increases in other areas. Late production models of the MiG-15bis, which was the variant built in the largest numbers, carried 23-mm (0.90-in) NR-23 revolver cannon in place of the slow-firing NS-23s.

The MiG-15bis was followed off the drawing board by the two-seat MiG-15UTI, codenamed Midget, with the instructor sitting behind and slightly above his pupil. Some fuel capacity was sacrificed, and the top speed dropped slightly. The two-seater was also used for ejection-seat experiments and formed the basis of the SP-5, the first all-weather fighter variant. An *Izumrud* (Emerald) fire-control radar (NATO codename Scan Fix) was fitted, the antenna being mounted in a bullet fairing in the centre of the intake splitter. A complementary ranging radar was installed in the top lip of the intake. The definitive all-weather fighter variant, the MiG-15P, was, however, a single-seater derived from the MiG-15bis.

A reconnaissance version fitted with a single nose-mounted vertical camera below the gun magazines was developed for high-altitude sorties over Korea and was additionally employed in Europe. A further variant was the MiG-15SB, which had twin beams extending from the wing leading edges to carry two 100-kg (220-lb) bombs, eight 55-mm (2.16-in) rockets or auxiliary fuel tanks. Rockets were fitted to reduce the takeoff run and a braking parachute similarly shortened the landing roll.

The MiG-15 was built under licence from 1953 in Czechoslovakia as the S.102 and by WSK in Poland as the LIM-1. The MiG-15bis followed under the designations S.103 and LIM-2, with the two-seat trainer constructed as the CS.102 and LIM-3. Spares were also built by the Chinese Shenyang National Aircraft Factory, Chinese MiG-15s being designated F-2s. Production in the Soviet Union ended in 1953-54.

The MiG-15 took part in the first-ever all-jet air combat when one was destroyed by a Lockheed F-80 Shooting Star of the US Air Force over Korea on November 7, 1950, some six days after the Russian type was deployed to that theatre. The Soviet aircraft was more manoeuvrable and had a higher ceiling than its US adversaries, and the slow-firing but hard-hitting cannon carried a heavier punch than the machine-guns of the

Fairey IIIA-F

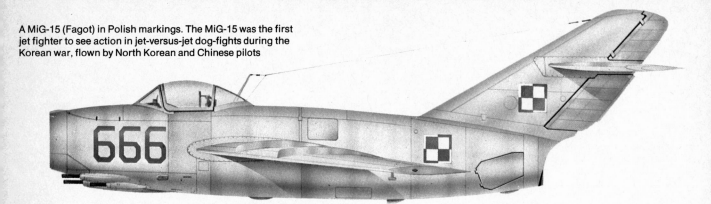

A MiG-15 (Fagot) in Polish markings. The MiG-15 was the first jet fighter to see action in jet-versus-jet dog-fights during the Korean war, flown by North Korean and Chinese pilots

opposing fighters. The USAF's response was to introduce the North American F-86A Sabre, which scored its first MiG kill on December 17, 1950. The North Korean and Chinese pilots could not hope to match the experience of their adversaries, and on May 20, 1951, Capt James Jabara bagged his fifth and sixth MiG-15s to become the first jet ace. The USAF alone claimed 792 MiG-15s destroyed over Korea, while the US Navy also notched up a creditable score, bringing the claimed kill-to-loss ratio to about 12:1. The MiG-15 should not be seen as merely fodder for opposing jet jockeys, however. The Soviet air force entered the era of effective jet fighters and it has run up numerous battle honours.

Span: 10.08 m (33 ft) *Length:* 10.86 m (35 ft 7½ in) *Gross weight:* 4960 kg (10 935 lb) normal *Maximum speed:* Mach 0.92

Fairey British aircraft See **Albacore, Baby (Sopwith), Battle, Barracuda, Campania, Fawn, Firefly, Flycatcher, Fox, Fulmar, Gannet, Gordon, Hendon, Seal, Swordfish**

Fairey IIIA-F

British two-seat floatplanes. One of the most successful Fairey designs was the III-series of float and landplanes which saw a wide variety of both service and civil use during the period 1918-30. The genesis of this long-lived design can be traced to the Fairey N.10 (F.128) which was modified in late 1917 as a landplane, with a wheeled undercarriage, and designated Fairey IIIA. Fifty examples were ordered as shipborne two-seat bombers, and production commenced in 1918 (N2850-N2899), and the first IIIA was flown on June 6, 1918. The end of the war prevented any widespread use of the IIIA, however. A variant, the IIIB, was also produced in small numbers as a two-seat floatplane bomber, and a few examples saw active service before the Armistice mainly on coastal patrols around the United Kingdom. Both versions employed a 260-hp Sunbeam Maori engine, and could carry a bombload of approximately 272 kg (600 lb) if required.

The third variant to be designed and produced during 1918 was the IIIC, a seaplane generally regarded as the best such design to emerge from the First World War. Powered by a Rolls-Royce Eagle VIII engine, the IIIC total production of 36 machines were all either IIIBs converted on the production line, or built as IIICs from that line. Too late for war service in 1918, at least seven examples saw operational duties with the North Russian Expeditionary Force, based at Archangel, in 1919. Four IIICs appeared on the Civil Register later, one of which, G-EBDI (ex-N9253), took part in an attempted global flight in 1922, but finally sank in Far Eastern waters on August 24,1919.

Progression in design next produced the IIID variant; probably the most successful Fairey design of its era. An overall total of 227 IIIDs were eventually built, and the type's versatile adaptability in both float and landplane configurations gave it a relatively long life. The prototype IIID, N9450, made its first flight in August 1920 as a seaplane, and an initial production batch of 50 machines was put in hand. Six IIID seaplanes went to the Australian government in August 1921, and one of these was flown around the

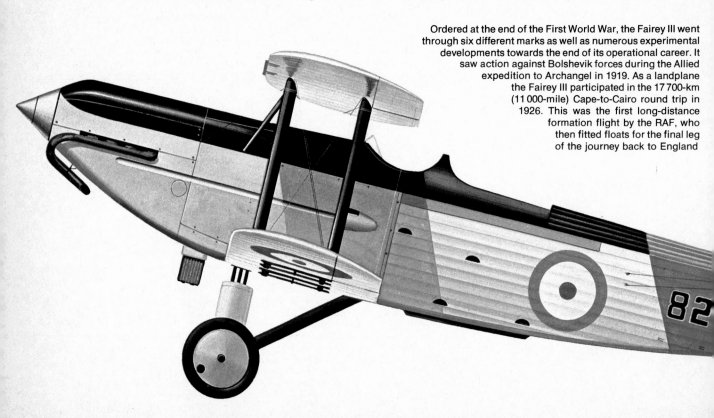

Ordered at the end of the First World War, the Fairey III went through six different marks as well as numerous experimental developments towards the end of its operational career. It saw action against Bolshevik forces during the Allied expedition to Archangel in 1919. As a landplane the Fairey III participated in the 17 700-km (11 000-mile) Cape-to-Cairo round trip in 1926. This was the first long-distance formation flight by the RAF, who then fitted floats for the final leg of the journey back to England

whole Australian coastline in 1924—13 789 km (8570 miles) in 44 days, approximately 90 flying hours—to earn the 1924 Britannia Trophy for its crew, Wing Commander S J Goble DSC, and Flying Officer I E McIntyre. Portugal also ordered a total of 11 IIIDs, one of which was specially prepared for a trans-Atlantic attempt in 1922. Finally three aircraft were needed to complete the flight successfully. Several other European countries purchased a few machines in the same period.

The most outstanding achievement involving IIIDs was the first long-distance RAF formation flight of some 17 700 km (11 000 miles) from Cairo to the South African Cape, and return to Cairo, in 1926. For this overland flight the IIIDs had a wheeled undercarriage, but reverted to floats on the return journey from Egypt to England. With the Fleet Air Arm, IIIDs were first issued to 441 Flight in 1924, and soon a total of seven such Flights were operating the type in home waters, the Mediterranean and the Far East zone. Fairey IIIDs continued in FAA service until 1930 before being finally replaced by more modern designs. Only two examples found their way onto the Civil Register: G-EBKE (ex-N9630) and G-EBPZ (S1076), both of which ceased to exist by 1929.

Last in the III-series was the IIIF, probably the most-used FAA aircraft of the inter-war years. With the exception of the Hawker Hart variants, the Fairey IIIF was also produced in greater numbers than any other British military aeroplane in the 1918-35 period. Originally designed to meet a 1924 specification, the IIIF was a much-modified development of the IIID, having an all-metal fuselage and propeller, folding wings, and easy changeability to either wheeled or float undercarriage. The first prototype, N198, first flew in March 1926, and initial deliveries of production aircraft went to various naval units during 1927. In the same year, six examples were issued to 47 Squadron RAF, based at Khartoum, Egypt, to undertake another Cairo-Cape-Cairo goodwill flight. The same unit later received further general purpose versions for normal duties. Other Middle East-based RAF units to receive IIIFs included 8 and 14 Squadrons. In England, 207 Squadron replaced its DH.9As with IIIFs, and several machines also went to 24 Squadron (Communications) fitted with special seating for VIP passengers; while

others subsequently equipped both 35 and 603 Squadrons.

It was in Fleet Air Arm use that the IIIF made its largest contribution, serving aboard every British aircraft carrier of the time, as well as ashore with many naval air stations, training establishments, and specialized naval schools. It also became the vehicle for a bewildering variety of experiments and testing in many roles; including catapult trials, landing on a carrier with strengthened float and empennage, and many trials of radio-controlled aircraft. The IIIF was also subjected to many years of scientific tests at the RAE, Farnborough. At least 25 IIIFs were purchased by non-British governments, including Russia, Ireland, Argentina, Greece, Chile and New Zealand. In all a total of 622 Fairey IIIFs were built, of which 243 were RAF versions and the rest FAA variants. These gave splendid service for almost 14 years, with at least three examples recorded as still in RAF service (as target tugs) as late as February 1941.

Two further developments, the IIIF Mk V and Mk VI, were to give further service under the designations Gordon and Seal respectively, but were merely the final examples of a line of Fairey III-series aircraft which had spanned almost 23 years of service usage. Flying in a myriad of roles, climates, and circumstances, the Fairey IIIs had been a virtual 'spine' for the infant RAF and FAA, providing priceless experience to two generations of British servicemen.

A British paratrooper armed with an L1A1 SLR, a British development of the Belgian FAL

Span: 14.07 m (46 ft 2 in) (IIIA) 19.13 m (62 ft 9 in) (IIIB) 14 m (46 ft 1 in) (IIIC) 14 m (46 ft 1 in) (IIID) 13.94 m (45 ft 9 in) (IIIF) *Length:* 9.45 m (31 ft) (IIIA) 11.3 m (37 ft 1 in) (IIB) 10.97 m (36 ft) (IIIC) 11 m (36 ft 1 in) (IIID) 11.07 m (36 ft 4 in) (IIIF proto) *Height:* 3.25 m (10 ft 8 in) (IIIA) 4.27 m (14 ft) (IIIB) 3.7 m (12 ft 2 in) (IIIC) 3.96 m (13 ft) (IIID) 3.83 m (12 ft 7 in) (IIIF proto) *Engines:* 260-hp Sunbeam Maori (IIIA & IIIB) 375-hp RR Eagle VIII (IIIC & IIID) 450-hp Napier Lion II (IIID) Various Napier Lion (IIIF) *Maximum speed:* IIIA 175.4 km/h (109 mph); IIIB 152.9 km/h (95 mph); IIIC 177.8 km/h (110.5 mph); IIID 193 km/h (120 mph); IIIF (Mk I landplane) 241.4 km/h (150 mph) *Service ceiling:* IIIA 4572 m (15 000 ft); IIIB 3139 m (10 300 ft); IIIC 2774 m (9100 ft); IIID 6096 m (20 000 ft) (landplane/Lion)

FAL

Belgian rifle. The Fusil Automatique Legere (FAL), a semi-automatic rifle developed and manufactured by Fabrique National of Liege, Belgium, was adopted as the standard service rifle by some 30 countries and manufactured under licence in many of them.

The Belgian designer Dieudonne Saive had begun work on a semi-automatic rifle in the 1930s and, upon the German occupation of Belgium in 1940, he fled to England where he continued his work at the Royal Small Arms Factory, Enfield. After the war he returned to Belgium and the rifle was produced as the 'SAFN' model. Saive then incorporated the same basic mechanism into a more modern

Falco, Fiat C.R.42

The Italian Fiat C.R.42 Falco was test flown in 1939 and served with both Fascist and Co-Belligerent Air Forces during the Second World War

design, basing the weapon on the German 7.92-mm (0.312-in) 'short' cartridge and later on the experimental British 7-mm (0.275-in) cartridge. After the British cartridge was rejected by NATO and the 7.62-mm (0.30-in) cartridge standardized, Saive redesigned the rifle once again and the final design, the FAL, appeared in 1950. After extensive testing it went into quantity production in 1953. The British Army began trials with it in 1955 and it was formally adopted as the L1A1 rifle on July 19, 1957.

The basic FAL is gas operated, using a bolt carrier and bolt driven by a sharp blow from the short-stroke gas piston rod mounted above the barrel. The bolt is locked by being tipped downward at the rear end so as to wedge in front of a prepared face in the receiver. As the bolt carrier moves back, cams lift the bolt free from its lock and withdraw it. On the return stroke, a fresh round is collected from the magazine and chambered, and the final movement of the bolt carrier cams the bolt down and locks it. Fire is normally confined to single shots, but the rifle can be modified to fire automatic at about 650 rds/min if the purchaser requires.

Several other modifications are available to suit the rifle to various roles: the barrel may be plain, or fitted with a flash-hider or with a grenade-launching attachment; a heavy barrel and bipod can be fitted in order to adapt the weapon to the light machine-gun role; the butt can be of metal tubing and fitted to fold alongside the receiver for more compact carriage by airborne troops; the furniture can be of wood, metal, or plastic material; and various sighting telescopes can easily be fitted.

Calibre: 7.62 mm (0.30 in) NATO *Length:* 110 cm (43.3 in) *Weight, loaded:* 5.06 kg (11 lb 2 oz) *Barrel length:* 53 cm (21 in) *Magazine:* 20-round detachable box *Rate of fire:* 650 rds/min

Falco, Fiat C.R.42

Italian fighter aircraft. Although the biplane as a fighting machine was virtually obsolete at the outbreak of the Second World War, many such aircraft participated successfully during the early part of the conflict.

The C.R.42 Falco (Falcon), designed by Celestino Rosatelli, was the last in the family, begun in 1923 with the C.R.20 and 30 series and followed by the C.R.33, 40 and 41 prototypes, to become one of these successes. It was an unequal-span biplane, with an oval-section fuselage. The fixed two-leg undercarriage was fitted with oleo-pneumatic shock-absorbers and enclosed in streamlined fairings. The tailwheel was retractable on the prototype, but fixed on production aircraft. Test flights began in early 1939 and, powered by an 840-hp Fiat A74R.1C.38 two-row radial engine, the sturdily-built prototype proved to be highly manoeuvrable, with a rapid rate of climb and a maximum speed of 441 km/h (274 mph).

It was put into production the same year, and when Italy entered the war on June 10, 1940, a total of some 330 were in front-line service with Stormi or Gruppi of the Regia Aeronautica in Italy and in North and East Africa. Armament comprised one 7.7-mm (0.303-in) and one 12.7-mm (0.5-in) Breda-SAFAT machine-gun, which both fired through the disc of the Fiat 3D41 propeller, and a rounds counter was fitted in the instrument panel. On later production models, the 7.7-mm (0.303-in) gun was replaced by another of 12.7-mm (0.5-in) calibre. For some inexplicable reason, radio equipment was not installed.

Italian C.R.42s drew their first blood on June 13, 1940, attacking air bases at Fayence and Hyères in southern France; they also escorted Fiat B.R.20s on bombing missions over Toulon harbour during the battle for France. They met strong opposition from French Dewoitine D 520s and Bloch 152s, but losses were minimal and during the remainder of the campaign they were also used on escort duties with S.M.79 bombers over the Mediterranean and North Africa.

On the strength of the achievement in this theatre, the Italian government decided on a closer collaboration with the Luftwaffe, and created the Corpo Aereo Italiano (Italian Air Corps) to assist mainly in the Battle of Britain. Fifty C.R.42s and 48 Fiat G.50s, together with other Italian fighter, bomber and reconnaissance aircraft, formed the contingent. They were sent to Ursel and Maldeghem in Belgium. Unfortunately, the speedier German Bf 109s found it a hard task to keep formation with the biplanes, and the latter's lack of radio also hampered activities. Nevertheless, it was decided to send the Falcos into combat against Hurricanes and Spitfires. Their first raid was on Harwich on November 11, 1940. They also participated in action off the Kent coast a few days later, and substantial victory claims were made by the Italians, although RAF records give a different picture. Their obvious inefficiency against superior aircraft, together with the Italian need for more air power in the Mediterranean, instigated the return of the Falcos to Italy in January 1941.

In the early stages of the desert campaigns in North Africa, during mid-1940 to 1941, C.R.42s were used extensively as fighters, until the advent of more advanced opposition in the form of Hurricanes and Tomahawks. They could not hope to compete against such types and were put to use in the ground attack role. Although improvements and modifications had been made to the original design—the C.R.42bis had two additional 12.7-mm (0.5-in) guns in underwing fairings —the C.R.42AS (Africa-Settentrionale: North Africa) was fitted with a special oil and

The Reggiane Re 2000 Falco I served with both the Hungarian and Swedish air forces, as well as the Italian navy and air force

air sand filter to cope with desert conditions, and a few were armed with two 20-mm (0.79-in) cannon under the lower wings. When used for night attacks, the C.R.42CN (Caccia Notturna) was equipped with radio and was also fitted with twin searchlights. One Falco, designated C.R.42B, had a 1010-hp Daimler-Benz DB 601 inverted-V-type engine installed, with which it was hoped the aircraft would achieve a speed of 520 km/h (323 mph), but this did not leave the experimental stage. Neither did the CMASA-built IC.R.42 (I= Idrovolante: seaplane), which was fitted with twin floats and was much heavier than the landplane, though speed loss from the increased weight was negligible.

However, demand for the type continued, and Falcos served extensively in Libya during 1940-41 and were used for attacks on Malta in the same period, as well as acting as escorts to bombers attacking Allied shipping in the Mediterranean. In October 1940, when Greece entered the war, the three squadrons of C.R.42s (together with other Italian aircraft) sent to the area showed marked superiority over the somewhat motley Greek air arm, which was soon defeated. Falco fighter units then combined with Luftwaffe forces to take the island of Crete, and remained in the Aegean theatre until they were replaced by Fiat G.50s in November 1941. After the Italian conquest of Ethiopia, bases there had, initially, little or no trouble in getting new C.R.42s or spares. However, after June 1941, increased Allied activity in North Africa, bad weather conditions and lack of radio equipment in the aircraft, all took their toll. By November 1941, all Falcos from the region had been either evacuated or destroyed.

Other parts of North Africa still covered by the ubiquitous little biplanes included Cyrenaica, where they were fitted with underwing racks for two 100-kg (220-lb)

bombs. Thus equipped, they received a new lease of life and enjoyed much success. As fighter-bombers, Falcos also participated in raids around Tobruk, Alexandria and Mersa Matruh and in the siege of Tripoli. Surviving aircraft from this last battle (some 82 Falcos) went back to Italy and were used in attacks on Allied convoys in the Mediterreanean—in which role the bombload was insufficient to do any great damage. They were phased out of this duty in favour of more modern types. In October 1941, a C.R.42CN night fighter unit was formed in Sicily and, although it did not see a great deal of active service there, it was reasonably effective later, in 1942-43, against RAF bombers over the industrial areas of northern Italy.

Utilization of the Falco was not confined to the Regia Aeronautica. In 1939, 34 were ordered by the Belgian air force; delivered from January 1940, they were in fact the first Falcos to fire their guns in anger, although they were relatively ineffective against the Luftwaffe opposition. Fifty were exported to Hungary, appearing on the Eastern Front from mid-1941; and in 1940-41 the Swedish air force took delivery of 72 aircraft. Designated J 11, they remained in service until 1945, after which a few remained in civil use.

Production of the type ceased in late 1942 when a total of 1781 had been built. Only 113 remained when the Italians surrendered in September 1943, of which 64 were still serviceable. Most of these were seized by the Luftwaffe or employed with the Repubblica Sociale Italiana, Mussolini's short-lived puppet regime, based at Salò, northern Italy; but a few escaped to join the Italian co-belligerent air force that fought on the Allied side, and continued with that Italian air arm until 1945, when they were finally declared obsolete. As a final gesture of defiance, some still remained, as modified two-seat trainers, until as late as 1950.

Span: 9.70 m (31 ft 9¾ in) *Length:* 8.25 m (27 ft) *Gross weight:* 2290 kg (5050 lb) *Maximum speed:* 430 km/h (267 mph)

Falco I, Reggiane Re 2000

Italian single-seat fighter aircraft. One of the three principal radial-engined Italian fighters of the Second World War (the others being the Fiat G.50 Freccia and the Macchi C.200 Saetta). The Re 2000 Falco I (Falcon) was a product of the Reggiane SA, a subsidiary of the Caproni group. Its designers, Alessio and Longhi, were strongly influenced by the contemporary US Seversky P-35 fighter, both types being dimensionally similar and having semi-elliptical wings, a 'wing-nut' tailplane shape and a short, tubby fuselage. The Italian design was lighter and had slightly more power (a 986-hp Piaggio P.XI RC 40 two-row 14-cylinder radial in the Serie I production model), and had easily the better performance. Just as the P-35, via the P-43 Lancer, developed into the celebrated Republic P-47 Thunderbolt, so was the Re 2000 the progenitor of a family of fighters whose principal other members were the Re 2001 Falco II, Re 2002 Ariete and Re 2005 Sagittario.

The Re 2000 prototype exhibited excellent manoeuvrability and handling qualities following its first flight in 1938. However, because it was less sturdily built than the C.200 and G.50, the Regia Aeronautica at first turned it down. The Italian navy later accepted 10 Falco I Serie II aircraft which, strengthened for catapult launching and fitted with arrester hooks, underwent shipboard trials during 1942. In addition, 12 Serie III Falcos, with a modified cockpit hood, extra fuel, and internal improvements, were assigned to the air force and deployed for overseas escort duties or as fighter-bombers (with an under-fuselage 200-kg [440-lb] bomb) from naval bases in Sicily. The Serie

Falco II, Reggiane Re 2001

II and III aircraft were converted from Serie Is and were powered by 1025-hp P.XIbis RC 40 engines; all three versions mounted a fixed armament of two 12.7-mm (0.5-in) Breda-SAFAT machine-guns in the fuselage decking over the engine.

Most of the 158 Re 2000s built in Italy were exported, the principal customer being the Hungarian air force, which ordered 70 Serie I Falcos. Deliveries of these began in 1940. These aircraft were known by the Hungarian air force as the Héja I (Hawk). In addition, a further 191 Re 2000s were built in Hungary under licence by MAVAG as the Héja II. These had 986-hp WMK 14 engines, a version of the French Gnome-Rhône Mistral Major K14 built in Hungary by the Manfred Weiss concern, and Hungarian Héja Is were despatched in 1941 to serve on the Eastern Front. In 1942-43, enough Héjas were deployed in the USSR to form an independent fighter group of the Hungarian air force. Others were utilized by units in Hungary as

The Reggiane Re 2001 Falco II.   A total of 236 were built and first saw action in Malta in 1942

major versions being the Serie I (100 built), with two 12.7-mm (0.5-in) Breda-SAFAT machine-guns over the engine; the Re 2001CN (Caccia Notturna: night fighter) Serie II and III with an additional 7.7-mm (0.303-in) gun in each wing or two German 20-mm (0.79-in) MG 151 cannon in underwing fairings; and the Re 2001CN Serie IV, which could carry an under-fuselage 640-kg (1410-lb) bomb or a drop-tank.

Various experimental models of the Re 2001 included a torpedo-carrying fighter con-

The Re 2000 was at first rejected by the Regia Aeronautica due to structural deficiencies and inadequate protection for fuel tanks which were inconveniently situated. However, the navy adopted it, and when it was subsequently flown in mock combat against the Bf 109E by both German and Italian pilots it proved the better aircraft

home defence fighters. The majority of Héja IIs were employed in the role of advanced fighter-trainer, but they too took on a defensive role in 1944, in an attempt to halt the advances of the Soviet ground forces across the Hungarian homeland.

Sweden also was a customer for the Re 2000 Serie I, the Flygvapnet operating a total of 60 between 1941-46 under the designation J 20. They were the fastest fighters in service in Sweden during the Second World War.

(Serie I) *Span:* 11 m (36 ft 1 in) *Length:* 7.99 m (26 ft 2½ in) *Gross weight:* 2850 kg (6285 lb) *Maximum speed:* 530 km/h (329 mph)

Falco II, Reggiane Re 2001

Italian single-seat fighter aircraft. Unlike the American P-35/P-43/P-47 line of fighter development, which remained radial-engined throughout, the Reggiane Re 2000 series at first followed a pattern similar to that adopted by its compatriot, the Macchi C.200 Saetta which, after a radial-engined start, switched to a V-type powerplant for further development. In both cases, the engine first chosen was the German Daimler-Benz DB 601A-1 inverted-V, known in its Italian licence-built form as the Alfa Romeo RA.1000 RC 41 Monsone, developing 1175 hp for takeoff.

After two prototypes had been completed in 1940 with German-built DB 601A-1s, the fighter was ordered into production in its new form as the Re 2001 Falco II. A total of 236 were built (including prototypes and 10 pre-production aircraft), in various sub-series, version (Re 2001G); an antitank conversion (Re 2001H); a prototype conversion with flush-mounted leading-edge wing radiators (Re 2001bis); two Serie Is converted for catapult-launching trials; and a testbed for the Isotta-Fraschini Delta RC 16/48 engine.

Production Serie I Re 2001s made their operational debut in attacks on Malta in the early summer of 1942, with subsequent production models following them into service later that year. Thirty-nine Serie I aircraft were adapted as Re 2001CBs, able to carry a 640-kg (1410-lb) bomb or torpedo, and a further 12 as land-based carrier trainers, fitted with arrester gear. The most widely used version of all was the Re 2001CN (50 Serie II and 74 Serie III/IV), which from 1943 served with five Gruppi of the Regia Aeronautica as a defensive night fighter in central and northern Italy. But, by the armistice only 21 Falco IIs remained serviceable, of which eight were used subsequently by the Italian co-belligerent air force.

(Serie III) *Span:* 11 m (36 ft 1¾ in)
Length: 8.36 m (27 ft 5¼ in)
Gross weight: 3280 kg (7230 lb)
Max speed: 542 km/h (337 mph)

Falcon

British self-propelled armoured AA equipment. Falcon is an antiaircraft tank designed with low cost and reliability well in mind. It consists of a Vickers chassis mounting two Hispano-Oerlikon 30-mm (1.18-in) automatic guns in a fully rotating turret. The chassis is based on that of the successful Abbot self-propelled gun and is fully tracked, being powered by a 216-hp General Motors GM 6V53 diesel engine through an Allison Torqumatic transmission. The forward section of the chassis is divided into two compartments, one holding the engine and transmission, the other the driver. The rear section of the chassis supports the turret, the prototype of which was designed and built by the British Manufacturing & Research company (BMARC).

The turret is armoured and carries the commander and gunner in the rear section separated from the guns and their mountings, to reduce their exposure to noise and fumes. The two guns are electrically cocked and fired, and produce a combined rate of fire of 1300 rds/min. Power control of the turret is by an electric metadyne system developed by GEC-AEI (Electronics), and is based on similar systems developed by them for the turret of the Vickers main battle tank. The

gunner has a periscope sight with a dual optical system, one of ×1 magnification and 50° field of view for antiaircraft use, and the other of ×6 magnification with 10° field of view for accurate engagement of ground targets. He controls the guns and turret by a joystick control, and the commander has a similar joy-stick with override so that he can direct the gunlayer to a fresh target. The fire control system incorporates a computer which is fed with the target's range—using a laser range-finder—and position in space by the gunner tracking the target. Computer information displaces an electronically generated marker in the sight picture by the required amount of aim-off. This is a cheap, simple and effective system which was selected on the assumption that aircraft would only attack a column of vehicles in good visibility. During 1978 Falcon was undergoing evaluation by the British Army.

Weight: 15 850 kg (34 945 lb) *Length:* 5.33 m (17 ft 6 in) *Width:* 2.64 m (8 ft 8 in) *Height:* 2.51 m (8 ft 3 in) *Powerplant:* GM 6V53 6-cylinder diesel, 216 hp at 2800 rpm *Speed:* 48 km/h (30 mph) *Range:* 385 km (239 miles) *Armament:* 2 30-mm (1.18-in) Hispano-Oerlikon H0831L cannon *Weight of shell:* 360 gm (12.5 oz) *Muzzle velocity:* 1080 m/sec (3545 ft/sec) *Rate of fire:* 650 rds/min (each gun)

The Vickers Falcon SP AA equipment combines twin Hispano-Oerlikon 30-mm (1.18-in) with the Abbot SP Gun chassis

Vickers

Falcon, Hughes

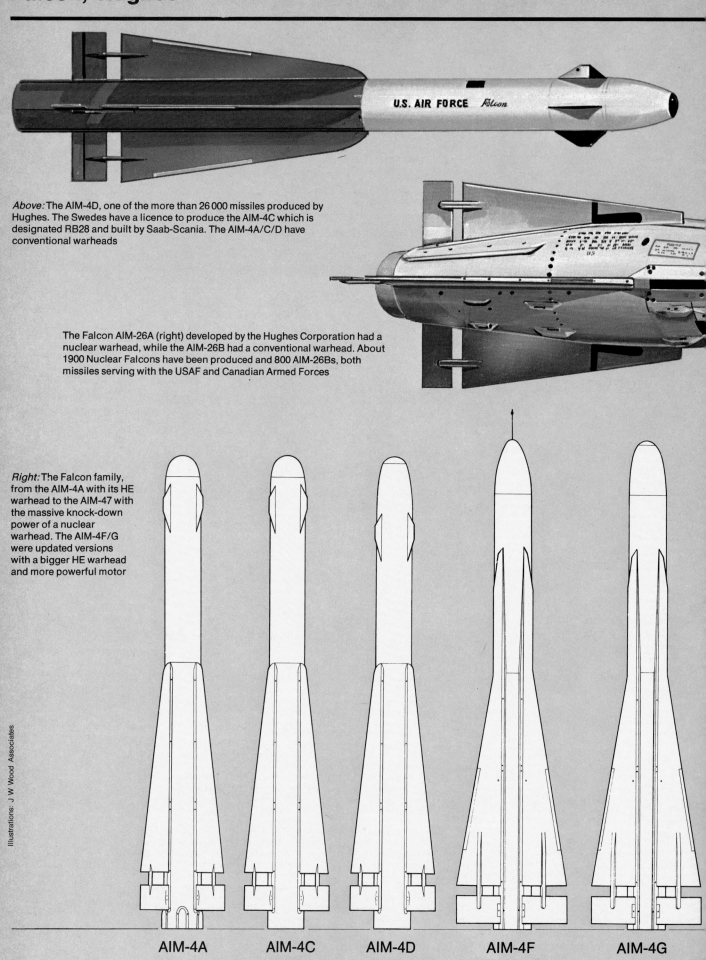

Above: The AIM-4D, one of the more than 26 000 missiles produced by Hughes. The Swedes have a licence to produce the AIM-4C which is designated RB28 and built by Saab-Scania. The AIM-4A/C/D have conventional warheads

The Falcon AIM-26A (right) developed by the Hughes Corporation had a nuclear warhead, while the AIM-26B had a conventional warhead. About 1900 Nuclear Falcons have been produced and 800 AIM-26Bs, both missiles serving with the USAF and Canadian Armed Forces

Right: The Falcon family, from the AIM-4A with its HE warhead to the AIM-47 with the massive knock-down power of a nuclear warhead. The AIM-4F/G were updated versions with a bigger HE warhead and more powerful motor

Illustrations: J W Wood Associates

| AIM-4A | AIM-4C | AIM-4D | AIM-4F | AIM-4G |

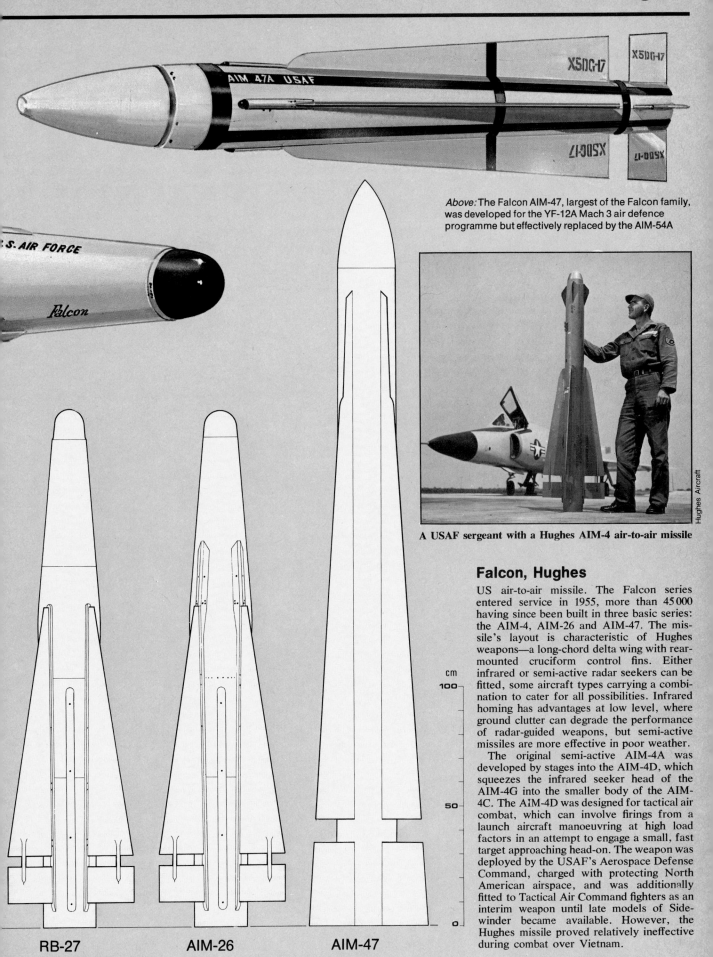

Above: The Falcon AIM-47, largest of the Falcon family, was developed for the YF-12A Mach 3 air defence programme but effectively replaced by the AIM-54A

A USAF sergeant with a Hughes AIM-4 air-to-air missile

RB-27   AIM-26   AIM-47

Falcon, Hughes

US air-to-air missile. The Falcon series entered service in 1955, more than 45000 having since been built in three basic series: the AIM-4, AIM-26 and AIM-47. The missile's layout is characteristic of Hughes weapons—a long-chord delta wing with rear-mounted cruciform control fins. Either infrared or semi-active radar seekers can be fitted, some aircraft types carrying a combination to cater for all possibilities. Infrared homing has advantages at low level, where ground clutter can degrade the performance of radar-guided weapons, but semi-active missiles are more effective in poor weather.

The original semi-active AIM-4A was developed by stages into the AIM-4D, which squeezes the infrared seeker head of the AIM-4G into the smaller body of the AIM-4C. The AIM-4D was designed for tactical air combat, which can involve firings from a launch aircraft manoeuvring at high load factors in an attempt to engage a small, fast target approaching head-on. The weapon was deployed by the USAF's Aerospace Defense Command, charged with protecting North American airspace, and was additionally fitted to Tactical Air Command fighters as an interim weapon until late models of Sidewinder became available. However, the Hughes missile proved relatively ineffective during combat over Vietnam.

Falcon, Curtiss

The Super Falcons, AIM-4F (semi-active) and AIM-4G (infrared), entered service in 1958. The former had greater immunity from jamming than its predecessors, and the latter also incorporated guidance improvements. Both models could be launched at higher altitudes and greater speeds than their forebears, and had longer ranges and more powerful warheads. The AIM-26A Nuclear Falcon was introduced in 1960, the AIM-26B, with a conventional warhead, being developed from it. Last in the series was the AIM-47A, a long-range version intended for the research YF-12A intercepter.

The AIM-26B and AIM-4D are built under licence by SAAB as the Rb27 and Rb28 respectively, and the AIM-26B—designated HM-55 in this case—is interfaced with the Hughes TARAN fire-control equipment in Mirage IIIS's of the Swiss air force.

(AIM-4D): *Length:* 2 m (6 ft 6¾ in) *Span:* 50.8 cm (20 in) *Diameter:* 16.25 cm (6½ in) *Weight:* 61 kg (134.5 lb) *Range:* 8-10 km (5-6 miles) *Speed:* Mach 4 *Propulsion:* Thiokol M58A2 solid rocket, 1770 kg (3900 lb) thrust

(AIM-26B): *Length:* 2.07 m (6 ft 9½ in) *Span:* 62 cm (24 in) *Diameter:* 29 cm (11½ in) *Weight:* 115 kg (253.5 lb) *Range:* 8-10 km (5-6 miles) *Speed:* Mach 2 *Propulsion:* Thiokol M60 solid rocket, 2650 kg (5840 lb) thrust

The Curtiss A-3B Falcon attack aircraft derived from the O-1E. The Falcon served with the US Army Air Force in the late 1920s and early 1930s where, besides observation and ground attack missions, some models were used for VIP transports and basic flight training

Falcon, Curtiss O-1/O-11/O-39 and A-3

US observation and attack aircraft. The Falcons were a diverse family of 184 O (observation) and 155 A (attack) biplanes produced by Curtiss in the latter half of the 1920s. All were single-bay biplanes with straight lower and sweptback upper wings, two (usually open) cockpits in tandem, and a two-wheel fixed undercarriage. Variants differed chiefly in powerplant, aerodynamic refinements and, in the case of the A-3s, armament.

The US Army Air Service staged two competitions, in late 1924 and early 1925, to find successors to the DH-4 series of observation and light bomber aircraft. In the former, Curtiss's Liberty-engined XO-1 was unsuccessful, but won the 1925 contract after refitting with a Packard 1A-1500. Ironically, this engine then proved a failure, and the 102 production O-1s were fitted instead with various models of the 435-hp Curtiss D-12 (V-1150) engine. They consisted of 10 O-1s ordered in 1925; 25 O-1Bs two years later, with wheel brakes and fuel jettison capability; 37 O-1Es, with Frise ailerons, horn-balanced elevators and improved engine cowling design; and 30 O-1Gs with improved streamlining—making them 16 km/h (10 mph) faster than the O-1B—slightly smaller wings, and redesigned rear cockpits. Following two

O-1 conversions (to O-1A and XO-11) to a 420-hp Liberty engine, 66 Liberty-engined models were produced for the US Army.

Several experimental Falcons flew with 600-hp Curtiss V-1570 Conqueror engines. They included the XO-13 and XO-13A (two converted O-1s) for the 1927 national air races; one O-13B; three YO-13Cs, otherwise similar to the O-1E; one YO-13D (supercharged Conqueror); one XO-16, a Conqueror-engined O-11 with Prestone (ethylene glycol) cooling; and one Y1O-26, similar to the O-1E but with a GIV-1570A-geared Conqueror and modified cooling system. However, the only Conqueror-powered production version, was the O-39, with Prestone cooling and a smaller rudder, but otherwise similar to the O-1G. Ten of these were built in 1932. Other one-off engine testbeds included the XO-12 (Pratt & Whitney Wasp), converted from an O-11, and XO-18 (Curtiss Chieftain). Other conversions, not involving an engine change, were four O-1Bs to O-1C unarmed VIP transports; one O-1E to an unarmed O-1F; another O-1E to XBT-4 basic trainer configuration, this later becoming the prototype for the O-1G; and one O-11 to O-11A (incorporating the improvements of the O-1E).

Except for the O-1C and O-1F, standard armament on the observation Falcons was four 0.30-in (7.62 mm) machine-guns: two

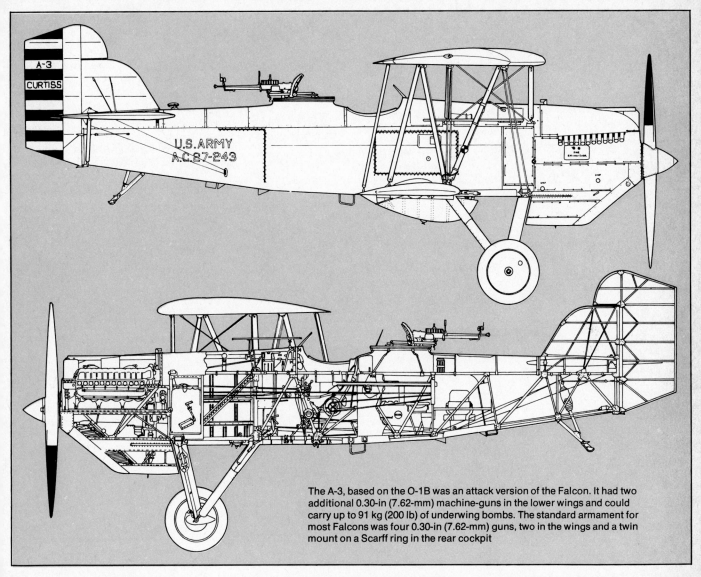

The A-3, based on the O-1B was an attack version of the Falcon. It had two additional 0.30-in (7.62-mm) machine-guns in the lower wings and could carry up to 91 kg (200 lb) of underwing bombs. The standard armament for most Falcons was four 0.30-in (7.62-mm) guns, two in the wings and a twin mount on a Scarff ring in the rear cockpit

fixed, forward-firing guns in the nose and two on a Scarff ring in the rear cockpit. Between 1927-30, Curtiss also produced 154 attack versions (76 A-3s, based on the O-1B, and 78 A-3Bs, based on the O-1E). These had two additional 0.30-in (7.62-mm) guns in the lower wings and could carry up to 91 kg (200 lb) of underwing bombs. There was also, in 1928, one XA-4, equivalent to the A-3, but with a 421-hp R-1340-1 Wasp engine.

(O-1B) *Span:* 11.58 m (38 ft) *Length:* 8.64 m (28 ft 4 in) *Gross weight:* 1989 kg (4385 lb) *Maximum speed:* 218 km/h (135.4 mph)

(A-3B) *Span:* 11.58 m (38 ft) *Length:* 8.28 m (27 ft 2 in) *Gross weight:* 2030 kg (4475 lb) *Maximum speed:* 224 km/h (139 mph)

Falke

German submarine torpedo. Experiments with homing torpedoes started in Germany in the mid-1930s, and it was soon found that the biggest limitation was 'self-noise' generated by the motion of the torpedo itself. Until further research on propeller-cavitation revealed the true source of this self-noise, it was assumed that a torpedo would not be able to home onto a ship-target at a speed of more than 25 knots.

From this point it was a simple step to modify a G7e electric torpedo to run slowly, and to fit it with a simple device to steer it in the direction of propeller-noise. The result was the T4 *Falke* (Falcon), and about 100 were made. They were issued in January 1943, and about 30 were fired in action. It was a relatively crude solution to the problem and was replaced by the T5 *Zaunkönig* (Wren).

Weight: 1397 kg (3080 lbs) *Speed:* 20 knots *Range:* 7498 m (8200 yards)

FA-MAS

French rifles, produced by Fusil Automatique, Manufacture d'Armes de St Etienne. The St Etienne arsenal is now part of the State-controlled Groupement Industriel des Armements Terrestres (GIAT), but the rifle continues to use the MAS identifying initials. It is the first French-designed 5.56-mm (0.219-in) assault rifle, and is of unorthodox appearance and construction. As is found with other modern designs, it is an attempt to produce a personal weapon which can function as a rifle, a submachine-gun, a squad light machine-gun, or a grenade-thrower, according to the needs of the moment. How well the designers have succeeded is yet to be determined, for the rifle is currently undergoing an exhaustive NATO evaluation.

The FA-MAS is a delayed blowback weapon using a two-part bolt and a hinged lever which bears against the gun body and, by means of differential leverage, holds one part of the bolt against the pressure of the recoiling cartridge case while allowing the second part to begin movement. By the time

Fancy

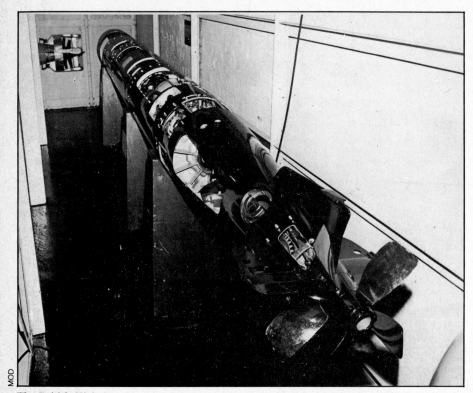

The British High-Test Peroxide (HTP) fuelled 53-cm (21-in) Mk 8 torpedo, code-named Fancy

this movement is communicated to the other part of the bolt, so as to open the breech and begin extracting the cartridge case, the chamber pressure has dropped to safe limits.

The rifle is laid out in 'bull-pup' configuration, with the bolt and chamber alongside the firer's face; it can be quickly adapted for right- or left-handed shooters by moving the cheek pad to one side or the other. This exposes an ejection port on the opposite side to the pad. The bolt is also removed and the extractor and ejector repositioned on the appropriate sides. Provision is made for single shots or automatic fire, and a three-round burst-fire counter is fitted, which allows a three-shot burst to be fired for a single pressure on the trigger. A full-length plastic carrying handle contains the open sights; a flash hider is fitted, and grenades can be launched without the need for additional attachments. For automatic fire a light bipod is permanently attached and folds alongside the receiver when not in use.

Calibre: 5.56 mm (0.219 in) *Length:* 757 mm (29.8 in) *Weight, loaded:* 4.165 kg (9 lb 3 oz) *Barrel length:* 488 mm (19.21 in) *Magazine:* 25-round detachable box *Rate of fire:* 900 rds/min *Muzzle velocity:* 960 m/sec (3150 ft/sec)

Fancy

British submarine torpedo. Out of a number of post-1945 experimental ideas in torpedo development, the British gained very few positive results. One of the most significant was the project Ferry (later renamed Fancy) which was a long-range submarine torpedo based on work done by the Germans in such torpedoes as the Steinbut. It was intended to be driven by High-Test Peroxide (HTP) and standard fuel. To save time and money, the vehicle chosen was the standard 21-in (53-

cm) Mk 8. It proved possible to modify the Mk 8's burner-cycle engine to run on HTP for long periods at high speed, but many other modifications had to be made to the torpedo.

The worst problem was that nearly all the standard materials used in a Mk 8 were incompatible with HTP, which was corrosive and explosive in contact with almost everything except synthetic rubber or porcelain. When the prototype was ready in 1953, the Ferry was renamed Fancy SR, and when pattern-running gyroscopes were ready in 1954 several were issued for testing in the submarines attached to *Maidstone*. More than 200 firing runs were made without any serious problems, but on June 16, 1955, a Fancy now known as the 21-in (53-cm) Mk 12, exploded while being loaded on board the submarine *Sidon* and sank it in Portland harbour. Another accident occurred some time later, when a torpedo exploded accidentally on the Arrochar torpedo range.

The enquiry into the *Sidon* disaster showed how necessary it was to make sure that all surfaces in the torpedo body which could possibly come into contact with HTP, must be compatible with the fluid. It also proved necessary to introduce drastic new standards for the HTP vessel, and these two factors raised so many new problems that in January 1959 the Admiralty cancelled the requirement for the Mk 12 torpedo. Nearly £1 million had been spent on it.

Fantan, Shenyang F-9

Chinese fighter-bomber. By 1975 preliminary reports had reached the West of a considerably modified version of the F-6, the MiG-19SF and PF built under licence in China. (Unlike the MiG-21, built in as small numbers as the Shenyang F-8, the earlier F-6 has continued in production and has proved

remarkably useful by China and various export customers.)

The Shenyang complex of the Chinese aerospace industry has long been known for painstaking quality and attention to detail, but also for a lack of original design experience. It cannot have been easy to derive a largely new twin-engined fighter from the F-6, differing in such respects as generally increased size, a large nose radar and lateral engine inlets.

First announced in the West by US Defense Secretary Rumsfeld in 1976, when it was described as 'the Fantan-A fighter-bomber', the F-9 still remains little known publicly and many of the published illustrations and specifications are little more than guesses. There have been several poor illustrations in Chinese naval and other newspapers, but their accuracy is suspect.

Most basic of all, it is not known whether the original Tumansky RD-9B engines, each rated at 3250-kg (7164-lb) thrust with maximum afterburner, remain the normal powerplant or whether they have been replaced by larger units.

In view of the greatly increased weight of both the major changes, it seems probable that the latter is the case, and it would be reasonable to suppose that the engines are the same as fitted to the early MiG-21, built as the F-8, namely the 5000-kg (11 244-lb) thrust Tumansky R11 series.

Existing illustrations of the Fantan-A show a nose resembling that of an F-4 Phantom, and a fair assumption is that at least this version is configured for all-weather interception.

Fifty F-9s powered by Rolls-Royce Spey turbofans are due to be built sometime in the late 1970s or early 1980s.

(Estimated data) Span: 10.2 m (33 ft 5 in) *Length:* 15.25 m (50 ft) *Gross weight:* 12 000 kg (26 450 lb) *Maximum speed:* clean, high altitude, 1910 km/h (1190 mph, Mach 1.8)

Fantasque

French destroyer class, built 1931-35. Between 1925 and 1931, the French navy laid down 24 super-destroyers or *contre-torpilleurs*. These were inspired by the big Italian destroyers or scouts of the *Carlo Mirabello* and *Leone* types, but took the idea even further. Although armed with a conventional destroyer-scale armament, five 138.6-mm (5.4-in) guns and torpedo tubes, the requirement for maximum speed was raised in each class, from 35 knots in the *Guepard* Class to 37 in the *Fantasque* Class, and 39 in the *Mogador* Class. The *Fantasque*s, however, by some mysterious process, proved to be capable of 27% more power than the contract required and this enabled them to average over 40 knots on trials. They were in fact the fastest destroyers ever built, and could operate as a division at speeds in excess of 37 knots, a feat unparalleled by any other class.

The six *Fantasque*s were ordered under the 1930 Programme, and were all laid down in the last months of 1931. *Le Triomphant* was the first to start her trials, in July 1934, but *l'Audacieux* was the first to become operational.

The design was a logical refinement of the

Name	launched	built
Le Fantasque	3/1934	Lorient arsenal
L'Audacieux	3/1934	Lorient arsenal
Le Malin	8/1933	Forge et Chantiers de la Méditerranée, La Syne
L'Indomptable	12/1933	Forge et Chantiers de la Méditerranée, La Syne
Le Terrible	11/1933	Chantiers Navals Francais, Caen
Le Triomphant	4/1934	Atelier et Chantiers de France, Dunkerque

previous *Guepard*, *Jaguar* and *Vauquelin*, but with more attention paid to a compact silhouette. Admiral Drujon, when reporting to the standing trials committee on the *Guepard* Class, insisted that the four tall funnels made the *contre-torpilleurs* too easy to identify at a distance. His recommendations were followed, and the original four funnels of the *Fantasque* design were trunked into a pair of short, wide funnels widely separated. Rounding the bridge-face and putting the pole mast on top of the range finder position helped by making it much harder to estimate the ship's angle of bearing.

The armament remained the same as before, five single 138.6-mm (5.4-in) guns disposed forward in A and B positions, and aft on two levels. However, the guns were the new 1929 Model, 45 cal in length instead of 40 cal. With a muzzle velocity of 800 m/sec (2624 ft/sec), they had a range of 20000 m (65617 ft) at 30° elevation and could fire 12 rounds a minute. The torpedo armament was increased to nine 55-cm (21.6-in) tubes, two triples abreast between the funnels and a third on the centreline abaft the second funnel. The torpedo was the standard 1929 Model DT, with an all-up weight of 2105 kg (4641 lb) and a charge of 415 kg (915 lb). At 39 knots it had a range of 10000 m (32808 ft), but at 35 knots this could be increased to 14000 m (45932 ft).

The machinery showed the most startling improvements. Following a bold departure in the *Milan* and *Epervier*, but without waiting for the results of their trials, the French navy adopted a new boiler developed by Chantiers et Ateliers de St Nazaire-Penhoët, with 325° superheat and a pressure of 37 kg/sq cm (526.26 lb/sq in). For comparison, one of the class, *le Terrible,* was given the same Yar-

row-Loire boilers as the *Milan* and *Epervier*. *Le Malin*, *l'Indomptabie* and *le Triomphant* had Parsons geared turbines, but the others had French-designed Rateau turbines. The designed horsepower has 74000 shp, with 81400 shp maximum output, but on her trials *le Terrible* reached the incredible speed of 45.029 knots with 94240 shp, and established a world speed record not broken until 1961.

It was rumoured at the time, doubtless by the builders, that *le Terrible*'s hull-form had been modified. In fact, she differed only in not having the propeller shaft-brackets specially designed for the class, and had to use the type used for the previous *Vauquelin* Class which may account for her better performance. The others, however, also had superb trials results.

The only questions which have never been answered are whether any realistic cost-limit was stipulated when the contracts were put out to tender, and whether the machinery specification laid down strict rules on output. In any other navy, but particularly the RN or USN, the extraordinary rise in the installed power would have been questioned, unless the builders were specifically permitted to ignore competitive costing and to go for maximum power. The effectiveness of the *contre-torpilleurs* must therefore be judged against their cost, and the comparative figures are not available. Their high speed was a mixed blessing, for it only allowed a range of 1126 km (700 miles), although at 25

knots this rose to 4667 km (2900 miles), with 4828 km (3000 miles) at 14 knots. By comparison, a war-built British destroyer of half the displacement could steam 7523 km (4674 miles) at 20 knots, and an American destroyer on two-thirds the displacement steamed 9656 km (6000 miles) at 15 knots.

The war record of the class was outstanding. All six, with the two later ships of the *Mogador* Class, formed part of the 2nd Light Squadron of the Raiding Force. They operated in the Atlantic in 1939-40, and in April 1940 *l'Indomptable*, *le Malin* and *le Triomphant* carried out a spectacular raid in the Skagerrak. They returned to the Mediterranean, and *l'Audacieux* ended her active career at Dakar in September 1940, when an 8-in (203-mm) salvo from the cruiser *Australia* demolished the forward guns and machinery. *L'Indomptable* was a victim of the scuttling of the fleet when the German army stormed Toulon arsenal in November 1942, and was never repaired, although her bow was used to repair *le Malin* in 1946.

After the fall of Toulon, the French forces overseas joined the Allies, and so *le Fantasque* and *le Terrible* went from Dakar to the US for modernization, as did the damaged *le Malin*, which had been shattered by a 16-in (406-mm) shell from the US battleship *Massachusetts* while lying at Casablanca. The refits rectified the ships' most glaring weakness by substituting one quadruple and two twin 40-mm (1.57-in) Bofors and 10 Oerlikon 20-mm (0.79-in) AA guns for the outdated 37-mm (1.46-in) and 8-mm (0.315-in) machine-guns. The ships were also given more fuel, and radar and Asdic, but to compensate for these additions they sacrificed the after set of triple torpedo tubes. As they now displaced nearly 4000 tons in full load condition they were re-rated as light cruisers.

The fourth ship, *le Triomphant*, had a very different career, for she had nearly been caught in Lorient undergoing machinery repairs when the Germans overran France in June 1940. She reached Plymouth with only one shaft working, and after being seized on July 3, was returned to Free French contro on August 28. It was necessary to rearm he with a British 4-in (102-mm) AA gun in place of the fourth 138.6-mm (5.4-in) gun aft and two 2-pdr (40-mm) pom-poms. For the time

The French destroyer *Fantasque*, name-ship of the fastest class of destroyers ever built

Name	1-hour trial	8-hour trial
Le Fantasque	42.71	40.48
L'Audacieux	43.18	41.41
Le Malin	43.11	41.49
Le Terrible	45.02	42.92
Le Triomphant	43.24	42.18
L'Indomptable	43.02	40.99

Farfadet

The MiG-19 made its maiden flight in September 1953. Since then it has been built under licence in Poland and Czechoslovakia and also in China. It was the first Russian production aircraft capable of exceeding the speed of sound. Since 1953 MiG-19 fighters have seen action in the Middle East, India and Far East, their performance varying according to pilot skill and the quality of the opposition. Clashes between Pakistani-crewed MiG-19s and Indian aircraft contrast with Syrian experiences against the Israelis

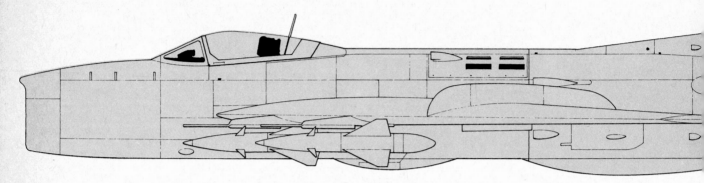

being, her remaining French weapons were retained but she was fitted with Asdic, being based on the Clyde as a convoy escort.

At the end of 1940, le Triomphant was sent to 'show the flag' in the Pacific, but here her short endurance was a crippling handicap. Apart from helping to evacuate Nauru Island when it was attacked by a German surface raider in December 1940, she spent her time escorting convoys. In December 1942, she completed a major overhaul at Sydney, and proved to be good for 40.4 knots at 3800 tons, only two knots less than she had achieved on her trials seven years earlier. A year later she was sent to the US to have the same modernization as her sisters, but while en route she was nearly overwhelmed by a cyclone and ran out of fuel. Eventually she made port in tow of a tanker, and went into Boston navy yard until March 1945.

The other three operated as the 10th Light Cruiser Division in the Mediterranean, and with conspicuous success in the Aegean. Here they were in their element, for the distances were short and the targets were ex-Italian and German light forces. In February 1944 they began a series of sweeps up the Adriatic, during which they sank a German cargo ship and the patrol vessel Uj 201 and severely damaged the ex-Italian destroyers TA.36 and TA.37 and Uj 205. In 40 days the division steamed 12874 km (8000 miles), and le Fantasque claimed to have dropped and weighed anchor 79 times. In September 1944 they were earmarked for the Pacific and began to refit, but finally it was only le Fantasque that went out, to arrive in Indo-China at the end of hostilities.

There she was reunited with her sister le Triomphant, which had been operating with the battleship Richelieu and the British Eastern Fleet. In 'Operation Bentre' le Triomphant led the reoccupation of Haiphong, and suffered considerable damage to her upperworks from Communist fire.

The ships continued in service for some years. Le Triomphant was the first to go, in December 1954, followed by le Fantasque in May 1957, but le Terrible and le Malin became harbour hulks in 1957, the former as a training ship for engineer-cadets and the latter as a mooring hulk for minesweepers. They were scrapped in 1962 and 1964.

Displacement: (As built) 2727-2800 tons (normal), 3200-3400 tons (full load); (After modernization) 3300 tons (normal), 4300 tons (full load) *Length:* 132.4 m (434 ft 4½ in) oa *Beam:* 12.25 m (40 ft 2½ in) *Draught:* 5.01 m (16 ft 5½ in) *Machinery:* 2-shaft geared steam turbines, 74 000-94 000 shp=37-42 knots *Armament:* (As built) 5 138.6-mm (5.4-in)/45-cal Model 1929 (5×1); 4 37-mm (1.46-in) AA Model 1925 (4×1); 4 13.2-mm (0.52-in) machine-guns (4×1); 9 55-cm (21.7-in) torpedo tubes (3×3); (le Triomphant, 1940) 4 138.6 mm (5.4-in)/45-cal (4×1); 1 4-in (102-mm) AA; 2 2-pdr (40-mm) AA (2×1); 4 37-mm (1.46-in) AA Model 1925 (2×2); 7 13.2-mm (0.52-in) AA machine-guns (1×4, 1×2, 1×1); 9 55-cm (21.7-in) torpedo tubes (3×3) (as modernized) 5 138.6-mm (5.4-in)/45-cal (5×1) 8 40-mm (1.57-in)/60-cal AA (1×4, 2×2) 10 20-mm (0.79-in) Oerlikon AA (10×1) 6 55-cm (21.7-in) torpedo tubes (2×3)

Farfadet

French submarine class, built 1900-1905. Four single-hulled boats (Q.7-10) were ordered to the plans of M Maugas in September 1899. All four were launched at Rochefort arsenal: *Farfadet* on May 17, 1901, *Korrigan* on January 25, 1902, *Gnôme* on July 24, 1902 and *Lutin* on February 12, 1903.

These boats were driven only by a single electric motor, and so had to recharge their batteries from a shore-based generator or from a depot ship. Despite this limitation they were highly regarded when they entered service. *Korrigan* became well known for entering the harbour of Bizerta fully submerged, and on manoeuvres she was awarded several successes. The main weakness lay in the absence of any deck-casing, so that the three hatches could easily be swamped by a big wave. The class was also liable to 'porpoise' without warning.

In 1904 *Korrigan* and *Farfadet* were towed from La Rochelle to Bizerta to form part of the *defense mobile* there, and shortly afterwards they were joined by *Lutin*. On July 5, 1905, *Farfadet* dived out of control in the harbour of Bizerta and was lost with all hands. Faith in the design was shaken when on October 16, 1906, her sister *Lutin* also sank at Bizerta, due to a kingston valve

failing to close. What made this disaster unusual was the fact that for the first time the French asked the Royal Navy for assistance in the attempts to rescue the crew. *Farfadet* was eventually raised and repaired and returned to service under the new name *Follet* in September 1909.

Lutin was discarded in September 1907 after being raised. *Korrigan* and *Gnôme* were laid up in 1906 and discarded in 1910, but *Follet* remained in service until the end of 1913 as an experimental boat.

Displacement: 185/202 tonnes (surfaced/submerged) *Length:* 41.35 m (135 ft 8 in) oa *Beam:* 2.9 m (9 ft 6 in) *Draught:* 2.68 m (8 ft 9½ in) *Machinery:* 1-shaft electric motor, 183 shp=6.1/4.3 knots (surfaced/submerged) *Armament:* 4 45-cm (17.7-in) torpedoes in dropcollars *Crew:* 16

Farmer, Mikoyan MiG-19

Soviet jet fighter. The MiG-19 was the first Russian production aircraft capable of exceeding the speed of sound in level flight and was the second type in the world to achieve this distinction, having been preceded by its approximate counterpart in the US, the North American F-100 Super Sabre. The first round, initiated in the late 1940s, produced the Lavochkin La-190 and Yakovlev Yak-1000; the former made its maiden flight in February 1951 but was grossly overweight and had unacceptable handling characteristics, while the latter was judged to be so unstable that permission to fly the prototype was refused.

Authorization for the development of the MiG-19 to succeed the MiG-17 then entering service was granted in 1951, although design work had begun the previous year. The MiG-19 followed the basic layout of its predecessors, the MiG-15/MiG-17 series, although twin engines were adopted, and was designed to perform similar roles—single-seat clear-weather interception, with ground attack as a secondary mission—but with performance improvements all round. Mikoyan's I-350 design, also known as the Type SM, made its maiden flight in September 1953 and entered production as the MiG-19 in the second half of the following year. Deliveries to the Soviet

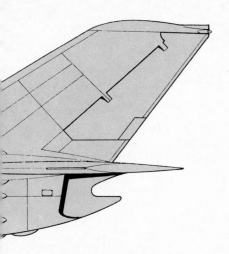

air force began early in 1955, and 48 flew in formation at that year's Soviet Aviation Day, held at Tushino. Early MiG-19s were powered by a pair of Mikulin AM-5 axial-flow turbojets each producing 2250 kg (5000 lb) of thrust dry and 3040 kg (6700 lb) with afterburning. The engines are mounted side-by-side in the rear fuselage and fed from a divided annular intake in the nose. The three-spar wings are tapered and swept back by 55° at 25% chord, with a full-chord fence on each side. Anhedral is about 4.5°. The large-area Fowler flaps can be used at up to 800 km/h (495 mph) in combat, and lateral control in later aircraft is effected by ailerons assisted by spoilers, this arrangement having been used first on the MiG-15SD.

The area-ruled fuselage has a cylindrical nose and carries a cluster of air scoops at the rear to cool the afterburners, with others on either side of the spine feeding the electronics bays. Air brakes were fitted to the fuselage sides in early models, later aircraft having an additional one mounted ventrally. The fin and fuselage-mounted tailplanes are swept back. Conventional elevators were fitted to the initial production MiG-19s, but were found to be relatively ineffective and were replaced by an all-moving tailplane with antiflutter weights at the tips. The type was then redesignated MiG-19S (*Stabilizator,* tailplane). Fuel is carried in four fuselage cells with a total capacity of 2170 litres (477 Imperial gal) and can be supplemented by a pair of underwing drop tanks containing 800 litres (176 Imperial gal) each. A dorsal spine housing control, running between the cockpit and the tail, was introduced into the MiG-19S. A fully duplicated hydraulic system was employed and the tailplane was geared electro-mechanically to operate at a nearly constant rate of stick-force per g. An electrical system was provided to operate the tailplane in the event of hydraulic failure.

Early MiG-19S carried a 37-mm (1.46-in) N-37 cannon with 40 rounds in the right-hand side of the forward fuselage and a 23-mm (0.90-in) NR-23 with 80 rounds in each wing. The MiG-19S, which entered full service in the second half of 1956, carried three 30-mm (1.18-in) NR-30 cannon in place of the earlier gun armament and was fitted with two air-to-surface weapon stations under the wings.

Typical weapons were a pair of UV-8-57 pods each containing eight 55-cm (21.6-in) S-5 rockets, two 250-kg (550-lb) bombs or a pair of 190-mm (7.5-in) TRS-190 or 212-mm (8.35-in) ARS-212 rockets.

In 1957, the original production aircraft codenamed Farmer-A by NATO was joined by the MiG-19SF (*Forsirovanny,* boosted), which was code-named Farmer-C. The Mikulin engines were replaced by a pair of Tumansky RD-9Bs each rated at 2600 kg (5730 lb) dry and 3250 kg (7165 lb) with reheat. Farmer-B was the MiG-19PF (*Perekhvatchik,* Intercepter), an all-weather version fitted with the X-band Scan Odd fire-control radar using dual pulse-repetition frequencies. The main antenna was housed in a bullet fairing mounted on the central intake splitter, with the complementary ranging radar installed in the upper lip. The last model built before the production line closed in 1959 was Farmer-D, the MiG-19PM, which followed the example set with the MiG-17 series and discarded gun armament in favour of four AA-1 Alkali radar-guided air-to-air missiles. A two-seat version, the MiG-19UTI, was also delivered.

The MiG-19 was built under licence as the S.105 in Czechoslovakia and as the LIM-7 in Poland. The type was supplied to China before relations soured in 1960, and the Shenyang National Aircraft Factory has copied the MiG-19 as the F-6. Chinese-built F-6s have been supplied to 'friendly' countries, including Pakistan, and are thought to incorporate indigenously developed improvements. The Pakistani aircraft have performed well in periodic clashes against Western-supplied types and MiG-21s operated by the Indian air force.

The MiG-19 has also been used as a testbed in a number of experimental programmes. Under the designation SM-10 it was used for in-flight refuelling trials from 1955, and in 1957 the SM-12PM was tested with RS-26 turbojets, a search/track radar mounted in a conical housing in the centre of the intake, and an enlarged dorsal spine. The SM-12PM carried two AA-1 Alkali air-to-air missiles and is claimed to have reached a speed of Mach 1.6 and an altitude of 17 400 m (57 100 ft), taking only four minutes to attain a height of 10 000 m (32 800 ft). A further modification, the SM-12PMU, was fitted with a Duchkin RU-01S liquid rocket boost motor which enabled the aircraft to peak at 24 000 m (78 740 ft) during trials in 1958.

SM-30 was the bureau designation of a pre-series MiG-19 which was used for catapult takeoff trials in 1956, and three years later the SM-50 underwent tests while fitted with RD-9BM turbojets of 3300 kg (7275 lb) thrust each with reheat, augmented by a U-19 rocket motor producing 3200 kg (7055 lb). A maximum speed of 1800 km/h (1118 mph) was attained, and a height of 20 000 m (65 600 ft) was reached in eight minutes.

MiG-19S: *Span:* 9 m (29 ft 6 in) *Length:* 13.09 m (42 ft 11 in) *Gross weight:* 8700 kg (19 180 lb) *Maximum speed:* Mach 1.4

Farquhar-Hill

British rifle. Colonel M G Farquhar, of Aboyne, Aberdeenshire, and Mr A H Hill, of Birmingham, collaborated in the development of an automatic rifle, their first joint patent being taken out in 1906. This was for a recoil-operated weapon in which the energy imparted by the recoiling barrel was stored in a spring until the chamber pressure had dropped, after which the spring power was used to open the bolt and complete the firing cycle.

In 1909 a fresh patent covered a system of gas operation. Subsequent patents improved on this, and a 1912 patent brought all the improvements together into a completely new design. It should be pointed out that many of the items in these patents applied equally well to the Beardmore-Farquhar machine-gun design which was proceeding at the same time.

A first prototype military service rifle was submitted for trial in 1912, without success. Various modifications were made, including a 20-shot rotary magazine, envisaged for possible air service or for 'assault fire', and improved models of the rifle were tested by

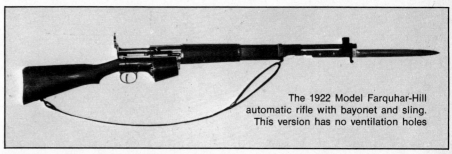

The 1922 Model Farquhar-Hill automatic rifle with bayonet and sling. This version has no ventilation holes

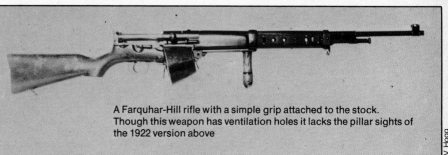

A Farquhar-Hill rifle with a simple grip attached to the stock. Though this weapon has ventilation holes it lacks the pillar sights of the 1922 version above

Farragut

Top: The USS *Dewey* a *Farragut* Class destroyer. *Above:* USS *Hull,* like her sisters, was modified during the war with air and surface warning radar and improved 40-mm and 20-mm AA guns

the army at various times until the early 1920s, but none were considered to be sufficiently simple and robust for military adoption, and the inventors finally gave up. No data can be given, since no two Farquhar-Hill rifles were alike.

Farragut

US destroyer. This vessel was the first of a class of eight destroyers authorized in 1916, but not laid down until 1932. They were the first destroyers to be built for the US Navy after the end of the First World War and formed part of a large programme of expansion and modernization. Although restricted by the naval arms limitations treaties then in force, the Americans took full advantage of technological advances in warship design resulting from experience in the First World War.

The design of the new destroyers differed radically from the flush-decked destroyers of First World War vintage, which at that time formed the backbone of the American destroyer fleet. Among the new features was a raised forecastle and enclosed bridge structure, while four gun mounts were in superimposed positions fore and aft with a fifth mount abaft the after funnel.

The Americans were determined to counter new Japanese destroyer designs and specified that the new class must incorporate the heaviest possible armament with a wide radius of action suitable for extended operations in the Pacific. As a result, bunkerage of the *Farragut* Class was much greater than that of the contemporary British 'E' Class destroyers. In spite of the increased bunkerage, however, fuel consumption of the *Farragut* Class was high. Although they carried 130 tons more fuel than the British 'E' Class, their radius of action was, in fact, inferior to the British destroyers—11 100 km (6900 miles) at 15 knots as opposed to 11 748 km (7300 miles) at 15 knots. Armament for the *Farragut* Class included a new dual purpose 5-in (127-mm) weapon which had been

designed for their new cruisers. Five of these guns were carried, in single mountings, those in A and E positions being fitted with splinterproof open shields, while the other three mountings lacked any form of protection. The *Farragut* Class also marked the introduction of the quadruple torpedo tube mounting to the US Navy.

Being the first destroyer to be built after the end of the First World War, and carrying a complete new weapons outfit as well as other modern equipment, the *Farragut* spent her early years carrying out trials and development programmes.

During the war, the 5-in (127-mm) gun mounting abaft the after funnel was replaced by two single 20-mm (0.79-in) mounts. Another 20-mm (0.79-in) gun was added in front of the bridge on a bandstand, two single mounts between the funnels and another single 20-mm (0.79-in) mount on the after superstructure. The mainmast was removed and various radars added. Later in the war, two twin 40-mm (1.57-in) guns were added.

The *Hull* and *Monaghan* foundered off the Philippine Islands on December 18, 1944, while the *Worden* was wrecked in the Aleutian Islands on January 12, 1943. The rest of the class was scrapped in 1947.

Aylwin (DD.355) was launched July 1934, at Philadelphia navy yard; *Dale* (DD.353) January 1935, at New York navy yard; *Dewey* (DD.349) July 1934, at Bath Iron Works; *Farragut* (DD.348) March 1934, at Bethlehem, Quincy; *Hull* (DD.350) January 1934, at New York navy yard; *MacDonough* (DD.351) August 1934, at Boston navy yard; *Monaghan* (DD.354) January 1935, at Boston navy yard; *Worden* (DD.352) October 1934, at Puget Sound navy yard, Bremerton.

Displacement: 1345-1410 tons (standard) *Length:* 104 m (341 ft 3 in) oa *Beam:* 10.4 m (34 ft 3 in) *Draught:* 3.1 m (10 ft 2 in) *Machinery:* 2-shaft Parsons geared turbines 42 800 shp=36½ knots *Armament:* 5 127-mm (5-in)/38-cal guns; 4 machine-guns; 8 53-cm (21-in) torpedo tubes *Crew:* 250

Fasen

German homing torpedo. In 1944 a number of active homing torpedoes were under development, starting with Boje and Geier. The Fasen (pheasant) resembled the Ibis in following the target's wake, but was unique in that it entered the wake and then went into a pre-set running pattern. It was dropped in favour of the Geier system.

Faulknor

British destroyer leader class. In 1912, Chile ordered six large destroyers from J S White of Cowes, Isle of Wight, of which two were completed and delivered before August 1914. The remaining four, *Almirante Goni, Almirante Simpson, Almirante Williams Robelledo,* and *Almirante Riveros,* were purchased by the Admiralty shortly after the outbreak of war and renamed *Broke, Faulknor, Botha* and *Tipperary* respectively. Being considerably larger than contemporary British destroyers, they were completed as flotilla leaders, *Broke* and *Faulknor* entering service in 1914 and *Botha* and *Tipperary* in 1915. The first pair mounted three 4-in (102-mm) guns, on each side, two on the forecastle and one aft, and two single torpedo tubes on each beam. In the second pair, the arrangement was modified to provide one centreline and two sided 4-in (102-mm) guns forward and aft and one twin torpedo tube mounting on each beam. The officers' accommodation was somewhat better than that found in contemporary British vessels, but the crews' quarters were considered below standard.

On completion, they were assigned to the destroyer flotillas of the Grand Fleet, and three of the class (*Botha* was refitting) took part in the Battle of Jutland in 1916. During the night actions of this battle, *Tipperary* was set on fire by the guns of three German cruisers at point blank range and sank about three hours later at 0200 hours on June 1. Shortly after this engagement, *Broke* was badly damaged by gunfire from the battleship *Westfalen,* and as a result collided with the destroyer *Sparrowhawk.* She survived and, after repairs, rejoined the fleet in August.

At the end of 1916, *Faulknor* and *Broke* transferred to the Dover Patrol where they were joined in 1917 by *Botha.* On the night of April 20, 1917, *Broke,* accompanied by the leader *Swift,* intercepted six German destroyers returning from a hit-and-run raid on the Dover area. In the subsequent engagement, *Broke* torpedoed the *G 85* and rammed the *G 42.* Both German vessels were sunk, and *Broke* was brought to a stop, badly damaged. As at Jutland, she survived and was towed back to Dover for repairs.

During 1918-19, the three destroyers were rearmed, four of their original 4-in (102-mm) guns being replaced by two 4.7-in (120-mm) weapons. *Botha, Broke* and *Faulknor* were sold back to Chile in 1920 and were renamed *Almirante Williams, Almirante Uribe* and *Almirante Riveros* respectively.

Displacement: 1700 tons (normal), 2000 tons (full load) *Length:* 101 m (330 ft 10 in) *Beam:* 9.9 m (32 ft 6 in) *Draught:* 3.35 m (11 ft) *Machinery:* 3-shaft geared turbines, 30 000 shp=31 knots *Armament:* 6 4-in (102-mm) (6×1) 4 53-cm (21-in) torpedo tubes *Crew:* 205

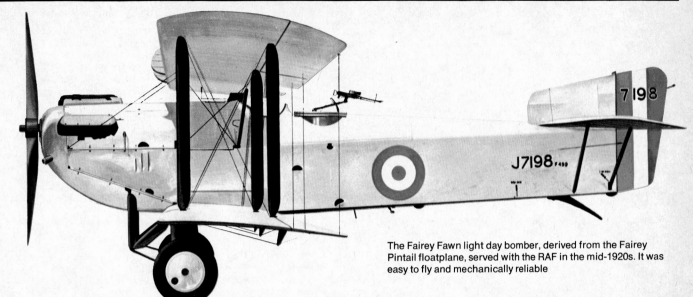

The Fairey Fawn light day bomber, derived from the Fairey Pintail floatplane, served with the RAF in the mid-1920s. It was easy to fly and mechanically reliable

Fawn, Fairey

British day bomber. Derived from the Fairey Pintail amphibian of 1920, the Fawn was the first post-1918 designed light day bomber to see RAF service. Intended as an army co-operation vehicle to replace the de Havilland 9A, the Fawn prototype, J6907, first flew in March 1923. After various modifications, including a longer fuselage, the design went into limited production, and the first production example appeared in January 1924, designated Fawn Mk II. This version entered RAF service, and eventually equipped Nos 11, 12, 100, 503 and 602 Squadrons. A further variant, the Mk III, fitted with turbo-supercharged Lion VI engine, was built but did not reach squadron use. Although ugly in appearance, the Fawn was pleasant to fly and proved to be a reliable workhorse. Several were fitted with external side-ladders and used for parachute-dropping exercises and demonstrations at Henlow; while machines of 12 and 100 Squadrons participated in the 1925 and 1926 RAF air displays at Hendon, demonstrating 'wing drill'.

Span: 15 m (49 ft 11 in) *Length:* 9.8 m (32 ft 1 in) *Height:* 3.6 m (11 ft 11 in) *Maximum speed:* 183 km/h (114 mph) at 3048 m (10 000 ft) *Climb to* 3048 m (10 000 ft):17 min 24 sec *Service ceiling:* 4220 m (13 850 ft) *Powerplant:* 470-hp Napier Lion *Armament:* 1 Vickers mg forward; 1 or 2 Lewis mg rear cockpit; External bombload to 209 kg (460 lb)

FB, Boeing

US Navy/Marine Corps single-seat fighter aircraft. The FB-1 was the US Marine Corps counterpart of the Army Air Service's PW-9 (Boeing Model 15), having the same 435-hp Curtiss D-12 engine and two-gun armament. Ten were completed (of 16 ordered) and were delivered in December 1925 to the shore-based fighter squadrons VF-1M, -2M and -3M. They were used in 1927 and 1928 by the US Expeditionary Force in China. The other six became FB-2s (two), FB-3s (three) or FB-4 (one), fitted variously with arrester gear, float undercarriage or alternative power-plants. The only other production version, however, was the FB-5 for the US Navy (Boeing Model 67), which differed from the FB-1 in having a 520-hp Packard 2A-1500 engine, increased wing stagger, and a balanced rudder. Twenty-seven were delivered in January 1927 to Marine fighter squadrons VF-1B and VF-6B for service aboard the *Langley*.

(FB-1) *Span:* 9.75 m (32 ft) *Length:* 7.14 m (23 ft 5 in) *Gross weight:* 1286 kg (2835 lb) *Maximum speed:* 256 km/h (159 mph)

FB.9, Vickers

British two-seat fighter/trainer aircraft. The success of the Vickers FB5 'Gunbus' on operations in France in 1915 led the parent firm to produce an improved variant, the FB.9, or 'Streamline Gunbus' as it was dubbed by the Royal Flying Corps. Basically similar in construction and 'pusher' config-uration to its predecessor, the FB.9 was slightly smaller in all-round size, with various minor improvements in shape and outline. Production was undertaken and eventually approximately 150 machines were built, including an unspecified number by the French Darracq firm.

The only FB.9s known to have seen opera-tional service were seven examples (Serials 7812, 7813, 7820, 7826, 7827 and 7828), all of which were flown on war patrols by 11 Squadron RFC in France in June-July 1916. On July 1, 7828 gained a confirmed aerial combat victory. All other FB.9s were rele-gated to RFC and RNAS training units, where their sterling qualities gave faithful service until late 1918. As trainers, several

Only seven examples of the Vickers FB.9 'Streamline Gunbus' saw action during the First World War, but the type was widely used by the RFC and RNAS as a trainer and remained in service until 1918

The Vickers FB.9 with dual controls was used for both pilot training and air gunnery practice

FB.9s were modified to have dual controls, and many had a Scarff ring fitted in the front cockpit for gunnery practice. At least one FB.9 was armoured and fitted with an oleo undercarriage.

Span: 10.3 m (33 ft 9 in) *Length:* 8.7 m (28 ft 5½ in) *Height:* 3.5 m (11 ft 6 in) *Engine:* 100-hp Gnome Monosoupape rotary, or 110-hp Le Rhône rotary *Maximum speed:* 132.9 km/h (82.6 mph) at ground level *Climb to 3048 m (10 000 ft):* 51 min *Service ceiling:* 3353 m (11 000 ft)

F B P

Portuguese submachine-gun. The weapon was manufactured at the Fabrica do Braco do Prata, Lisbon, and designed by Major Goncalves Cardoso of the Portuguese army in 1948. Cardoso made a careful analysis of existing successful submachine-guns and put together a design based on the best features of various models plus a few ideas of his own. The bolt and return spring were enclosed in a telescoping tubular cover, as in the German MP38, and the attachment of the barrel and cocking lever are from the same gun. The pressed-steel frame, firing mechanism and collapsible wire butt were taken from the American M3 submachine-gun, while the exposed, stepped, barrel, bayonet and bayonet fittings were of Cardoso's design. The result was a sound, if undistinguished, weapon which served the Portuguese army quite well, though users do not speak very highly of its accuracy.

Calibre: 9 mm (0.354 in) Parabellum *Length:* 813 mm (32 in) *Weight, loaded:* 4.43 kg (9 lb 12 oz) *Barrel length:* 250 mm (9.84 in) *Magazine:* 32-round detachable box *Rate of fire:* 500 rds/min

---

F.E2, Royal Aircraft Factory British aircraft

F.E.8, Royal Aircraft Factory British aircraft

F.E.2, Royal Aircraft Factory

British fighter/reconaissance biplane series. The first aircraft to carry the F.E. designation was the F.E.1, designed by Geoffrey de Havilland in 1910 and named Farman Experimental because of its resemblance to contemporary Farman pusher biplanes. The F.E.1 was rebuilt as the F.E.2 after a crash in 1911,

and the F.E.2 was itself rebuilt, to a different design but with the same designation, in 1913. However, the first of the Royal Aircraft Factory's series of F.E. fighters, the F.E.2a designed in the summer of 1914, had nothing but the basic fact of being a pusher-propelled biplane in common with the earlier machines, notwithstanding the similarity of the designations.

Twelve F.E.2as were ordered from the Royal Aircraft Factory in August 1914, and the first machine emerged in January 1915 as a large two-bay biplane with accommodation for the pilot and observer in an armoured nacelle forward of the wings and a 100-hp Green engine mounted above the lower wing driving a two-blade wooden pusher propeller. The centre section of the upper wing was hinged aft of the rear spar and could be lowered to act as an air brake, while an even

more radical innovation was a small tail-braking parachute tried on the first 2a. The tail assembly, with distinctive triangular fin, was mounted on converging booms extending aft from the upper and lower wing spars, while the oleo undercarriage incorporated a small nosewheel. A mounting for a Lewis machine-gun was provided in the observer's front cockpit, and it was the unobstructed forward field of fire provided by the pusher configuration and cockpit arrangement that was to make the later F.E.2s so successful over the Western Front.

The Green engine proved to have a poor power-to-weight ratio and later F.E.2as were modified to take the 120-hp Beardmore engine. This modification delayed completion of the remaining aircraft, and the last of the 12 was not finished until November 1915, by which time the first F.E.2bs had begun to

appear. The early 2b was essentially a simplified version of the 2a, having the same wings but without the centre-section air brake, and a somewhat smaller nacelle mounting the same engine and armament as the earlier type. However, later 2bs had modified wings of the same section as those fitted to the F.E.2c, and the 160-hp Beardmore was fitted in place of the 120-hp in order to improve performance, while other engines were fitted experimentally.

Many experimental armament installations were made in F.E.2bs, including a 1-pdr Vickers quick-firing gun in a raised cowling, twin Lewis mountings, additional Lewis mountings between the cockpits to give a rearward field of fire and a 0.45-in (11.43-mm) Maxim, and some examples were modified for home defence with a single cockpit and two internal Lewis guns firing through the nose. As the 2b became obsolescent as a fighting scout by early 1917 it was developed as a night bomber and antisubmarine aircraft, with the result that it remained in production until the end of the war. Bombload of the fighter/reconnaissance version was up to eight 9-kg (20-lb) bombs; for night-bombing missions the 2b could carry a variety of bombs in combinations ranging from 14 11.4-kg (25-lb) to a single 104-kg (230-lb).

Many F.E.2bs were built by contracting firms with little or no previous experience of building aircraft, notably Boulton & Paul, G & J Weir and Ransome, Sims and Jeffries, and at least 1000 were produced, the official total of 1939 probably including conversions of earlier aircraft for bombing, experimental and training purposes.

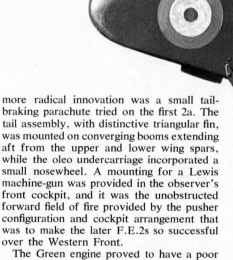

A 160-hp Beardmore-powered F.E.2b with the nose-wheel removed from the oleo undercarriage

Two variants of the 2b designated F.E.2c were produced in 1915. The first of these had a new nose cowling to the nacelle incorporating a Lewis gun with limited traverse fired by the pilot who now sat in the front cockpit, while the observer's gun was mounted behind the pilot's seat. The other F.E.2c also incorporated a new type of gun mounting, while small numbers of 2cs were also produced in 1918 as night bombers.

In April 1916, the prototype F.E.2d, a modified 2b mounting the 250-hp Rolls-Royce Mk 1 engine, was flown. The new engine gave a significant improvement in climb rate and performance at altitude, and quantities of FE.2ds with various marks of Rolls-Royce engines were produced. The additional power also permitted increased armament, and 2ds were equipped with various arrangements of Lewis guns, some having one or two fixed guns in the nose in addition to one or two free guns fired by the observer.

The F.E.2a had been designed from the outset as a fighting aircraft, and the distinguished record of the series over three years of war in a number of roles testifies to the soundness of the basic design. The first operational unit to fly 2as in France was 6 Squadron RFC, which had four on its strength by September 1915. The type's arrival in France coincided with the introduction of the German Fokker Eindekker (monoplane), which soon began to make an impact on the Western Front—and it was to a large extent the F.E.2b that helped to contain the 'Fokker scourge'. The wide field of fire of the observer's gun made it a potent aerial combat machine, and faster production in greater quantities might well have prevented the Fokker monoplanes becoming so much of a problem. Although it has been claimed that the German ace Max Immelman died as a

result of shooting off his own propeller, it was certainly after combat with an F.E.2b that his fatal crash occurred.

F.E.2bs continued to more than hold their own, but the effect of the introduction of the F.E.2d in June 1916 was adversely affected when the first machine to go to France was landed by mistake on the German airfield at Lille after the pilot had lost his way in fog. Nevertheless, the fixed forward-firing guns enabled 2ds to be flown as true fighters and they gained a number of successes. By the spring of 1917 F.E.2s were clearly becoming outclassed as fighters and the 2bs were withdrawn from offensive duties in April, though the 2d continued in front-line service until the following autumn.

Towards the end of 1916 the first night-bombing expeditions were being mounted, and F.E.2bs carrying bombs or heavy guns proved eminently successful in attacks on such targets as enemy airfields, railway stations and trains. Bombing raids were continued through 1917, and from mid-1917 onwards the number of F.E.2b-equipped night bomber squadrons in France steadily increased. Frequent raids against enemy communications and other targets continued until almost the end of the war.

The type was not so successful at home defence, since its ceiling of 3350 m (11 000 ft) was too low to permit the interception of enemy aircraft and airships. However, another use was found for the 2b in early 1918, when two flights were based on the northeastern coast of England to carry out coastal patrols. On the evening of May 31, one of these aircraft spotted the German submarine *UC49* moving submerged near Seaham, Co Durham, and dropped his two 45-kg (100-lb) bombs near the vessel. The destroyer *Locust*, attracted by the explosions, was guided by the F.E.2b, and depth-charged and sank the submarine.

Span: 14.55 m (47 ft 9 in) *Length:* 9.83 m (32 ft 3 in) *Gross weight:* (160-hp F.E.2b) 1378 kg (3037 lb); (F.E.2d) 1574 kg (3470 lb) *Maximum speed:* (160-hp F.E.2b) 147 km/h (91.5 mph); (F.E.2d) 151 km/h (94 mph)

F.E.8, Royal Aircraft Factory

British biplane fighter. The next fighter after the F.E.2 in the F.E. line was the F.E.8 of 1915. The 1913 F.E.3 was used in static tests with the 1-pdr COW gun, and the twin-engined F.E.4, of which two were built in 1916, was

Despite the early success of pusher fighters over the Western Front, the F.E.8 had a disastrous career during the First World War. They arrived at the front late in 1916 by which time they were outclassed by contemporary German types. During one black day on March 9, 1917 nine F.E.8s were attacked by Manfred von Richthofen's Jasta 11. Four were shot down, four forced to land and the pilot of the ninth was wounded and crash landed

F.E.9, Royal Aircraft Factory

A posed picture of the enemy-eye-view of an F.E.8. From behind they were tragically vulnerable

intended to be a ground attack aircraft. The F.E.6 was an unsatisfactory development of the F.E.3, while the F.E.5 and 7 were never built. Resembling the D.H.2, but designed before the de Havilland fighter, the F.E.8 was another two-bay pusher biplane. The prototype F.E.8 had a 100-hp Gnome Monosoupape engine and was armed with a remote-controlled Lewis firing through the nose of the all-metal nacelle. This installation proved troublesome, however, and production of F.E.8s had the gun mounted at eye level.

The prototype's service trials, beginning in December 1915, were successful, but production F.E.8s did not appear until May 1916. Although an eventual total of 182 were built, 147 of which were sent to France, only two RFC squadrons, 40 and 41, were fully equipped with F.E.8s. The second of these did not arrive in France until October 1916, by which time, in spite of some early successes, the type was completely outclassed by contemporary German fighters: the first production F.E.8 was shot down within a week of its arrival on June 22. On March 9, 1917, nine F.E.8s of 40 Squadron were attacked by Manfred von Richthofen's Jasta 11. Four were shot down, another four forced to land, and the pilot of the ninth was wounded and crash landed. In spite of this disaster, the last F.E.8s were not withdrawn until July 1917, one of their final operational uses being in ground strafing during the battle of Messines in June of that year.

Span: 9.6 m (31 ft 6 in) *Length:* 7.2 m (23 ft 8 in) *Gross weight:* 610.5 kg (1346 lb) *Maximum speed:* 151 km/h (94 mph)

F.E.9, Royal Aircraft Factory

British biplane fighter. Designed in 1916 as a replacement for the F.E.2b, the F.E.9, the last of the series to be built, was another pusher biplane at a time when machine-gun synchronizing gears had made the pusher configuration obsolete. The tail assembly was mounted on converging booms and the long nacelle was mounted high up between the wings with forward- and rearward-firing Lewis guns to improve the observer's field of fire; powerplant was a 200-hp Hispano-Suiza. Difficulties with control in flight and various modifications made in attempts to eradicate

them delayed production, and in the event only three F.E.9s were built, one serving with a home defence squadron.

Span: 11.5 m (37 ft 9½ in) *Length:* 8.6 m (28 ft 3 in) *Gross weight:* 1125 kg (2480 lb) *Maximum speed:* 169 km/h (105 mph)

Fearless

British destroyer class. The *Fearless* or 'F' Class destroyers of the 1932 Programme were in all but a few minor details repeats of the previous *Eclipse* Class. All eight were laid down in 1933, launched in 1934, and completed in 1935, except for the name ship which completed in 1934. The ships were very little altered until 1940 when the after bank of torpedo tubes was replaced by a 12-pdr AA gun and the after funnel was shortened and the mainmast removed to clear its area of fire. Y gun was later removed to provide space and weight for additional depth charge equipment (except in *Foresight* and *Fury*) and two 20-mm (0.79-in) AA guns were added in the bridge wings. During 1943-44 *Fame, Forester, Fortune* and *Foxhound* were fitted with a Hedgehog ASW on the fore-

castle and had their 0.5-in (12.7-mm) guns replaced by two 20-mm (0.79-in) AA guns. All, except *Fearless, Firedrake* and *Fury*, had a third pair of 20-mm (0.79-in) added abreast the searchlight platform and all, except *Fearless, Foresight* and *Fury*, had their bridge director replaced by surface warning radar.

The class became the 8th Destroyer Flotilla in August 1939 and served with the Home Fleet until mid-1940 when they transferred to Force H at Gibraltar. In October 1940, *Fame* returned to the Home Fleet, but on October 17 ran aground in fog on the east coast off Sunderland. She was subsequently salvaged, repaired and returned to service as an Atlantic escort vessel in 1942. On July 23, 1941, both *Fearless* and *Firedrake* were seriously damaged by torpedoes dropped by Italian aircraft. As part of Force H, the two destroyers were taking a convoy through to Malta in the operation codenamed Substance. The convoy—six merchant ships and a troop transport—had been organized in anticipation of a German airborne attack on the island. *Fearless* had to be abandoned and was sunk by *Forester* north of Bone, Tunisia, but *Firedrake* was towed to Gibraltar and subsequently refitted in the US. Not long after the completion of this refit, on December 16, 1942, she was torpedoed and sunk by the German submarine *U 211* in the North Atlantic. *Foresight* returned to the Home Fleet in September 1941 to be followed by *Forester* and *Fury* in January 1942, all three taking an active part in covering Russian convoys during 1942. *Fury* and *Foresight* returned to the Mediterranean in August 1942 to take part in the 'Pedestal' convoy. During this operation, on August 12, *Foresight* was hit by an aerial torpedo. She was taken in tow, but sank the following day.

In March 1942, the last pair in the Mediterranean, *Foxhound* and *Fortune*, were transferred to the Eastern Fleet. They returned to the UK in mid-1943 and were transferred to the Royal Canadian Navy, being renamed *Qu'Appelle* and *Saskatchewan* respectively. They, and the other survivors of the class, served most of the remainder of the war as Atlantic Escorts. *Fury*, however, served in the Mediterranean during 1943-44 and (with

The prototype F.E.9. It had horn-balanced ailerons similar to those of the original B.E.12a

Forester) she took part in the Normandy landings, during which, on June 21, she was mined off the beachhead and driven ashore. Her hulk was scrapped in late 1944.

The antisubmarine record of the class was quite outstanding and covered the entire period of the war. In September 1939, *Forester* and *Fortune* sank the *U27*, and *Faulknor* and *Foxhound* the *U39*. During 1940, *Fortune* sank *U44* and *Firedrake* sank the Italian *Durbo*. In 1941, *Forester*, *Foresight* and *Foxhound* combined with their leader, *Faulknor*, to sink the *U138*. In 1942, *Fame* sank *U353*, *Fury* sank *U585* and *Foxhound* assisted in sinking *U179*. In 1943, *Fame* sank *U201* and in 1944 assisted in sinking *U767* while *Forester* helped to sink *U845* and *U413*.

The survivors of the class were sold for scrap during 1945-47 except for *Fame* which was sold to the Dominican Republic in 1948 and renamed *Generalisimo*.

Fame, Firedrake—built by Vickers Armstrong
Fearless, Foresight—built by Cammell Laird
Forester, Fury—built by White
Fortune, Foxhound—built by J Brown
Faulknor—built by Yarrow

Displacement: 1405 tons (standard), 1940 tons (full load) *Length:* 100.28 m (329 ft) *Beam:* 10.13 m (33 ft 3 in) *Draught:* 2.59 m (8 ft 6 in) *Machinery:* 2-shaft geared steam turbines, 36 000 shp= 25.5 knots *Armament:* 4 4.7-in (120-mm) (4× 1); 8 0.5-in (12.7-mm) AA (2× 4) guns; 8 53-cm (21-in) torpedo tubes (2× 4) *Crew:* 145

Fearless

British assault ship class, built 1962-67. By 1946, the original Landing Ships, Dock (LSD) built in 1943-44 had all been returned to the US, and when the British Ministry of Defence decided to expand the amphibious capability of the Army and Navy in the late 1950s it was decided to build two expanded and up-to-date versions of this unusual type.

C & S Taylor

The British assault ship *Fearless* (L.10). She carries both landing craft and helicopters

Fearless can carry four LCM(9) (Landing Craft, Mechanized) in dock and four LCVP (Landing Craft, Vehicle or Personnel) on davits, with a flight deck for five Wessex helicopters above the stern dock. In an assault the stern dock is flooded to allow the LCMs to float out under their own power. She has a capacity for 380-400 troops or 700 marines for short periods

C & S Taylor

Fearless

The British assault ship *Fearless*, launched in 1963 as an expanded and up-dated version of the original US LSDs (Landing Ships, Dock), and basically—together with her sister *Intrepid*—a self-propelled floating dock. Both ships have seakeeping qualities superior to those of tank landing ships and greater speed and range. They can operate independently and each ship is equipped as a Naval Assault/Brigade HQ capable of launching and controlling an assault landing by air and seaborne troops. By 1978 *Fearless* was a training ship at the Royal Naval College, Dartmouth and had been tested with Harrier V/STOL aircraft

Feather

C & S Taylor

HMS *Fearless* showing her flooded stern dock. She is armed with four Seacat missile launchers and two 40-mm Bofors light antiaircraft guns

The *Fearless* was launched by Harland and Wolff, Belfast, in December 1963 and her sister *Intrepid* was launched six months later by John Brown on the Clyde. They are basically self-propelled floating docks, with a large well-deck and a stern gate; the ship can be flooded down, and when the stern gate is open landing craft can ferry men and vehicles to the beach-head. The main advantage of these big and complex ships over LSTs (Landing Ships, Tank) and LCTs (Landing Craft, Tank) is their seaworthiness, speed and range and the fact that a large number of assault troops can be accommodated in reasonable comfort. There is also room for the HQ and staff as well as tanks and vehicles.

The ships carry only a light close-range defence against air attack: four Seacat missile-launchers and two single 40-mm (1.57 in) Bofors guns. The pendant members were originally *L.3004* and *L.3005*, but they are now *L.10* and *L.11*. Each ship carries four LCM (9) ramped landing craft in davits. Both ships are fitted with helicopter landing-platforms and *Fearless* has tested the Harrier V/STOL aircraft. In 1969 *Intrepid* was fitted with the Skynet satellite communications system but this has since been removed.

In 1976 *Intrepid* went into reserve, leaving *Fearless* as a training ship attached to the Royal Naval College, Dartmouth. The *Intrepid* was due to relieve *Fearless* in 1979.

Displacement: 11 060 tons (standard), 12 120 tons (full load), 16 950 tons (ballasted) *Length:* 158.5 m (520 ft) oa *Beam:* 24.4 m (80 ft) *Draught:* 6.2 m (20 ft 6 in) *Machinery:* 2-shaft geared steam turbines, 22 000 shp=21 knots *Armament:* 2 40-mm (1.57-in) AA (2×1); 4 Seacat GWS 22 quadruples SAM-launchers *Crew:* 580 (including 400 troops)+700 troops for short periods

Feather, Yakovlev Yak-17

Soviet jet fighter. The Yak-17 was developed from the Yak-15, a minimum-change conversion of the piston-engined Yak-3U to accept jet propulsion. In 1945 the Soviet authorities instructed four bureaux to design fighters around the captured German jet engines which were becoming available. Mikoyan/ Gurevich and Sukhoi were allocated responsibility for twin-engined types, with Lavochkin and Yakovlev concentrating on single-jet aircraft. The powerplant was to be the Kolesov RD-10, an adaptation of the Junkers Jumo 004B developing 850 kg (1874 lb) of thrust. Lavochkin started from scratch with a new airframe, but Yakovlev and his co-designer, Adler, based their contender on the Yak-3U. The resulting Yak-15 became the second Soviet jet aircraft to fly, being beaten by the Mikoyan I-300 by a matter of an hour on April 24, 1946.

The Yak-15 incorporated the wings, rear fuselage, tail and tail-wheel undercarriage of the Yak-3U. Installation of the turbojet in place of the piston engine necessitated modification of the wing-spar centre section, which was arched over the jet-pipe in order to keep the nozzle as high as possible. The forward fuselage was completely redesigned and the main longerons were strengthened to take the increased load. A stainless-steel sheet was attached beneath the rear fuselage to protect it from the hot exhaust gases, and a roller replaced the tail wheel, with protection against the jet blast being given by a shield.

The Yak-15 completed its acceptance trials in May 1947 and 280 were ordered as single-seat jet conversion trainers. The initial production batch used the tail-roller undercarriage, but this proved unsatisfactory and the type was redesigned as the Yak-15U (*Usover-*

shenstvovanny, or improved) with a tricycle layout. The nose wheel could not retract fully, since it was mounted beneath the air intake, so it was housed in a bulged fairing when in the up position. The change to a nose-wheel layout altered the Yak-15's balance, so the main undercarriage was modified to retract between the main spars instead of in front of the forward member.

Flutter problems with an airframe which had been designed to accept a piston engine resulted in the Yak-15's top speed being limited to Mach 0.68, thus preventing full power being used below 3200 m (10 500 ft). Some 400 Yak-15s are thought to have been built between October 1946 and March 1948, when the type was succeeded by the Yak-17 Feather.

The Yak-17 was powered by the uprated RD-10A rated at 1000 kg (2205 lb) of thrust. The Feather was slightly faster and lighter than its competitor, the La-150, and was substantially superior in range; rough-field performance of the Yak-17 was very much better than that of the Lavochkin design, which had a heavy narrow-track undercarriage. The La-150 was abandoned in April 1947 and the Yak-17 was ordered into production.

The two-seat Yak-17UTI Magnet is thought to have preceded the single-seater so that Russian crews could build up their jet experience. A second cockpit was added in front of the existing position and a long sliding canopy was fitted; an enlarged fin was also adopted for both the Magnet and Feather. The types remained in production from March 1948 to August 1949, at least 430 and possibly as many as 700 being built. The Yak-17UTI was the Soviet air force's first specialist jet trainer and remained in service until replaced by the MiG-15UTI.

The Yakovlev Yak-15 (NATO codenamed Feather) used a powerplant based on captured German jet engines, and was the second Soviet jet to fly

Span: 9.2 m (30 ft 2 in) *Length:* 8.78 m (28 ft 9½ in) *Gross weight:* 3323 kg (7326 lb) *Maximum speed:* 750 km/h (466 mph)

Calibre: 6.5 mm (0.256 in) *Weight:* 4.31 kg (9 lb 8 oz) *Length:* 1045 mm (41.14 in) *Barrel length:* 525 mm (20.67 in) *Magazine:* 25-shot detachable box *Rate of fire:* 600 rds/min *Muzzle velocity:* 731 m/sec (2400 ft/sec)

Federov

Soviet rifle. Vladimir Federov was born in 1874 and later entered military service in the artillery of the Czarist Russian army. After technical training at the artillery academy, he was appointed to a technical commission, examining weapon designs, and here he became interested in small arms and particularly in automatic weapons, a new field of study at that time. He began to design an automatic rifle, his first attempt being a gas-driven conversion of the Mosin-Nagant bolt-action rifle which, like most such conversions, was a failure. He then worked out a totally new design in which the barrel recoiled for a short distance to unlock the bolt, after which blowback action completed the bolt cycle of action.

One or two prototypes were made (reputedly by V A Degtyarev, then working 'on the bench' at Oranienburg arsenal) but it was not entirely successful. Much of the trouble lay with the 7.62-mm (0.30-in) Mosin-Nagant cartridge which was a powerful round with a fat, bottle-necked, rimmed case. It was an awkward shape for feeding and did not function well in a partially-blowback action.

After the Russo-Japanese war the Russian Army possessed a quantity of Japanese 6.5-mm (0.256-in) rifles and ammunition and they had conducted a number of tests and projects in this calibre. Federov saw that this slender, rimless round overcame most of his problems, and he redesigned his rifle around the 6.5-mm (0.256-in) cartridge. Since this round was less powerful than the 7.62-mm (0.30-in) one, it gave less recoil. This was good for the firer, but not so for the mechanism, and Federov had to incorporate a bolt accelerator into the mechanism to ensure positive operation. As finally developed, his 'Automat' was a short rifle with a forward pistol grip, firing from a 25-round box magazine.

A small number of these rifles were made in 1916, but the revolution a year later halted production. After a pause, work began again and the rifles remained in limited production until about 1924. Quantities of these rifles were used in the civil war, but they were apparently scrapped in the late 1920s and specimens are extremely uncommon.

Federov continued to work on arms design, though principally as an organizer and coordinator. He was awarded many decorations, including the Order of Lenin, and was promoted to Lieutenant General of the artillery technical service.

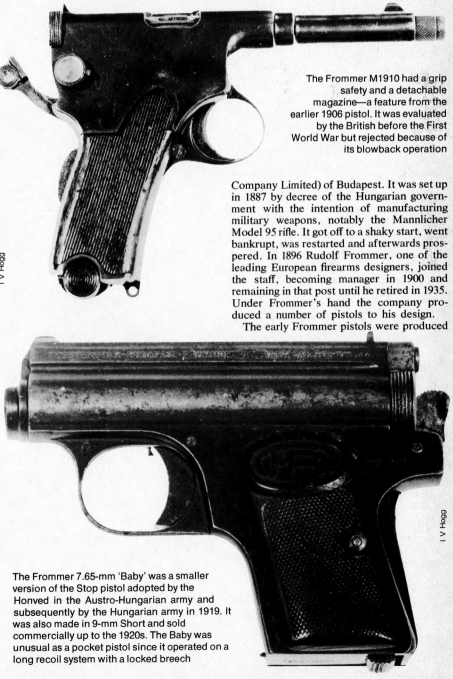

I V Hogg

The Frommer M1910 had a grip safety and a detachable magazine—a feature from the earlier 1906 pistol. It was evaluated by the British before the First World War but rejected because of its blowback operation

The Frommer 7.65-mm 'Baby' was a smaller version of the Stop pistol adopted by the Honved in the Austro-Hungarian army and subsequently by the Hungarian army in 1919. It was also made in 9-mm Short and sold commercially up to the 1920s. The Baby was unusual as a pocket pistol since it operated on a long recoil system with a locked breech

I V Hogg

Fegyvergyar

Hungarian firearms manufacturer. Abbreviated form of the full title Fegyver és Gépgyár Reszvenytarsasag (Arms and Machinery Company Limited) of Budapest. It was set up in 1887 by decree of the Hungarian government with the intention of manufacturing military weapons, notably the Mannlicher Model 95 rifle. It got off to a shaky start, went bankrupt, was restarted and afterwards prospered. In 1896 Rudolf Frommer, one of the leading European firearms designers, joined the staff, becoming manager in 1900 and remaining in that post until he retired in 1935. Under Frommer's hand the company produced a number of pistols to his design.

The early Frommer pistols were produced

Felix

The Frommer M1937 7.65-mm pistol was made during the Second World War for Hungarian armed forces and also for the Luftwaffe

I V Hogg

only in small numbers, but in 1912 the Stop model appeared; this achieved considerable success, being adopted by the Honved, the Hungarian element of the Austro-Hungarian army and, in 1919, by the newly-formed Hungarian army, as well as being widely adopted by police forces and sold commercially. The Stop was a locked-breech pistol operating on the long recoil system. On firing, the barrel and bolt, which are locked together, recoil for a distance greater than the length of the cartridge. The bolt is then held fast and the barrel allowed to return to the forward position. As it does so, the bolt head revolves to unlock from the breech and the spent case is extracted. Once the barrel has returned, the bolt is released to run forward, chamber a fresh round, and rotate to lock. This is a very elegant system, but quite superfluous in the context of a 7.65-mm (0.301-in) ACP cartridge. However, it sold well and proved to be reliable in use. In postwar years a 9-mm (0.35-in) Short version was produced, and a vest-pocket version, the Baby, was made in both calibres for commercial sale.

In 1921 a simple blowback automatic, the Lilliput, in 6.35-mm (0.25-in) calibre, appeared. This much simpler weapon sold well and in 1929 an enlarged version in 9-mm (0.35-in) Short chambering became the Hungarian army's Model 1929 pistol. This was later refined into the Model 37, which was also adopted by the army in 1937. During the Second World War, several thousand of these pistols were made in Budapest for the Luftwaffe; these were in 7.65-mm (0.301-in) calibre and had a manual safety catch fitted. All previous Frommer designs had relied entirely on a grip safety device, no manual safety being used.

After the Second World War and the arrival of a Communist regime, the arms industry was nationalized and the company became known as Femaru és Szerszamgepgyar NV. Their principal products have been the Tokagypt and Walam pistols. The Tokagypt was a redesign of the Soviet Tokarev TT33 pistol to fire 9-mm (0.35-in) Parabellum cartridges, and was developed to meet an Egyptian order in 1958. The Egyptian army, however, changed their mind and the pistols went to the Egyptian police, but after the first few batches had been delivered, the contract was cancelled and the remaining pistols were disposed of commercially, most of them being sold in Germany as the Firebird. The Walam was a near-copy of the Walther PP pistol, also made for an Egyptian order, also cancelled, and also disposed of commercially.

(M1919 Stop) *Calibre:* 7.65-mm (.301-in) *Weight:* 0.61 kg (1 lb 5 oz) *Length:* 165 mm (6.5 in) *Barrel length:* 95 mm (3.7 in) *Magazine:* 7-round detachable box *Muzzle velocity:* 280 m/sec (920 ft/sec)

(Model 1937) *Calibre:* 7.65-mm (.301-in) *Weight:* 0.77 kg (1 lb 11 oz) *Length:* 182 mm (7.16 in) *Barrel length:* 110 mm (4.33 in) *Magazine:* 7-round detachable box *Muzzle velocity:* 280 m/sec (920 ft/sec)

Felix

US homing bomb. One of the many avenues of research explored by the US National Defense Research Committee during the Second World War was the possibility of detecting a target by heat radiation. The most obvious target would be one which radiated considerably more heat than its surroundings, such as a ship at sea at night, and the outcome of the research was the VB-6 Felix, so named from the ability of cats to see in the dark.

Felix consisted of a standard 453-kg (1000-lb) general-purpose bomb to which was attached a nose unit containing the heat-seeking 'eye' and an octagonal stabilizing tail unit. The missile was designed for use in clear weather, and was sighted and released by standard procedures. Once the eye had

located a target, it applied mechanical controls to the tail rudders and elevators to correct range and direction, while gyro-stabilized ailerons prevented it from swinging and a tail flare allowed it to be tracked from the launch aircraft. However, although it achieved good test results, and was in production by the summer of 1945, it arrived too late for operational use against Japanese shipping.

Total weight: 545 kg (1202 lb) *Length:* 231.6 cm (91.2 in) *Diameter:* 47.2 cm (18.6 in)

Felixstowe

British flying boats. On the outbreak of the First World War, among the Admiralty's chief responsibilities was the aerial defence of Britain, as well as the more traditional role as guardian of the island's surrounding seaways. At that time the Royal Naval Air Service was almost wholly equipped with floatplanes of limited range and unreliable performance. The obvious need for a sea-going aircraft of long range led Captain Murray Sueter, Director of the Naval Air Department, to purchase two Curtiss flying boats; a decision based in no small part on the advice of Squadron Commander John C Porte, commander of the RNAS station at Hendon (site of the present RAF Museum).

Porte had plenty of aeronautical experience, particularly in connection with the American designer Glenn Curtiss and his products. After some operational use of these initial Curtiss flying boats, Porte set out to improve some of the more obvious weaknesses in the design.

In September 1915, Porte was appointed in command of RNAS Felixstowe and while there finally produced his own design of flying boat. It was a large, three-engined aircraft, and was allocated the serial number 9800. Quite unofficially, it was titled the 'Porte Baby'. The largest flying boat design of its day, the 'Baby' was put into limited production—some 20 machines—and most of

A Felixstowe F.2a flying boat. The dazzle-painting was introduced to identify individual pilots

The Felixstowe F.3. Some types were built in Malta by the Dockyard Constructional Unit

The Felixstowe Fury, popularly known as the Porte Super Baby

these saw operational service in 1916-17.

While the 'Baby' began production, Porte designed a new form of flying boat hull, and tested it on a modified Curtiss H4 (No 3850). The resulting aircraft was at first titled the Porte I, and later officially designated Felixstowe F.1—the true father of all subsequent F-boats to enter RNAS and RAF service in later years. By July 1916, however, first examples of a larger Curtiss flying boat design began arriving in England. Designated H.8, these were quickly modified to accept more powerful twin 250-hp Rolls-Royce engines, and redesignated Curtiss H.12s, or 'Large Americas' as the RNAS crews usually referred to them. The Curtiss H.12 hull soon proved to be inadequate for its tasks, so Porte designed a new hull (the Porte II), resulting in all-round improvement in performance. With a new tail unit added, the modified craft was designated Felixstowe F.2, and its general structure became a prototype for succeeding F-boats.

Large-scale production of the F.2 was ordered, and the type began to equip RNAS units in late 1917. Carrying a crew of four, and a bombload of approximately 272 kg (600 lb), the F.2a (its production designation) could achieve a maximum speed of some 145 km/h (90 mph), with an endurance of perhaps six hours. It was cumbersome to handle and slow in manoeuvre, yet gave formidable operational service for the rest of the war. With at least four machine-guns in nose, tail, and flank locations, it also gave a good account of itself when engaged by German seaplanes. The F.2a's main duty was antisubmarine hunting; an air deterrent which undoubtedly proved successful in the protection of Britain's vital mercantile shipping.

Porte next designed the F.3, a slightly enlarged variant of the F.2, which was put into production swiftly. The F.3 soon proved to be inferior in many respects to the F.2, but by the time this was realized full-scale production was well under way and could not be halted. This accent on F.3 production inadvertently prevented full importance being given to Porte's final biplane flying boat design, the F.5.

The F.5 prototype, N90, underwent its official trials in May 1918 and was clearly superior in virtually all aspects over the F.3; yet production of the F.5 was only permitted on condition that many F.3 components, then easily available, were utilized. As a direct result of this unimaginative edict, the F.5's performance suffered unnecessarily. The delay also prevented any F.5 from seeing active service in 1918; although the type gave excellent service for many years after in the RAF, and an American version, titled F5-L, gave equally good service in the peacetime US Navy air arm.

Porte's ultimate design was a massive triplane flying boat, unofficially nicknamed the 'Porte Super-Baby', but officially designated Felixstowe Fury. With wings spanning 37.5 m (123 ft), the Fury was powered by five 360-hp Rolls-Royce Eagle engines. Flying controls, initially, were power-assisted by servomotors. After successful flying trials, the Fury was in the last stages of preparation for a projected flight to South Africa on August

Fencer, Su-19 Sukhoi

A production Felixstowe F.3, an enlarged but in many ways inferior version of the F.2

11, 1919, when it was wrecked in Harwich harbour. All work on a second Fury was then stopped and the Fury programme cancelled. In October 1919, John Cyril Porte, the man whose inventive genius had conceived the F-series of flying boats, died in Brighton of tuberculosis.

Span: (F.1) 22 m (72 ft) (upper), 14 m (46 ft) (lower); (F.2) 29 m (95 ft 7½ in) (upper), 20.8 m (68 ft 5 in) (lower); (F.3) 31 m (102 ft) (upper), 22.6 m (74 ft 2 in) (lower); (F.5) 31.6 m (103 ft 8 in) (upper), 22.6 m (74 ft 2 in) (lower); (Fury) 37.5 m (123 ft) *Length:* (F.1) 11 m (36 ft 2 in) (hull only); (F.2) 14.1 m (46 ft 3 in); (F.3) 15 m (49 ft 3 in); (F.5) 15 m (49 ft 3 in); (Fury) 19.2 m (63 ft 2 in) *Height:* (F.2) 5.3 m (17 ft 6 in); (F.3) 5.7 m (18 ft 8 in); (F.5) 5.7 m (18 ft 9 in); (Fury) 8.4 m (27 ft 6 in) *Maximum speed:* (F.1) approx 125.5 km/h (78 mph); (F.2) 153.7 km/h (95.5 mph) at 609.5 m (2000 ft); (F.3) 150 km/h (93 mph) at 609.5 m (2000 ft); (F.5) 141.6 km/h (88 mph) at 609.5 m (2000 ft) (full load); (Fury) 156 km/h (97 mph) at 609.5 m (2000 ft)

Fencer, Su-19 Sukhoi

Soviet attack aircraft. In early 1974 the chairman of the US Joint Chiefs of Staff, Admiral Thomas H Moorer, described this aircraft as "the first modern Soviet fighter to be developed specifically as a fighter bomber for the ground-attack mission." Though it is still remarkably little-known in the West, it is misleading to use the word fighter at all in connection with this aircraft, just as it is in connection with the F-111. The two aircraft, one Russian, the other American, have many points of similarity, but the Su-19 most resembles the European Panavia Tornado, both in design and in mission. Where they differ is in timing, to the disadvantage of the West.

Although this extremely important aircraft entered squadron service with the Soviet air forces in 1975, very little was known about it in the West until a single blurred photograph became available at the end of 1977. This showed an extremely efficient wing with large and acutely-swept fixed gloves, and pivoted outer sections of remarkably high aspect ratio. It also has a conventional and not especially wide body, with variable lateral inlets ahead of the wing gloves leading to

twin turbofans or turbojets with afterburner nozzles projecting behind the delta-shaped tailplanes. It has an extremely large nose radar and main landing gears attached on each side of the fuselage, leaving the belly clear for pylons, with at least two wheels on each leg. There are small fences, possibly doubling as pivoted pylons, on the wings, and small aft-facing projections on the trailing edge of the tailplane (probably rear-warning radar).

It has long been believed that the crew of two sit side-by-side, an innovation in Soviet tactical aircraft and made a more attractive arrangement by the size of the radar dish aerial. Flight controls are almost certainly similar to other aircraft of this configuration, with full-span high-lift flaps, leading-edge slats or droops, wing spoilers locked inoperative at high sweep, and left and right tailplanes serving for roll control and trim in all regimes (backed up by secondary spoilers at low speeds). It is possible that there is an internal weapon bay, but a load that may be as great as 8000 kg (17 637 lb) can be carried externally on pylons on the body, gloves and outer wings. There is said to be a GSh-23 twin-barrel 23-mm (0.90-in) gun, although the MiG-27—a smaller aircraft with a similar spectrum of missions—has a new multi-barrel 'Gatling' of unknown type.

It would be logical if the engine installation and engine-type were the same as in the Su-15 'Flagon F' intercepter by the same design bureau. This engine is the Lyulka AL-21F-3, rated with maximum afterburner at 11 113 kg (25 000 lb); dry rating is 7800 kg (17 196 lb). Although far from new, this engine has the right thrust and is fully proven in several roles, with variable inlet systems; it is also used in the single-engined Su-17, which has a swing-wing. On the other hand, it is quite an old turbojet, and mission radius would be considerably extended by a later turbofan, such as an augmented Lotarev D-36. There is considerable disparity between the Su-19 fuselage and that of the Su-15, and no similarity at all with other components.

One odd feature in the available photograph is that it clearly shows a long nose probe but offset either upward or to the left: it is not aligned with the direction of flight. Most Soviet intercepters have long nose booms to carry pitot heads and accurate

air-data instrumentation feeding air-temperature, yaw, pitch and possibly g or gust information to the weapon-delivery and flight-control systems. Almost certainly the radar is backed up by a terrain-following radar and a laser designator and ranger in an under-nose chisel mount. The photograph shows a small bump exactly where one would expect to find CW (Continuous Wave) missile-guidance radar, of the kind fitted to the smaller and simpler MiG-27.

Beyond doubt, the Su-19 carries the full range of Soviet tactical weapons, including guided missiles. Air-to-surface missiles (ASMs) have been notably and unaccountably absent from the Soviet armoury known to the West (except in the largest strategic size, with cruise-type heavy-bomber missiles). Although brief supposed details of new ASMs were published in 1977, they are generally regarded as a mixture of rumour and guesswork.

These are: AS-7 Kerry, radio command guidance, weight 1200 kg (2645 lb), range 10 km (6.2 miles); AS-8, helicopter antitank; AS-X-9, antiradiation missile, range 80-90 km (50-56 miles); and AS-X-10, electro-optical homing, range 10 km (6.2 miles). Except for AS-8 all are specifically associated with the Su-19, but the ranges seem unaccountably low and radio-command guidance extremely unlikely (it is apparently becoming a habit to invest 1975 Soviet hardware with 1955 performance, a highly dangerous and unhelpful assumption). There is also said to be a SATASM (Soviet advanced tactical ASM) with a range of 40 km (25 miles).

Small numbers of early production Su-19 attack aircraft were deployed with the GSFG (group of Soviet forces in Germany) in early 1975, in what is thought to have been part of the operational evaluation programme. By the spring of 1978, approximately 400 Su-19s were in service in the European theatre, not including others on the Chinese front and in the Far East, with conversion schools and reserve units. Many regiments had been identified in the western Soviet Union and in Soviet units occupying members of the Warsaw Pact. No example had been identified serving with any Warsaw Pact air force.

Spearheading the transformation of the Soviet air force's Frontal Aviation (the close-support force that forms the backbone of Soviet air power) from a close-range battlefield weapon into a powerful striking force with continent-wide range, Su-19 is by far the greatest single aerial threat to the NATO countries of Western Europe. Its range is considerably greater than that of any previous Soviet tactical offensive aircraft, and it is widely reported that this aircraft also has the capability for in-flight refuelling, again a new feature among Soviet tactical aircraft. With internal fuel only, the Su-19 is considered to have an 800-km (497-mile) radius, sufficient to cover almost all continental Western Europe. Flying hi-lo-hi existing examples could reach the United Kingdom. Developed versions are estimated to have a radius of 1900 km (1180 miles).

(Estimated) Span: (70°) 9.52 m (31 ft 3 in); (16°) 17.37 m (57 ft) *Length:* 21 m (68 ft 10¾ in) *Gross weight:* 32 000 kg (70 548 lb) *Maximum speed:* (lo, clean) 1530 km/h (950 mph, Mach 1.25); (hi, clean) probably Mach 2.5.

The submarines *Ferré* and *Palacios*, built in 1912, had a bow torpedo tube and four drop-collars for externally stowed torpedoes

Ferdinand German self-propelled gun
See **Elefant**

Ferré

Peruvian submarine. *Ferré*, and her sister *Palacios*, were built for the Peruvian navy by the French firm of Schneider, and completed in 1912-13. At the time Schneider had a virtual monopoly in constructing submarines for the French navy, being in the process of completing an order for two almost identical classes totalling 33 submarines. Peru had previously purchased a number of warships from France and the French navy was in the process of setting up a naval college for the Peruvian navy at Callao when these two submarines were ordered.

Ferré and *Palacios* were almost identical to the French *Brumaire* Class, differing mainly in internal layout and lacking the upper deck casing of the French boats. They were distinguished by two tall tubes for the periscopes and engine exhausts. The *Brumaire* Class had pioneered the use of the heavy oil engine in the French navy and the same Schneider-Carel heavy oil engine was used to propel the Peruvian vessels. Following their completion in 1912-13 the two sub-

The Peruvian submarine *Palacios* which, with her sister *Ferré*, was built by Schneider in France

marines were shipped out to Peru in a special transport.

See also *Brumaire*.

Displacement: 300/400 tons (surfaced/submerged) *Length:* 52.12 m (171 ft) oa *Beam:* 5.41 m (17 ft 9 in) *Draught:* 3.04 m (10 ft) *Machinery:* (surfaced) 2-shaft heavy oil engines 840 bhp= 13 knots; (submerged) electric motors 460 ehp=9 knots *Armament:* 1 bow 45-cm (17.7-in) torpedo tube and four drop collars carrying 46-cm (18-in) torpedoes *Crew:* 29

Ferret

British armoured scout car. Ferret was developed by the Daimler company in 1949, production began in 1952 and continued until 1971, during which time some 4500 were built. As well as being used by the British Army, they have been adopted by 36 other countries.

The Ferret is basically a four-wheeled car with an all-welded armour steel body. The driver sits in the front of the hull, the centre

British Army Ferret scout cars on Exercise Arctic Express in Norway. The crew have stowed their snowshoes and stores on the glacis plate

Ferret

A Ferret on NATO exercises with Italian troops. The Browning mg is fitted for blank firing

is the commander's compartment, and the engine and transmission are at the rear. The first model (Mk 1/1 in British service) had an open-topped hull and mounted a light or medium machine-gun on a simple pivot. The Mk 1/2 had an enclosed turret with a 0.30-in (7.62-mm) Browning machine-gun carried on top, while the Mk 2/3 had the machine-gun inside the turret. The Mk 3 is similar to the Mk 1/1 but with larger wheels and a flotation screen, normally carried folded down into a trough around the hull top. With the screen erected the vehicle can swim, propelling itself by paddle-wheel action of the road wheels. The Mk 4 is similarly an amphibious version of the Mk 2/3.

The final model was the Mk 5, which incorporates the larger wheels and flotation screen and also has a new turret of aluminium alloy armour and four Swingfire missile launchers. An earlier antitank guided weapon (ATGW) model was the Mk 2/6 which carried two Vigilant missiles, one on each side of the turret. Both these missile vehicles carry remote-control equipment allowing the commander to dismount and control the missiles from a distance. This enables the controller to keep the target under observation while the launch vehicle remains hidden.

Ferret was to have been replaced in the late 1970s by a new vehicle, the Vixen, but development of this was stopped in 1974 and by 1978 there was still no scheduled replacement for Ferret.

(Ferret Mk 5) *Weight:* 3485 kg (7683 lb) *Length:* 3.38 m (11 ft 1 in) *Width:* 1.90 m (6 ft 3 in) *Height:* 1.88 m (6 ft 2 in) *Power:* Rolls-Royce B-60 6-cylinder, 129 bhp at 3750 rpm *Speed:* 93.3 km/h (58 mph) *Range:* 300 km (186 miles) *Armour:* 16 mm (0.63 in) *Crew:* 2 *Armament:* 4 Swingfire missiles housed in armoured containers forming part of fully-rotating turret, further 2 Swingfires carried; 1 7.62-mm (0.30-in) machine-gun

A Ferret Mk 2/3 armoured car. The Ferret has been in service with the British Army since the early 1950s. Used in every internal security campaign from Malaysia through Aden and Cyprus to Ulster, it is a fast and handy vehicle and one of the few AFVs that it is politically acceptable to use on the streets

Despite its biplane configuration and rear-gunner's position resembling those of First World War aircraft, the Grumman FF-1 was an advanced design. It was the first US Navy fighter to have a retracting undercarriage and was faster than many contemporary single seat types. The US Navy bought 27, some of which were fitted with dual controls. As the Goblin 1, this aircraft was also built and operated in Canada

Feuerlilie

German research rocket. Two types of rocket were built in the Feuerlilie (Orange Lily) series, the F-25 of 25-cm (9.8-in) diameter and the F-55 of 55 cm (21.6 in). The F-25 was designed in 1941 to provide aerodynamic information at transonic speeds and was similar to the Hecht vehicle, the main difference being the use of a solid-propellant booster. The rocket, developed at Braunschweig using bodies produced at Ardeltwerke in Breslau, was accelerated from a 60° ramp by a Rheinmetall-Borsig solid-propellant rocket burning diethylene glycol-dinitrate. The motor produced 500 kg (1102 lb) of thrust for six seconds to boost the rocket to 220 m/sec (722 ft/sec). Roll stabilization was provided by a gyro acting on ailerons mounted on the single-plane wings, which were swept back by 40°. The F-25 was test-flown six times in Pomerania—three flights were made in April 1943 and a further three in July.

The F-55 was much larger, the project being begun in early 1942. The vehicle was used for research into solid-fuel rockets and possibly other fields. The tailless F-55 had wings swept back by 50° and was launched from a ramp angled at 70°. Early models were boosted by a single rocket developing 6000 kg (13 230 lb) of thrust for 21 seconds; later versions had four rockets clustered round the centre of gravity, each producing 2000 kg (4410 lb) of thrust for six seconds. Cruise propulsion was taken over by a sustainer motor: a solid-propellant unit developing 4000 kg (8820 lb) of thrust for six seconds in early models, with a liquid oxygen/alcohol powerplant producing 1000 kg (2205 lb) for 25 seconds being fitted in later F-55s. The largest variant of Feuerlilie could reach an altitude of 9000 m (29 530 ft) with a booster or 4800 m (15 750 ft) without.

Feuerlilie F-55 reached Mach 1.25 during tests with a Rheinmetall-Borsig solid-propellant motor in Pomerania during May 1944, but was unsuccessful when fired with a Konrad liquid-fuel rocket at Peenemünde on

A squadron of nine Grumman FF-1 fighters. They were armed with three browning mgs

December 11 of that year. A third rocket was delivered to Peenemünde in November 1944, but was never fired, and the project petered out by the following January.

(F-25) *Length:* 2 m (6 ft 6¾ in) *Span:* 1.12 m (3 ft 8 in) *Diameter:* 25 cm (9.84 in) *Launch weight:* 120 kg (264.5 lb); (F-55) *Length:* 4.8 m (15 ft 9 in) *Span:* 2.28 m (7 ft 5¾ in) *Diameter:* 31.5 cm (12.40 in) *Launch weight:* 470 kg (1036 lb) with solid-propellant motor, 656 kg (1446 lb) with liquid-propellant motor

FF and SF, Grumman

US Navy fighter aircraft. This two-seat biplane, ordered on April 2, 1931, was the first aircraft designed by Grumman for the US Navy, and the first USN fighter with retractable landing gear. The prototype XFF-1 flew in late 1931, powered by a 575-hp Wright R-1820E Cyclone radial engine giving it a top speed of 314 km/h (195 mph). Later, with a 750-hp R-1820F Cyclone, it achieved 323 km/h (201 mph). Deliveries of 27 FF-1s, with R-1820-78 engines, began to VF-5B (*Lexington*) in June 1933. Armament comprised two 0.30-in (7.62-mm) Browning machine-guns in the upper front fuselage, with another in the rear cockpit, and there was provision for one 45.36-kg (100-lb) bomb beneath each lower wing.

A second prototype was completed as a scout aircraft (XSF-1), and 33 SF-1s were ordered with revised internal equipment and R-1820-84 engines. These also served in the

FG-42

Lexington, with Scout Squadron VS-3B. All FF-1s and SF-1s were withdrawn from front-line service by the end of 1936, but served with reserve units (the former as FF-2 trainers) until late 1940. Of 57 FF-1s built as GE-23s by the Canadian Car and Foundry company, 15 served as Goblin Is with the Royal Canadian Air Force from 1940; 40, purchased by Turkey, went in fact to the Spanish Republican air force in 1937; one was delivered to Nicaragua and one, it is believed, to Japan. The Canadian Goblins were used for coastal patrols, while the Spanish machines carried out bombing and ground strafing attacks; eight survived the civil war.

(FF-1) *Span:* 10.51 m (34 ft 6 in) *Length:* 7.47 m (24 ft 6 in) *Gross Weight:* 2110 kg (4655 lb) *Maximum speed:* 333 km/h (207 mph)

F.F.V.S. Swedish aircraft   See **J22**

The Grumman FF-1. Twenty-seven of these fighters were delivered to USS *Lexington* in 1933

FG-42

German rifle. The Fallschirmjagergewehr 42 was a selective-fire automatic rifle developed expressly for use by the parachute and airborne troops of the German army during the Second World War.

By 1939 the airborne troops were asking for something better than the standard Gewehr 98 bolt-action Mauser rifle. When the army began developing their short cartridge assault rifle, the airborne force expressed interest, since this looked like giving them the high firepower and light weight they were seeking.

However, after examining the project they turned it down. They were not happy with the idea of the short cartridge, and demanded a weapon firing the standard, full-power, 7.92-mm (0.312-in) Mauser cartridge, giving them the long-range performance they felt they needed. The army would have none of this, so the airborne force, being part of the Luftwaffe, put their demands through the aviation ministry and thus by-passed the army weapons office. Specifications were issued in 1940 to six firms: Gustloff, Grossfuss, Haenel, Krieghoff, Mauser and Rheinmetall-Borsig.

All the manufacturers submitted models and after discussion and testing, the Rheinmetall design was selected for further development as the FG-42. Since Rheinmetall did not have the facilities to manufacture the weapon, the production was undertaken by Krieghoff. About 7000 are believed to have been made. By the time it reached production the airborne force had been reduced in size and importance and no longer had sufficient priority to obtain greater production.

The gun operation was by a long-stroke gas piston beneath the barrel. The rear end of this piston carried an upright post which engaged in a helical cam on the bolt. As the piston was driven back, so the bolt was revolved to unlock and was then drawn backward by the movement of the post. In single shot firing,

A Fallschirmjagergewehr 42 automatic rifle in its production form with a metal butt and folding bayonet. The Americans adapted the piston and bolt assembly in their M60 GPMG developed after the Second World War. The FG-42, unlike the heavier M60, was difficult to fire accurately due to its light weight and flimsy bipod

the bolt was returned by the usual spring, chambering a cartridge, but the piston was held about 25 mm (1 in) from its forward position, so that although the bolt was closed and locked, the piston post, which carried the firing pin, had not completed its stroke. When the trigger was pulled, the piston was released and went forward to carry the firing pin on to the cartridge. Thus single-shot fire was obtained from a closed bolt and gave the weapon commendable accuracy. When set for automatic fire, releasing the trigger after a shot caused the bolt to be held to the rear so as to allow the barrel and chamber to cool. When the trigger was pulled, the bolt and piston ran forward to chamber a cartridge and fire it immediately.

The FG-42 was a remarkable design, achieving the near-impossible feat of firing a full-power cartridge at automatic rates in a light weapon, as well as giving high accuracy for single shots.

Calibre: 7.92 mm (0.312 in) *Length:* 94 cm (37 in) *Weight:* 4.50 kg (9 lb 15 oz) *Barrel length:* 510 mm (20.08 in) *Magazine:* 20-shot detachable box *Rate of fire:* 750 rds/min

---

FGM-77   US antitank missile   See **Dragon**

FH 70

NATO 155-mm (6.1-in) howitzer, jointly developed by Britain, West Germany and Italy, and scheduled to enter service in 1979. FH 70 (which stands for Field Howitzer of the 1970s) was originated by a NATO

The prototype model of the Rheinmetall-Borsig FG-42 with wooden butt, early flash eliminator and conventionally angled pistol grip

requirement stated in 1963, which laid down basic parameters for a medium howitzer to replace the existing British 5.5-in (40-mm) gun and the US 155-mm (6.1-in) howitzer M1, in both towed and self-propelled versions. Early development was shared between Britain and West Germany, Italy joining the project in 1970, and the three countries divided the design between them. Britain was to be the coordinating authority and was to design the carriage and the high explosive shell and cartridge; Germany was to be responsible for the 'elevating mass'—the gun, breech and muzzle brake—plus the

sighting system, auxiliary propulsion unit, and ammunition other than high explosive. Italy dealt with the recoil system and cradle and the elevating gear.

The basic requirement called for a weapon weighing not more than 8 tonnes, with a range of 24 000 m (26 247 yards) with conventional shell and 30 000 m (32 810 yards) with sub-calibre or rocket-assisted shells, and a rate of fire of six rds/min. It also had to be capable of firing any 155-mm (6.1-in) ammunition currently in NATO service and, while normally to be towed by a vehicle, was to have an auxiliary propulsion unit on the

carriage which would give it limited country performance to a distance of at least 20 km (12.4 miles) in the absence of the towing tractor.

The resulting weapon was first displayed in September 1972. Since then there have been numerous modifications, but development has now been completed and production is getting under way. The FH 70 uses a split-trail carriage of conventional form upon which a saddle unit carries the gun. This saddle can be revolved to the rear so that the barrel lies above the folded trail legs and is secured to them for travelling. Small dolly

A British-crewed FH 70 fires at high angle during trials on ranges in Sardinia. The weapon is a joint British, German and Italian development

Toby Bowbin, MOD

An FH 70 in Sardinia undergoing evaluation by gun crews from Britain, Germany and Italy

Calibre: 155 mm (6.1 in) *Weight in action:* 8800 kg (8.66 tons) *Barrel length:* 675 cm (265.75 in) *Length of bore:* 603 cm (237.4 in) 39 calibres *Elevation:* —5½° to +70° *Traverse:* 28° right and left *Auxiliary power:* 1700-cc 4-cylinder 68 bhp at 4500 rpm *Shell weight:* 43.5 kg (96 lb) *Maximum range* (conventional): 24 000 m (26 250 yards) *Maximum range* (assisted): 30 000 m (32 810 yds) *Rate of fire:* 6 rds/min *Detachment:* 10

FH 77

Swedish 155-mm (6.1-in) gun. At much the same time that NATO developed the FH 70 howitzer, Sweden developed a very similar weapon, the FH 77. The notable difference being that since this design was to a specification made by a single authority, the Swedish army, and was developed and built by a single company, AB Bofors, the time from inception to completion was about half that required for the NATO weapon. The Swedish government issued a 35-million kronor contract to Bofors in 1970, trials with prototypes began in January 1974, and entry into field service was expected in 1978.

The general specification stressed mobility, but excluded a self-propelled equipment on financial grounds. It had to fire to 22 km (13.7 miles) with standard projectiles and weigh about 10 tonnes. The result is a split-trail weapon with auxiliary propulsion which is, in many respects, remarkably akin to the FH 70, which suggests that if similar requirements are given to separate competent designers, then similar results are often obtained.

FH 77 has an auxiliary propulsion unit powered by a Volvo engine driving a hydraulic transmission to power the main wheels, the trail legs being supported on two hydraulically-lowered dolly wheels; the driver sits high, alongside the gun breech. An electric hoist on one trail leg lifts the ammunition to an automatic hydraulic loader/rammer unit mounted on the rear end of the cradle, behind the breech. Fixed, cased ammunition is used, and the powered loading system means that a 'burst fire' rate of fire equal to 18 rds/min can be sustained for brief periods. The range of ammunition includes conventional high explosive, illuminating and smoke shells. While no announcement had been made by 1978, it is likely that a form of long-range projectile is under development.

Calibre: 155 mm (6.1 in) *Weight in action:* 11 000 kg (10.82 tons) *Length of barrel:* Not known *Elevation:* —3° to +50° *Traverse:* 30° right and left *Power:* Volvo B20B petrol engine *Shell weight:* 43 kg (96 lb) *Maximum range:* 22 000 m (24 059 yd) *Detachment:* 9

wheels on the trail ends assist manoeuvring and turn the carriage into a four-wheeled unit for movement under the power of the auxiliary propulsion unit. This, which is contained in the forward section of the carriage, ahead of the main wheels, consists of a 1700-cc Volkswagen engine. As well as moving the gun, it is employed to drive a hydraulic pump from which pressure is available for steering the dolly wheels, lifting them so as to lower the trail, and for lifting the main wheels to lower the carriage on to a 'sole plate' platform for firing.

The gun uses a vertical sliding breech with ring obturation for firing bagged charges. As well as the standard HE shell, a fin-stabilized sub-calibre long-range shell is under development and illuminating and smoke shell have been standardized and a special antiarmour carrier shell, loaded with dispensible mines, is also planned.

A self-propelled version, known as SP 70, is also under development, though to a later time schedule. Little has been publicly announced about this equipment, but it has been said that the chassis development was to be tied to the development of the proposed MBT70 battle tank. Since that project has run into problems, it can be assumed that SP 70 is still some distance from finalization.
See also SP 70.

The 155-mm (6.1-in) Field Howitzer 70 has a 1700-cc Volkswagen engine as auxiliary power. This feature, found in some Soviet guns, allows the FH 70 to be moved in and out of a firing position without using a large and noisy towing vehicle. It can also assist if the gun is bogged down in heavy mud

The Fiat-Revelli Model 1914 served with Italian forces from 1914 until the end of the Second World War, but despite this record it was typical of the poor quality of Italian automatic weapons. A blowback design, it had an oil pump to lubricate the cartridges and an operating rod which protruded clear of the gun and carried dirt into the mechanism, producing heavy wear and jams in action

FH, McDonnell US Navy jet fighter aircraft See **Phantom**

Fi 103 Factory designation for German flying bomb See **F29-76**

Fiat Italian aircraft See **B.R. 1/2/3, Centauro, Cicogna, C.R.1, C.R.20, C.R.25, C.R.30, C.R.32, Falco, Freccia, G.91, R.S.14**

Fiat

Italian machine-guns. During the First World War, like most engineering companies, Fiat became involved in munitions production and was called upon to manufacture the Revelli medium machine-gun. This was a retarded-blowback, water-cooled gun with an unusual feed system in which ten five-round rifle chargers were dropped into a cage on the left of the gun. As the gun fired so the rounds were stripped from the chargers in turn. Like most Italian machine-guns, the design did not allow a slow opening of the bolt to give initial unseating of the empty cartridge case. Therefore, the ammunition had to be lubricated to facilitate extraction; an oil pump was built into the receiver and gave each cartridge a squirt of oil as it was being chambered.

At the end of the war, Fiat set up a subsidiary company, Societe Anonyme Fiat Armamente Torino (SAFAT), to develop machine-guns. In 1926 this firm produced an infantry light machine-gun, which was basically the Revelli mechanism in an air-cooled gun. The magazine was a box type hinged to the side of the gun; it could be swung forward, loaded from a special charger, and then swung back into place for firing. Some 2000 of these guns were made for the Italian army.

In 1928 the company abandoned the Revelli blowback system and introduced a new gun with a locked breech, a system devised by an employee called Mascarucci. This had a hooked claw mounted on the barrel which dropped into a recess in the breech block; among other things, this system improved the extraction and did away with the need to lubricate the ammunition. However, very few were taken by the Italian army. Later in that year an aircraft gun, belt-fed and using the same breech-locking system, was developed and the Italian air force purchased some, but it seemed to Fiat that there was little benefit to be gained from the arms business, and they sold their SAFAT company to Ernesto Breda in 1930 and retired from the weapons field.

In 1935, on the insistence of the Italian government, Fiat put the Revelli gun back into production, this time in modified form. It was now chambered for a new 8-mm (0.315-in) cartridge, belt-fed, and air cooled. The mechanism was altered so that the bolt chambered a round and stayed closed, ready to fire, when the trigger was released. If the gun had been fired previously for any length of time the cartridge was loaded into a hot chamber and soon 'cooked off'. Instead of lubricating the ammunition, the cartridge chamber was fluted with shallow grooves so as to 'float' the case on a layer of gas and thus ease extraction. In spite of all these changes —or, more probably, because of them—the Fiat 35 machine-gun turned out to be a worse weapon than the 1914 model it set out to replace.

Having fulfilled their obligations by manufacturing this weapon (which, it should be stressed, they did not design) the Fiat company once more left the firearms field, this time for good.

(Model 1914) *Calibre:* 6.5 mm (0.25 in) *Weight:* 17 kg (37½ lb) *Barrel length:* 65 cm (2 ft 2 in) *Feed:* 50-round box *Rate of fire:* 400 rds/min

(Model 1928) *Calibre:* 6.5 mm (0.25 in) *Weight:* 9.52 kg (21 lb) *Barrel length:* 50 cm (1 ft 11½ in) *Feed:* 20-round attached magazine *Rate of fire:* 500 rds/min

(Model 1935) *Calibre:* 8 mm (0.315 in) *Weight:* 18.15 kg (40 lb) *Barrel length:* 65 cm (2 ft 2 in) *Feed:* Belt *Rate of fire:* 500 rds/min

Fiat

Italian tanks. Shortly after the first British tanks appeared in battle in 1916, the Fiat company decided to design one. The Italian army had not shown any interest, but Fiat set to work at their own expense. The design became the Fiat 2000 and proved to be very good, the more so since Fiat were working in the dark, with no specialized technical advice or assistance. Because of this, the two prototypes were not completed until late 1918 and were not used in the war. Four more were subsequently built, and the six remained in use by the army until the mid-1930s.

The 2000 was an armoured box with a low track line, the tracks being almost entirely shrouded by armour. The driver sat in front, with the transmission beneath him, while the

Fiddler, Tupolev Tu-28P

An Italian officer in service dress and crash helmet stands with his overall-clad crews during an inspection of two troops of Fiat 3000B tanks, the type which came too late for the First World War and served from 1920 to 1939. The 3000 was originally armed with two machine-guns, but in 1929 they were rebuilt as the 3000B with a new engine and 37-mm (1.46-in) gun

IWM

engine was at the rear. A central turret mounted a 65-mm (2.56-in) gun, and there were seven machine-guns spaced around the hull, three down each side and one facing to the rear. Though somewhat lacking in cross-country performance, the 2000 had good protection and gunpower and, for its day, was one of the better designs. Had production been achieved in time, it could have been a useful combat vehicle.

By early 1918 the Italian army had made some decisions about tanks and had bought some Renault light tanks from France. These seemed to suit their ideas of tactics and more were requested, but at that time the French could not supply their own needs, let alone those of the Italians. The army therefore turned to three Italian companies—Fiat, Ansaldo and Breda—ordering 1400 copies of the Renault, the first to be delivered by the spring of 1919.

The three firms each submitted modified designs, making small alterations to the Renault in order to suit various Italian army requirements, and the Fiat 3000 was selected to be the standard product. Before much more could be done, the war ended and the contracts were terminated. One hundred tanks which were in process of manufacture were allowed to be completed. The first of these was delivered in 1920, and they were to remain in service until the Second World War. For most of that time they formed the principal strength of the Italian tank corps.

The 3000 was an improvement on the Renault, since it was mechanically simpler, more reliable, lighter, and had a lower centre of gravity. It was armed with a pair of SIA or Fiat air-cooled machine-guns in the turret. In 1929 most of them were rebuilt as the 3000B by fitting a more powerful engine and sub-

stituting a 37-mm (1.46-in) gun for the twin machine-guns.

In later years, Fiat worked in conjunction with Ansaldo and Breda, producing components for their tanks, but the Fiat name did not again attach to an armoured vehicle until the early 1970s when, in conjunction with OTO-Melara, the Fiat 6616M armoured car was produced. This is a four-wheeled car mounting a 20-mm (0.79-in) cannon in its turret, plus a 40-mm (1.57-in) grenade launcher and a co-axial 7.62-mm (0.30-in) machine-gun. An initial delivery of 30 cars to the police and 20 to the army had been made, and were expected to be followed by more. Another vehicle produced by the two firms is the Type 6614 amphibious armoured personnel carrier designed for use by police and internal security forces.

(2000 tank) *Weight:* 39 920 kg (39 tons) *Length:* 7.39 m (24 ft 3 in) *Width:* 3.09 m (10 ft 2 in) *Height:* 3.81 m (12 ft 6 in) *Armament:* 1 65-mm (2.56-in); 7 6.5-mm (0.25-in) mg *Armour:* 15-20 mm (0.59-0.79 in) *Power:* Fiat 240-hp 6-cylinder gasoline *Speed:* 7.5 km/h (4.7 mph) *Crew:* 10

(3000 tank) *Weight:* 5588 kg (5.5 tons) *Length:* 4.19 m (13 ft 9 in) *Width:* 1.65 m (5 ft 5 in) *Height:* 2.19 m (7 ft 2¼ in) *Armament:* 2 6.5-mm (0.25-in) mg *Armour:* 6-16 mm (0.24-0.63 in) *Power:* Fiat 54-hp 4-cylinder gasoline *Speed:* 24 km/h (15 mph) *Crew:* 2

(6616M armoured car) *Weight:* 7400 kg (7.28 tons) *Length:* 5.23 m (17 ft 2 in) *Width:* 2.48 m (8 ft 1¾ in) *Height:* 1.89 m (6 ft 2¾ in) *Armament:* 1 20-mm (0.79-in); 1 40-mm (1.57-in) grenade launcher; 1 7.62-mm (0.30-in) mg *Armour:* 8 mm (0.31 in) *Power:* Fiat 147-hp 6-cylinder diesel *Speed:* 95 km/h (59 mph) *Crew:* 3

Fiddler, Tupolev Tu-28P

Soviet jet intercepter. Fiddler is the world's heaviest intercepter, if reports of a Tu-22P version of the Blinder bomber are discounted. The Tu-28, which carries the design bureau designation Tu-102, is thought to have evolved from the Tu-98 Backfin bomber which, like the Il-54 Blowlamp, was abandoned when the Yak-28 Brewer was selected to meet the requirement for an attack bomber. Fiddler itself was originally thought to be intended for strike and reconnaissance, and was described by the commentator at the 1967 Soviet Aviation Day as being a descendant of the *Shturmovik*, capable of engaging targets in the air or mobile targets on the battlefield. When revealed to Western eyes in 1961, the Tu-28 Fiddler-A was fitted with a large ventral blister which was thought to contain, variously, a reconnaissance pack, an early-warning radar, avionics, fuel or weapons. By the time of the 1967 display, however, this bulge had disappeared and the Tu-28P Fiddler-B was revealed as carrying twice the armament, in the form of four AA-5 Ash air-to-air missiles.

The Tu-28 was developed in competition with the Lavochkin La-250 Anaconda and made its maiden flight in 1957, a year after its

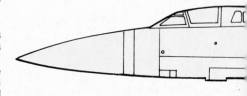

Only two Carro Armato Fiat 2000 tanks were built, but they were the first Italian-designed heavy tanks. With a crew of 10, seven machine-guns and a turret-mounted 65-mm (2.56-in) gun they weighed 40 tons and, being powered by a 6-cylinder 240-hp Fiat engine, were capable of only 7 km/h (4.5 mph)

rival. The La-250 was abandoned in 1958 after a series of accidents, and Fiddler entered service in 1962-63. The Tu-28's layout is similar to that of the Tu-98, although the bogie main-gears retract into underwing fairings—thus freeing space in the fuselage—and a fire-control radar replaces the glazed nose. The wing, mounted part-way up the area-ruled fuselage, is slightly tapered and has 56° of leading-edge sweepback at the wing centre section, reducing to 50° on the outer panels. The all-moving tailplane is mounted low on the fuselage, and the original Tu-28 was fitted with two ventral fins; these have been discarded on the Tu-28P.

Air is fed from two shoulder-mounted intakes to a pair of afterburning turbojets side by side in the rear fuselage. The original powerplant was the Lyulka AL-7F, developing 6440 kg (14 198 lb) of dry thrust and 10 000 kg (22 046 lb) with afterburning, but later models may be powered by an alternative

engine such as the AL-21F-3. The fire-control radar is also thought to have been updated progressively.

The Tu-28P is understood to have been employed primarily on standing patrols around the periphery of the Soviet Union, beyond the belts of surface-to-air missiles (SAM) and in areas unprotected by SAM. Maximum frontline strength is thought not to have exceeded 150 Fiddlers, most of which were based in the Moscow military district. Others are reported to have been deployed in the Arctic alongside Tu-126 Moss early-warning and control aircraft. Normal endurance of the Tu-28P is thought to be 3.5 hours, but this could be increased to 5.5 hours with the addition of auxiliary fuel tanks. The standard armament is four AA-5s, two with infrared seekers and the other pair with semi-active radar guidance. Normal Soviet practice is to ripple-fire the weapons, the radar-guided missile following its IR counterpart

after a delay of approximately one second.

Some sources claim that the Fiddler was replaced from late 1974 by a Tu-22P interceptor version of the Blinder bomber. Such a development may have been deployed as an interim measure, but the definitive successor to the Tu-28P is expected to be a variant of the Su-19 Fencer strike fighter.

Span: 20 m (65 ft 7½ in) *Length:* 27.5 m (90 ft 2½ in) *Gross weight:* 43 500 kg (95 900 lb) *Maximum speed:* Mach 1.65 (all figures estimated)

Fido

US antisubmarine homing torpedo. When the US began research into homing torpedoes in the late 1930s the effort was hampered by the lack of a suitable torpedo and by lack of acoustic data. Fortunately in 1940-41 American scientists were given timely assistance by the British, who made available the results of

The Tupolev Tu-28P Fiddler is the world's heaviest intercepter, at 43 500 kg (95 900 lb). The original powerplant, which may have been replaced by the AL-21F-3, was a Lyulka AL-7F capable of 6440 kg (14 200 lb) of dry thrust and 10 000 kg (22 045 lb) with afterburning. Fiddlers are armed with four AA-5 missiles, two with infrared seekers and two with semi-active radar guidance

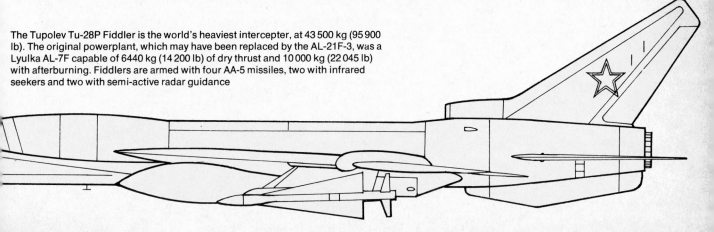

Le Fier

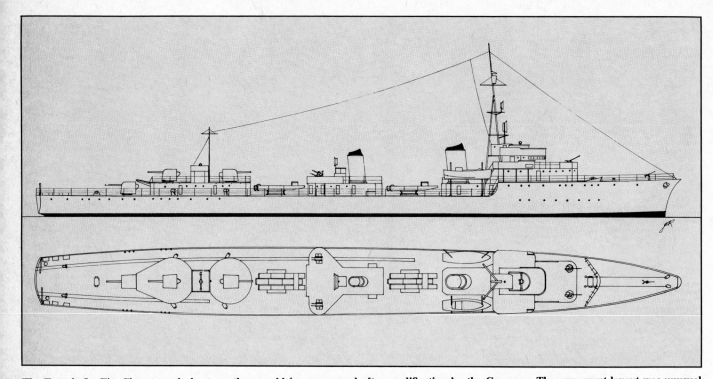

The French *Le Fier* Class torpedo boats as they would have appeared after modification by the Germans. The armament layout was unusual with the three 105-mm (4.1-in) guns in turrets aft and two 37-mm (1.46-in) AA guns and a single 20-mm (0.79-in) AA gun forward

their investigations into acoustics since the late 1930s.

Project NO-94 was started in 1941 to produce a 12-knot torpedo air-launched against diving submarines. It was to have passive homing in three dimensions, and although the normal diameter of 53 cm (21 in) was chosen, it was to be only 213 cm (84 in) long. Cooperation between Harvard University, Bell Telephone Laboratories, and General Electric led to the successful development of the Mk 24 torpedo. For security reasons it was always referred to as the Mk 24 Mine, or Fido; to aircrew it was more affectionately known as 'Wandering Annie'.

The idea behind Fido was simple. The fast-running propellers of a diving U-Boat caused 'cavitation', a sound-effect of bubbles forming on the propeller-blades, and a homing device could pick these up if dropped close to the point of diving. The homing head developed for the Mk 24 mine had four hydrophones mounted around the body of the torpedo, with simple steering toward the source of noise, but they would only register on the noise of a cavitating propeller, and as the torpedo itself was slow-running there was no self-noise problem.

On entry into the water, the torpedo dived to a set depth. If no sound was detected it then began to ascend in a spiral path to allow the homing head to sweep through a 360° arc. The running time was about 15 minutes, and under good conditions the hydrophones could pick up noises at 1370 m (4500 ft). The total weight was about 272 kg (600 lb) and the warhead was filled with Torpex.

Elaborate precautions were taken by the Allies to ensure that the German U-Boat Command did not find out too soon about Fido's limitations, and it was decided that the new weapon should be introduced simultaneously on both sides of the Atlantic. Therefore stocks in the United Kingdom had to be

built up in total secrecy, and in the first three months of 1943 supplies were sent over from the US. This led to an astonishing breach of security, when the senior RAF officer in charge of the first consignment learned from HM Customs that he had failed to declare the importation of 'some form of aerial homing torpedo for use against submarines'. The first British squadron to use Fido was Coastal Command's No 86 Squadron, whose VLR Liberators each carried two. On May 12, 1943, one of the Liberators damaged *U 456* so severely that she sank the next day. The first outright sinkings claimed were *U 266* and *U 657*, both on May 14, but by a Liberator of RAF 86 Squadron and a Catalina of USN VP-84 respectively. On May 19 another attack was made against a U-Boat, and the two Mk 24s dropped may have sunk *U 954*, which disappeared in the area. The Allied scientists' fears that the Mk 24 would have only a short life proved unfounded as the Germans took much longer to realize its existence, and it continued to be a useful weapon through to the end of 1944. It was replaced by an improved, longer version called the Mk 27.

Weight: 272 kg (600 lb) approx *Length:* 213 cm (84 in) *Water speed:* 12 knots *Maximum detection range:* 1370 m (4500 ft) *Endurance:* 15 minutes

Le Fier

French torpedo boat. The 14 vessels which were to have made up this class were the last destroyer type to be designed for the French navy until after the Second World War. They were a much improved design of the earlier 600-tonne type whose design had suffered from the tonnage limitation imposed by the London Naval Treaty. The new design provided for a much greater displacement (1400 tonnes full load as against 914 tonnes full load

for the 600-tonne type) with corresponding increase in dimensions. Installed power was increased to 30 800 hp from 22 000 hp which it was hoped would provide a top speed of about 34 knots, the same as the smaller 600-tonne type. Increased bunkerage was provided raising the radius of action by 1609 km (1000 miles) at 20 knots as designed.

The layout of the armament showed a radical departure from normal practice where it was usually sited fore and aft, with the light AA amidships. In *Le Fier* the main armament was sited aft in twin turrets and the light AA concentrated forward. Amidships two sets of twin torpedo tubes were to be installed.

Seven vessels were laid down in 1939 and by June when France surrendered, three had been launched and it was hoped to be able to tow them to a free port: none of the other vessels were ever laid down, although material for their construction had been assembled. All seven vessels laid down were captured by the Germans, but lack of French cooperation prevented their completion for the German navy, and they were either scuttled in harbour by the Germans in 1944 or sunk during air raids.

The Germans had planned to rearm the vessels with three 105-mm (4.1-in) guns in single mountings aft with two single 37-mm (1.46-in) and nine 20-mm (0.79-in) guns in a quadruple and single mounting forward.

The Spanish *Audaz* Class light frigates built with French assistance between 1945 and 1964 were closely modelled on the original design of the *Le Fier* Class.

Displacement: (1026 tonnes) (standard) *Length:* 95 m (311 ft 8 in) oa *Beam:* 9.37 m (30 ft 9 in) *Draught:* 3.25 m (10 ft 8 in) *Machinery:* 2-shaft geared turbines, 30 800 shp=33 knots *Armament:* 4 100-mm (3.9-in) (2×2); 8 13.2-mm (0.52-in) (4×2) guns; 4 55-cm (21.6-in) torpedo tubes (2×2); 2 A/S mortars *Crew:* 136

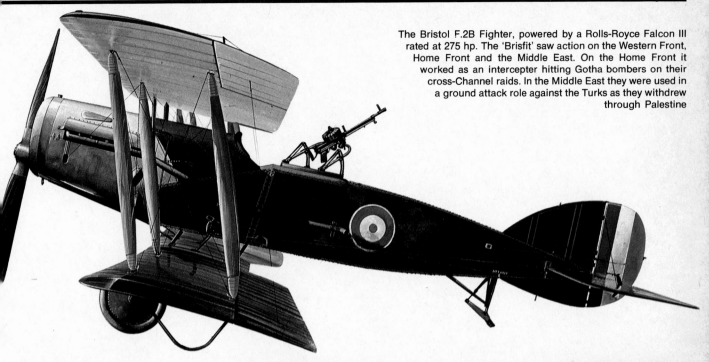

The Bristol F.2B Fighter, powered by a Rolls-Royce Falcon III rated at 275 hp. The 'Brisfit' saw action on the Western Front, Home Front and the Middle East. On the Home Front it worked as an intercepter hitting Gotha bombers on their cross-Channel raids. In the Middle East they were used in a ground attack role against the Turks as they withdrew through Palestine

Fighter, Bristol F.2A and F.2B

British fighter/reconnaissance biplane. In March 1916 the design was begun of a 120-hp Beardmore-powered tractor replacement for the B.E. pusher scouts. The type was designated R.2A and was intended to be armed with one wing-mounted Lewis machine-gun and another for the observer on a Scarff ring. At the same time a similar design using the 150-hp Hispano-Suiza was produced, but lack of power from the Beardmore caused the designer, Captain Frank Barnwell, to produce a new design using the new 190-hp Rolls-Royce Falcon and with the designation F.2A. This was an unequal-span two-bay biplane with its fuselage, tapered to the rear, mounted mid-way between the wings: as the Bristol Fighter it was to become one of the most famous aircraft of the First World War.

Two prototypes were completed by the early autumn of 1916, one with the Rolls-Royce engine, the other with the 150-hp Hispano-Suiza, and after successful trials a first batch of 50 Rolls-Royce-powered production F.2As was ordered with a synchronized Vickers machine-gun mounted in the top of the engine cowling in addition to the Scarff-mounted Lewis. Meanwhile the second, Hispano-Suiza-powered, prototype had been modified to improve the pilot's view and given a larger fuel tank and increased ammunition stowage. Further production machines were ordered with the 190-hp Rolls-Royce Falcon I and the designation F.2B; after the first 150 the 220-hp Falcon II was substituted for a further 50, and production was intended to continue with the 275-hp Falcon III. By the autumn of 1917 production of the aircraft was outstripping that of the engine, and the 200-hp Hispano-Suiza was substituted in the aircraft intended for reconnaissance squadrons, but this proved unreliable and was replaced by the 200-hp Sunbeam Arab in a modified nose. Some later F.2Bs were fitted with the 220-hp Siddeley Puma and a number of subcontractors were given contracts to produce the F.2B, 3050

Pilot and observer/gunner in First World War flying dress by their Bristol F.2B Fighter

being completed by the end of 1918 and production continuing until 1926 for a final total of over 3500.

The greatest number of F.2Bs used the Falcon engines, however, and it was these fighter/reconnaissance machines which won the Bristol Fighter its reputation—though only after some severe early setbacks.

The first F.2A unit to arrive in France was 48 Squadron, RFC, in March 1917, and their first patrol ended in disaster. On April 5 six of their Fighters were attacked by Manfred von Richthofen's Jasta 11 and four were shot down. Further combat failures followed before it was realized that the fault lay in the tactics, not in the aircraft. Previous fighting scouts had the observer's gun as their primary—if not only—armament, but the F.2As synchronized Vickers was a much more potent combat weapon, and once the pilot's learned to aim the whole aircraft at the target the Fighter never looked back. After the nadir of 'Bloody April', and once the pilots had recognized the necessity for a different technique, the F.2B quickly won an

outstanding reputation among both its pilots and their opponents.

F.2Bs of 48 Squadron, the first unit equipped with the type to arrive in France, in March 1917, accounted for 148 enemy aircraft by the time of the Armistice, and almost all of the Canadian ace A E McKeever's 30 victories were scored with the type. McKeever and his fellow pilots of 11 Squadron eventually found that enemy airmen would only attack their F.2Bs if they were flying alone or in pairs, refusing to engage larger numbers. As well as mounting offensive scouting patrols, F.2Bs were used as bomber escorts and bomber intercepters and on ground attack missions, for which they could carry up to 12 9-kg (20-lb) fragmentation bombs. Because of their success their introduction to reconnaissance squadrons was delayed almost until the end of the war.

Bristol Fighters also served with distinction in Italy, while in Palestine they equipped 1 Squadron of the Australian Flying Corps and made a substantial contribution to the Allied victory in that theatre. Numbers were

Fighter, Bristol

also used by Home Defence squadrons.

After the First World War the F.2B became the standard RAF army cooperation aircraft, serving with the RAF until 1932 in Germany, the Middle East and India. Small numbers were supplied to Belgium, Greece, the Republic of Ireland, Mexico, New Zealand, Norway and Spain, and SABCA in Belgium built 40, with 300-hp Hispano-Suiza engines, under licence in 1925.

The US Army had become interested in the type when the United States entered the First World War in 1917, and ambitiously large orders were placed with the Fisher Body Corporation and later with Curtiss. Unfortunately, a redesign of the aircraft to accommodate the 400-hp Liberty engine hindered production, and Curtiss only produced 27, which were given the designation O-1, remaining orders being cancelled in July 1918. Two prototypes of another modified F.2B design were produced as the B-3 and B-4 (later XB-1 and XB-2), and 40 production aircraft with the designation XB-1A, powered by 300-hp Wright engines and armed with twin Browning machine-guns, were built by Dayton-Wright as night observation aircraft.

The Bristol Fighter was the RAF's best two-seat fighter, and its long postwar service testifies to the soundness of the original design. The Royal New Zealand Air Force F.2Bs were not retired until 1936, and it is further testimony to the aircraft's virtues that all the redesigns carried out in the United States failed to make any improvement to the standard F.2B. A great many British Fighters were also later registered as British civil aircraft, Bristol producing a number of passenger-carrying conversions.

(F.2A, 190-hp Falcon I) *Span:* 11.96 m (39 ft 3 in) *Length:* 7.85 m (25 ft 9 in) *Gross weight:* 1210 kg (2670 lb) *Maximum speed:* 177 km/h (110 mph)

(F.2B, 275-hp Falcon III) *Span:* 11.96 m (39 ft 3 in) *Length:* 7.87 m (25 ft 10 in) *Gross weight:* 1292 kg (2850 lb) *Maximum speed:* 198 km/h (123 mph)

Right: **F.2B Fighter cockpit. 1** Position of Vickers gun. **2** Radiator water temperature indicator. **3** Revolution counter. **4** Engine oil pressure gauge. **5** Petrol tank air pressure gauge. **6** Gun bar—alternative position of Vickers gun firing lever. **7** Front and rear petrol tanks on and off taps—air pressure supplied by (a) engine pump (b) air-driven pump. **8** Hand-operated emergency pump. **9** Radiator shutter adjustment lever. **10** Starting magneto. **11** Tail plane angle of incidence adjustment lever. **12** Rudder bar. **13** Extra air control lever. **14** Engine throttle. **15** Engine main switch (lever outside fuselage). **16** Position of Constantinesco interrupter gear handle for Vickers gun (missing). **17** Control lever (joystick) with Vickers gun firing lever alternative position (missing). **18** Altimeter. **19** Air speed indicator. **20** Inclinometer. **21** Position of Aldis periscopic gun sight (missing). **22** Position of Prideaux articulated ammunition links shute.

Below: The Bristol F.2B Fighter showing its metal and fabric construction and the position of the pilot's and observer's machine-guns. There were a number of experiments with different powerplants, but Rolls-Royce Falcons rated at 190, 220, or 275-hp were the standard. Bristol Fighters built for the US were fitted with 400-hp Libertys but other engines proved unsuitable. After the war, the F.2B was widely exported to Spain, Belgium, Mexico, Norway, Sweden, Greece, Bulgaria and Ireland

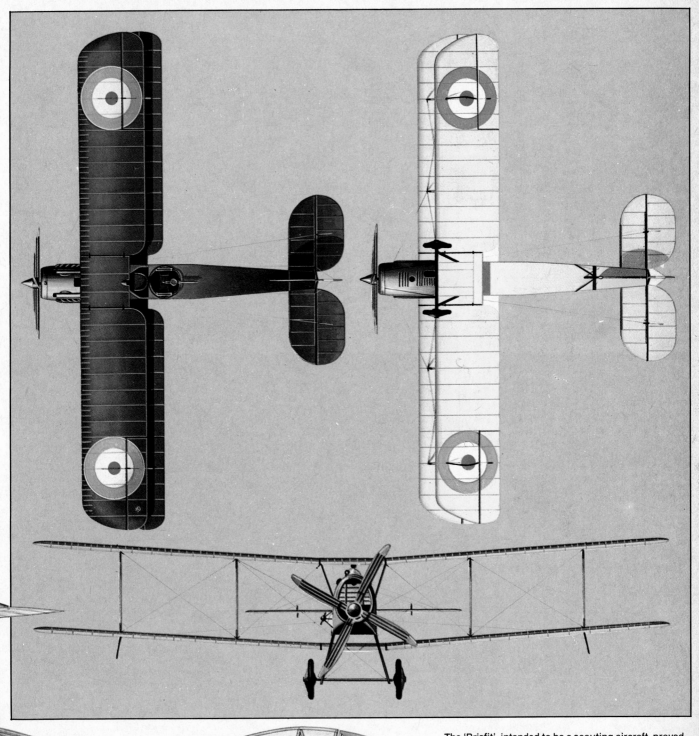

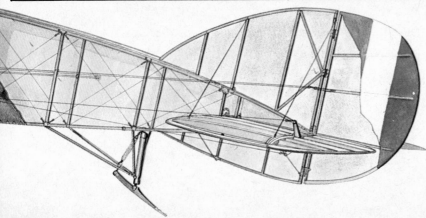

The 'Brisfit', intended to be a scouting aircraft, proved to be an ideal machine for dogfights. Its fixed forward-firing guns could be used offensively while the observer, besides protecting the rear, could also engage targets of opportunity. This combination worked so well that when two aircraft of No 22 Squadron were attacked by seven Fokkers on May 7, 1918, they downed four and carried on the fight when 15 more enemy aircraft appeared. When the two Fighters broke off the action, having run out of ammunition, they had shot down a total of eight enemy aircraft. A Canadian F.2B crew, Lt A E McKeever and Sgt L F Powell, downed the remarkable total of 30 aircraft in six months in 1917. In the same year, a Bristol Fighter shot down a Gotha bomber in a raid on Harwich on July 22

HMS *Mauritius*, a *Fiji* Class cruiser. Her 6-in (152-mm) guns supported the landings at Sicily, Salerno and Anzio and the Normandy landings

Fiji

British cruiser class. The 11 ships of the *Fiji* Class were constructed under the Estimates for 1937 *(Fiji, Mauritius, Kenya, Nigeria* and *Trinidad)*; 1938 *(Bermuda, Gambia, Jamaica* and *Ceylon)*; and 1939 *(Newfoundland* and *Uganda).* The first group were laid down in 1938 and completed during 1940-41, the remainder were laid down in 1939 and completed during 1942-43. They were the first and only British cruisers designed within the 8000 tons maximum standard displacement specified under the terms of the London Naval Treaty of 1936. This replaced the earlier 10000-ton limit, but at the same time restrictions on numbers of cruisers were abandoned, an object that the Admiralty had been trying to achieve for some years.

The ships were designed with the same armament as the 9000-ton *Southampton* Class, weight being saved by a reduction in protection and machinery which allowed for a smaller hull, producing the greatest saving at 450 tons. The magazine box protection of the *Southampton* Class was abandoned in favour of a thinner belt and a thicker protective deck, both of which were extended to cover the magazines and shell rooms as well as machinery spaces. The engine power was reduced to 72 500 shp which, because the ship was smaller, gave a slightly greater designed speed. The hull was 10.9 m (36 ft) shorter overall than that of *Southampton,* but only 6 m (20 ft) shorter between perpendiculars, the difference being largely due to the adoption of a transom stern (which also improved speed and saved weight). The actual design weights were slightly greater than the specified limit, but it was assumed that close attention to detail during construction and improvements in machinery design would bring them within 8000 tons. In the event, holding the displacement down proved unnecessary as the outbreak of the Second World War automatically ended the treaty

limitations. A combination of wartime additions and the difficulty of maintaining strict weight controls under wartime conditions, led to the entire class exceeding 8500 tons standard displacement at the time of completion.

Although the class proved of great value during the war, their restricted size resulted in the ships being cramped and overcrowded when additional wartime crew and equipment became necessary. The fitting of radar and AA weapons also produced a serious increase in topweight which necessitated limiting the number of AA guns added. In the last three ships to complete *(Newfoundland, Uganda* and *Ceylon)* the aircraft equipment and X triple 6-in (152-mm) turret were omitted to provide additional space and weight for these weapons. The aircraft equipment was removed from the remainder of the class during 1943-44 and X turret from all except *Nigeria* and *Gambia* during 1944-45. By the end of the war, three 4-barrelled 2-pdr pom-pom mountings had been added to most of the class the exceptions being *Nigeria* and *Gambia,* which retained X turret, *Kenya* which mounted a uniform close-range armament of 28 40-mm (1.57-in) Bofors (5×4+8×1), *Uganda* and *Newfoundland* which mounted one 4-barrel pom-pom and two 4-barrel Bofors. They were also fitted with between 12 and 28 20-mm (0.79-in) AA guns (removed from *Kenya* 1945).

All served initially with the Home Fleet; *Jamaica* serving with this force until the end of the war and becoming famous for her part in the sinking of *Scharnhorst* on December 26, 1943. *Fiji* transferred to the Mediterranean in 1941, where she was bombed and sunk during the battle for Crete on May 22, 1941. *Kenya* was temporarily transferred to the Mediterranean to cover Malta convoys during 1941 and 1942 and in the 'Pedestal' convoy of August 1942, was joined by *Nigeria,* both vessels being torpedoed and damaged by Italian submarines during the

operation. In March 1942, *Trinidad* was struck by one of her own torpedoes (which had failed to run true because its gyroscope had frozen) during an action with German destroyers while covering the Russian Convoy PQ13. Temporary repairs were carried out at Murmansk, but during her return journey on May 14, she was attacked by German aircraft in the Barents Sea and so seriously damaged that she had to be abandoned. She was torpedoed and sunk on the following day by the British destroyer *Matchless. Mauritius* was transferred to the Eastern Fleet in 1942, and then to the Mediterranean in 1943, where she covered the landings at Sicily, Salerno and Anzio before returning to the Home Fleet to cover the Normandy landings in 1944. *Newfoundland* and *Uganda* also served in the Mediterranean in 1943, where the former was damaged by a submarine torpedo while covering the Sicily landings. *Uganda* was damaged by a glider bomb while covering the Salerno landings. After repairs, *Uganda* was transferred to Canada and renamed *Quebec.*

During 1943-44, *Gambia* (manned by the Royal New Zealand Navy until 1946), *Kenya, Ceylon* and *Nigeria* joined the Eastern Fleet but *Gambia* returned to the Home Fleet in 1944. In 1945 *Ceylon, Newfoundland, Quebec, Bermuda* and *Gambia* transferred to the British Pacific Fleet.

In 1957, *Nigeria* was transferred to India and renamed *Mysore.* In 1959, *Ceylon* and *Newfoundland* were sold to Peru, being renamed *Coronel Bolognesi* and *Almirante Grau* respectively. The remaining ships of the class were sold for scrap from 1961-68.

Fiji, Bermuda—built by John Brown
Kenya, Ceylon—built by Stephen
Mauritius, Gambia, Newfoundland—built by Swan Hunter
Nigeria, Jamaica, Uganda—built by Vickers Armstrong
Trinidad—built by Devonport dockyard

A prototype Blackburn Firebrand Mk II. Planned as a fighter, the type was redesigned to take a torpedo and designated 'torpedo fighter'

Displacement: 8500-8800 tons (standard), 10350-10850 tons (full load) *Length:* 169.31 m (555 ft 6 in) *Beam:* 18.9 m (62 ft) *Draught:* 5.03 m (16 ft 6 in) *Machinery:* 4-shaft geared steam turbines, 72500 shp = 33 knots *Protection:* 88.9 mm (3½ in) sides, 51 mm (2 in) deck *Armament:* 12 6-in (152-mm) (4×3); 8 4-in (102-mm) (4×2); 8 2-pdr (2×4); 16 0.5-in (12.7-mm) (4×4) guns; 6 21-in (53 cm) (2×3) torpedo tubes *Aircraft:* 2 *Crew:* 730

FiM-43 US man-portable antiaircraft missile   See **Redeye**

Firebar, Yakovlev Yak-28P

Soviet jet intercepter. The Yak-28 series, comprising the Brewer bomber in addition to the Firebar intercepter, was based on the Yak-25 Flashlight. Substantial redesign was involved, however: the wing was raised from halfway up the fuselage to a shoulder position, partly to keep the larger engine nacelles and intakes clear of the ground and to correct the Yak-25's nose-up sit on the ground; a twin tandem main-wheel layout was adopted in place of Flashlight's nose-wheel/zero-track undercarriage, thus freeing space in the centre fuselage; many aerodynamic modifications were made; and different engines were installed.

The aircraft which emerged was substantially larger and more powerful than its predecessor. Area ruling was adopted for the fuselage and the wing, of increased area, carried 50° of sweepback on the inboard leading edge. Firebar is powered by a pair of Tumansky R-11 turbojets, the power of which has progressively been uprated since the aircraft entered service. Late production versions are powered by variants rated at an estimated 4600 kg (10 140 lb) of dry thrust each, or 6200 kg (13 670 lb) with afterburning.

The prototype Firebar flew in 1960 and the type entered service some three years later.

The major differences from the Brewer, which was developed in parallel, lay in the forward fuselage. A radome replaced Brewer's glazed nose, and the windscreen of the two-crew cockpit was, along with the forward undercarriage leg, mounted some 76.2 cm (2.5 ft) further forward in the intercepter version. The internal weapons bay fitted to Brewer was deleted from the intercepter, and Firebar's lengthened fuselage was later also adopted for the strike variant. A longer and more pointed radome was fitted to later production Firebars.

Firebar is fitted with an X-band Skip Spin search and fire-control radar operated by the rear crew member. Standard armament comprises four AA-3 Anab air-to-air missiles, two of which use infrared guidance while the other pair employ semi-active radar homing. A Yak-28P has been displayed with one Anab and one AA-2 Atoll under each wing, but this is thought to have been only an experimental installation. Firebar had by 1978 been mainly replaced by the Flagon-E variant of the Sukhoi Su-15.

Span: 12.5 m (41 ft) *Length:* 22 m (72 ft 2¼ in) *Gross weight:* 18 500 kg (40 785 lb) *Maximum speed:* Mach 1.15 (all figures estimated)

Firebird, Ryan

US air-to-air missile. The XAAM-A-1 Firebird was developed as a test vehicle to investigate various aspects of propulsion, control and guidance, and was considered as possible armament for the Convair B-36 bomber. Trials with parasite fighters proved unsuccessful, and missile armament was therefore examined as a means of bomber defence. Firebird was cancelled in 1952, however, and the distinction of being the first fully operational US missile system went to Nike Ajax in the following year.

Firebird was powered by a bi-fuel liquid-propellant rocket sustainer motor, being

accelerated initially by a solid-propellant booster. Semi-active radar guidance was to have been employed, possibly with a command link from the launch aircraft in the early stages of the missile's flight. Trials were carried out at Holloman Air Force Base, Alamagordo, using an F-82 Twin Mustang and a B-26 carrying radars for target illumination. The Firebirds were mounted on underwing pylons and could be fired singly or in salvoes of two or four.

Length: 3.3 m (10 ft 10 in) including booster *Span:* 90 cm (2 ft 11 in) *Diameter:* 15 cm (5.9 in)

Firebrand, Blackburn

British torpedo bomber. Owing to official indecision, this capable machine missed the Second World War. Originally designed to Specification N.11/40 as a carrier-based fighter, it emerged about twice as large as was necessary and was ineffectual as a dogfighter despite the power of its Sabre engine. Nine Firebrand Is were built (preceded by the prototype, flown in February 1942), followed by 12 TF.IIs redesigned to carry a torpedo. The odd concept was officially called a 'torpedo fighter', but a torpedo bomber could hardly achieve success in air combat. All Firebrands had four 20-mm (0.79-in) Hispano cannon, but the air fighting role was progressively made secondary and finally forgotten.

In 1944, the 2500-hp Bristol Centaurus VII or XI sleeve-valve radial was substituted for the highly unsuitable Sabre, and 24 Firebrand IIIs went through carrier trials that belatedly showed the need for a larger fin. In September 1945, Fleet Air Arm No 813 Squadron was equipped with the excellent Firebrand IV, of which 140 were built, supplemented by converted IIIs. Restyled TF.4 (torpedo fighter) and later S.4 (strike) this mark was followed by the S.5 and 5A, of which 105 were built, closing the line in December 1947. Features included larger aileron tabs and

Fireflash, Fairey

The Blackburn Firebrand TF Mk 5 production aircraft powered by a 2520-hp Centaurus IX

horn-balanced elevators, and the 5A had powered ailerons. The torpedo crutch was hinged to rotate the weapon into the minimum-drag attitude after takeoff.

(Mk 5A) *Span:* 15.63 m (51 ft 3½ in) *Length:* 11.87 m (38 ft 11½ in) *Gross weight:* 7945 kg (17 515 lb) *Maximum speed:* (with torpedo) 550 km/h (342 mph)

Fireflash, Fairey

British air-to-air missile. Fireflash was briefly operational with the Royal Air Force, a guided weapons development squadron of Supermarine Swift F.7 fighters armed with the missile being formed at RAF Valley, Anglesey, in April 1957. The Swift failed to live up to expectations, however, and Fireflash was itself succeeded in 1958 by the infrared-guided de Havilland Firestreak. Fireflash was also installed experimentally on the Hawker Hunter and Gloster Javelin

before being replaced by Firestreak on the latter aircraft.

Fairey Aviation began work on air-to-air missiles in early 1949 and was later awarded the development contract for Fireflash, which completed its Ministry of Supply acceptance trials in early 1957. Several hundred test rounds were fired from Meteor T.7 and NF.11 test installations and from operational types. A high proportion of small targets were destroyed by direct hits, even when the missiles were carrying no warheads.

The weapon system comprised the beam-riding missile, an Ekco radar mounted in the fighter's nose, a gunsight, a simple permission-to-fire computer and various ancillary services. Fireflash consisted of an unpowered central dart to which were attached a pair of solid-propellant boost motors. The boosters burned for some two seconds—during which the unguided round was spun by offset venturis to minimize dispersion caused

by asymmetric thrust—before being jettisoned explosively. Stabilizing fins prevented the spent motor cases from toppling after separation and decelerating sufficiently to endanger the launch aircraft.

The fins on the central dart unlocked at booster separation, reduced the roll rate and then steered the missile on to the centreline of the radar beam. The beam was kept pointing at the target by means of the pilot's gunsight, a receiver in the rear of the dart detecting the missile's position relative to the beam axis. The beam-riding method of guidance was claimed to be virtually invulnerable to countermeasures, although this was doubtful. The gunsight graticule also had to be kept over the target if a successful interception was to be carried out, and the coasting missile's kinetic energy—and hence range—was reduced every time the beam wandered off its target, causing the Fireflash to manoeuvre.

Length: 2.84 m (9 ft 4 in) *Span:* 71 cm (2 ft 4 in) *Diameter:* 14 cm (5.5 in)

Firefly

Anglo-American self-propelled gun, and, later, tank. The first Firefly was a Morris wheeled 'tank destroyer', a four-wheeled armoured car mounting a 6-pdr antitank gun alongside the driver. The requirement, put forward early in 1942, was for a vehicle of minimum size, mounting a gun with an automatic loading device so that the crew could be reduced to a driver and one gunner. The Molins Machinery company produced an efficient autoloader in only five months and one prototype was built. During this period, however, German tanks with thicker armour and heavier guns had appeared and the 17-pdr

A Sherman VC(M4A4) Firefly. This effective upgunning by the British of the standard Sherman used a 17-pdr Mk 4 antitank gun. It became an excellent tank killer in Normandy in 1944, and later with US forces in Europe

A 35-ton Sherman Firefly (M4A4) showing its redesigned turret with the stowing cradle for the 17-pdr gun bolted to the rear hull decking

gun had become the standard British antitank gun. The 6-pdr could no longer hope to defeat this heavier opposition at practical ranges and therefore the Firefly project was cancelled in 1943 and the name went into abeyance.

It was revived the following year. The British Army were by then using the American Sherman M4 medium tank, armed with a 75-mm (2.95-in) gun. While this was an improvement on the 6-pdr and 2-pdr guns of earlier tanks, it still could not deal with German Panther and Tiger tanks, except at suicidally short ranges. The US Armor Board had recommended up-gunning the Sherman to take a 90-mm (3.54-in) gun, but the Ordnance Department refused to attempt this since the 90-mm (3.54-in) breech was so large that a new turret would have had to be designed and built.

In October 1943, Woolwich arsenal had successfully fitted a 17-pdr gun into a Sherman turret, and this was offered to the US Army as being a more practical solution than using the 90-mm (3.54-in) gun, as well as being a better antitank gun. However, US Army ground forces refused to contemplate this. The British went ahead on their own and converted about 600 Shermans, calling the converted tank the Firefly. The first conversions were ready for use in the 1944 invasion of Europe, and the numbers were steadily increased thereafter as the necessity for the powerful gun became more obvious. Once British units had a minimum allocation of the Firefly, 160 were allotted to American units in Europe.

Firefly, Avions Fairey

Anglo-Belgian fighter aircraft. The original Felix-engined Firefly I was a private-venture single-seat biplane fighter, first flown on November 12, 1925. Although it was much faster than contemporary RAF fighters—top speed 302 km/h (188 mph)—it did not go into production, but an improved all-metal version, the Firefly IIM, was entered for an RAF fighter competition in 1929. Apart from its construction, this differed considerably from the Mk I, having a pronounced stagger to the wings, much-improved interplane and landing gear struts, modified vertical tail surfaces,

a ventral radiator (instead of wing-mounted), and a more powerful engine (480-hp Rolls-Royce Kestrel IIS) in an aerodynamically cleaner cowling. A 0.303-in (7.7-mm) Vickers machine-gun was mounted in each side of the fuselage, forward of the cockpit, to fire forwards through the propeller disc.

The Mk IIM lost the RAF competition to the Hawker Fury, but in a home-based competition, against strong continental opposition, it proved superior to all its rivals and was the only one of them to demonstrate a terminal velocity dive. As a result, in 1930 Belgian's Aéronautique Militaire ordered 45 (later increased to 88), of which all but the first 25 were manufactured by Fairey's Belgian subsidiary at Gosselies. Deliveries began in late 1931 and were completed during 1933. Although they were no longer in first-line service at the outbreak of the Second World War, about 50 were still on charge in May 1940 when Germany invaded Belgium, and took part in the brief fighting which followed. Most of the Fireflys that survived this period succeeded in escaping to France.

Fairey in Britain also built one Firefly Mk III/IIIM, a carrier version with bigger area wings, strengthened fuselage, catapult and arrester gear, bomb racks, and provision for floatplane landing gear. This competed unsuccessfully for a Royal Navy order against the Hawker Nimrod, but was later used as a practice floatplane by the 1931 RAF Schneider Trophy team. Two other Firefly IIMs were converted to Firefly IVs with 758-hp Hispano-Suiza 12 Xbrs engines.

(Firefly IIM) *Span:* 9.60 m (31 ft 6 in) *Length:* 7.52 m (24 ft 8 in) *Gross weight:* 1490 kg (3285 lb) *Maximum speed:* 282 km/h (175 mph)

Firefly, Fairey

British naval fighter. A natural development of the Fulmar two-seat fighter, the Firefly was designed by a team led by H E Chaplin to meet specification N.5/40, an amalgamation of earlier requirements which had called for a carrier-based fighter with a turret. However, the turret was dropped, and when chief test pilot Chris Staniland flew the first Firefly I on December 22, 1941, it was a clean tandem-seater with manually-folding wings containing four 20-mm (0.79-in) cannon and retractable Youngman area-increasing flaps. At first there was no requirement for the type to

A rocket-assisted Fairey Firefly roars down the flight deck of HMS *Glory* during the Korean war

Firefly, Fairey

A Fairey Firefly Mk I. Though the first prototype flew in 1941, the production aircraft did not see action until mid-July 1944. Firefly fighters of HMS *Indefatigable* covered the attack on the *Tirpitz* in July 1944 and as part of the British Pacific Fleet became the first British aircraft to fly over Tokyo in the Second World War. During the Korean war they attacked land targets and conducted antisubmarine patrols

Flight deck crew of *Unicorn* ready a Firefly Mk V for strike missions during the Korean war

be able to carry bombs or rockets.

Development was satisfactory, and the F.I, with 1730-hp Rolls-Royce Griffon IIB, entered service with 1770 Squadron of the Fleet Air Arm in October 1943, subsequently seeing extensive action in all theatres, especially in air-to-surface attacks against the Japanese. Manoeuvrability and long range made up for poor speed, and the good pilot view and comfortable rear observer cockpit were most welcome. Fairey, at Hayes and Stockport, and General Aircraft built 429 F.Is followed by 376 FR.Is (fighter reconnaissance) with ASH ship- and submarine-detection radar. Then followed 37 NF.II night fighters, with the large AI.X radar packaged into pods on the leading edge of both wings and with the forward fuselage

lengthened to preserve centre of gravity position, which was disturbed by the heavy displays in the rear cockpit. Conversions included the NF.1, with American 3-cm AI radar (usually APS-6) in a ventral pod, with other changes including shrouded exhausts, and the FR.IA which was a Mk I rebuilt almost to FR.I standard. From the 471st aircraft the engine was the 1990-hp Griffon XII.

Availability of the two-stage Griffon led to the F.III, reaching 562 km/h (349 mph) with the 2035-hp Griffon 61, but handling was poor. An extensive redesign resulted in the greatly improved F.IV (postwar FR.4) with 2250-hp Griffon 74 driving a four-blade Rotol propeller. New square-tipped wings had reduced span and neat leading-edge pods

housing fuel (left) and radar (right). Radiators were moved to the inboard leading edge and the aerodynamics improved. New underwing racks could carry up to 907 kg (2000 lb) of bombs, 16 rockets or drop tanks. Production, all by Fairey, amounted to 160, of which 40 went to the Royal Netherlands Navy. Nearly all those in front-line service with Royal Navy carriers saw action in Korea in 1950-53.

The main postwar Firefly was the Mk 5, similar to the 4, but with the wing folding and locking powered hydraulically, and with additional role equipment. There were several versions, including the AS.5 antisubmarine aircraft, NF.5 night fighter and FR.5 day fighter-reconnaissance, all with better communications, navigation and IFF, and the NF and AS having night and search/attack radar. Production totalled 352, including batches for the Royal Australian and Canadian Navies which served throughout the Korean campaign.

In 1951, the Firefly AS.6 entered service as an interim ASW aircraft pending delivery of the Fairey Gannet. It abandoned all fighter pretensions and carried only radar, sonobuoys and antisubmarine weapons. Fairey built 133, followed by 151 of the final version (making total production 1638), the AS.7. This was a complete redesign, with long-span wing, chin radiator, swept-forward wing roots, new cockpits for a crew of three,

new radar and sensors and a much larger vertical tail as well as a large number of internal changes.

In the 1950s more than 450 Fireflys were rebuilt for new roles. The first was the TT.1 target tug, with Mk 2B windmill winch and 2150 m (7053 ft) of cable for a drogue target; some of these had a long career in Sweden. The T.1 operational trainer, 30 of which were supplied to the Royal Navy and a few to other countries, had two separate stepped cockpit canopies, dual control and changed equipment. Most were unarmed, but some had two cannon. The U.8, U.9 and U.10 were all radio-controlled drones or targets, of the kind today styled an RPV (remotely piloted vehicle). The U.9 was the standard target for development and training with the Seaslug ship-to-air missile, while the U.10 was a similar rebuild of the AS.7. All targets had large multi-angle high-speed camera pods on the wingtips.

(AS.5) *Span:* 12.55 m (41 ft 2 in) *Length:* 11.56 m (37 ft 11 in) *Gross weight:* 7300 kg (16 100 lb) *Maximum speed:* 618 km/h (384 mph)

Firestreak, de Havilland

British air-to-air missile. Development of Firestreak began in 1951 to counter the threat to Britain from Russian subsonic bombers carrying nuclear weapons. These aircraft could not manoeuvre at more than about 2g, an important factor in the early days of missile development. Work proceeded in parallel on the beam-riding Fairey Fireflash, which entered service briefly, and the radar-guided Vickers-Armstrongs Red Dean, which was later cancelled.

Missile design in Britain was in its infancy when Firestreak (originally codenamed Blue Jay) was begun, and there were many constraints. Wingspan had to be less than about 1 m (3 ft 3 in) so that the weapon would not hit the ground if its launch aircraft burst a tyre on landing, when the undercarriage oleos would be fully depressed. Pylon length was limited by flutter considerations, and forward-fuselage mountings could adversely affect aircraft handling.

Twist-and-steer control, using only two aerodynamic surfaces, was examined. However, it needed a long time to react and had no real weight advantages. Canard (forward-mounted) control surfaces were also a possibility, but at that time very little was known about their performance at high Mach numbers. Alternatively, a moving wing could have been employed; this would have required large actuators, resulting in a loss of lift at the wing/body junction. The weight inherent in missiles designed before the advent of microelectronics meant that lateral accelerations had to be kept low to avoid overstressing the weapon. Sustainer motors had low specific impulses and were heavy, so booster burn-out was followed by coasting flight. Rapid terminal manoeuvring was thus impossible.

Firestreak's infrared seeker was sufficiently sensitive to track the target's hot engines only if the missile was launched from behind its adversary and followed a pursuit course to impact. Despite all these difficulties, the weapon was still in service 20 years after its introduction.

Firestreak became operational in 1958, arming de Havilland Sea Vixens of the Royal Navy and the Royal Air Force's Gloster Javelins. These carried four rounds each, while the English Electric Lightning was

Rocket-armed Firefly fighters are moved onto the flight deck of a British carrier in preparation for a strike against Japanese oil depots

Fishbed, MiG-21

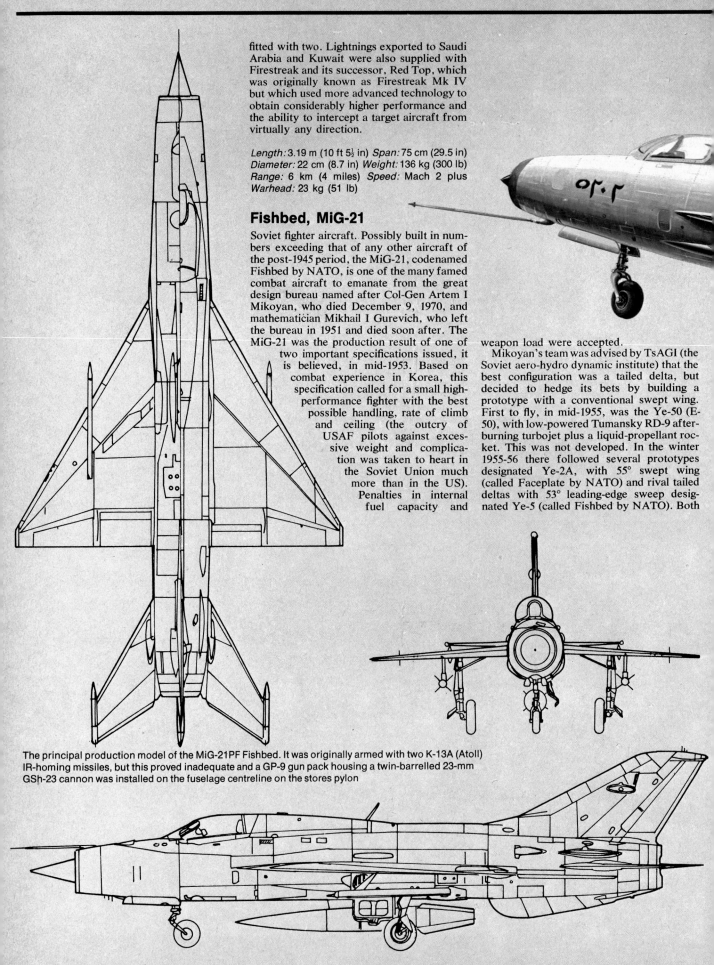

fitted with two. Lightnings exported to Saudi Arabia and Kuwait were also supplied with Firestreak and its successor, Red Top, which was originally known as Firestreak Mk IV but which used more advanced technology to obtain considerably higher performance and the ability to intercept a target aircraft from virtually any direction.

Length: 3.19 m (10 ft 5½ in) *Span:* 75 cm (29.5 in)
Diameter: 22 cm (8.7 in) *Weight:* 136 kg (300 lb)
Range: 6 km (4 miles) *Speed:* Mach 2 plus
Warhead: 23 kg (51 lb)

Fishbed, MiG-21

Soviet fighter aircraft. Possibly built in numbers exceeding that of any other aircraft of the post-1945 period, the MiG-21, codenamed Fishbed by NATO, is one of the many famed combat aircraft to emanate from the great design bureau named after Col-Gen Artem I Mikoyan, who died December 9, 1970, and mathematician Mikhail I Gurevich, who left the bureau in 1951 and died soon after. The MiG-21 was the production result of one of two important specifications issued, it is believed, in mid-1953. Based on combat experience in Korea, this specification called for a small high-performance fighter with the best possible handling, rate of climb and ceiling (the outcry of USAF pilots against excessive weight and complication was taken to heart in the Soviet Union much more than in the US). Penalties in internal fuel capacity and weapon load were accepted.

Mikoyan's team was advised by TsAGI (the Soviet aero-hydro dynamic institute) that the best configuration was a tailed delta, but decided to hedge its bets by building a prototype with a conventional swept wing. First to fly, in mid-1955, was the Ye-50 (E-50), with low-powered Tumansky RD-9 after-burning turbojet plus a liquid-propellant rocket. This was not developed. In the winter 1955-56 there followed several prototypes designated Ye-2A, with 55° swept wing (called Faceplate by NATO) and rival tailed deltas with 53° leading-edge sweep designated Ye-5 (called Fishbed by NATO). Both

The principal production model of the MiG-21PF Fishbed. It was originally armed with two K-13A (Atoll) IR-homing missiles, but this proved inadequate and a GP-9 gun pack housing a twin-barrelled 23-mm GSh-23 cannon was installed on the fuselage centreline on the stores pylon

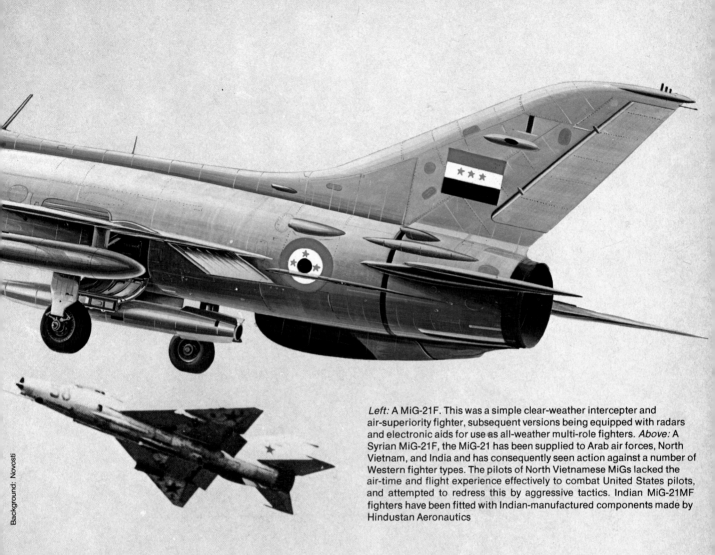

Left: A MiG-21F. This was a simple clear-weather intercepter and air-superiority fighter, subsequent versions being equipped with radars and electronic aids for use as all-weather multi-role fighters. *Above:* A Syrian MiG-21F, the MiG-21 has been supplied to Arab air forces, North Vietnam, and India and has consequently seen action against a number of Western fighter types. The pilots of North Vietnamese MiGs lacked the air-time and flight experience effectively to combat United States pilots, and attempted to redress this by aggressive tactics. Indian MiG-21MF fighters have been fitted with Indian-manufactured components made by Hindustan Aeronautics

types were convincingly demonstrated at the Soviet Aviation Day show at Tushino on June 24, 1956. Later the production designation of MiG-21 became known to the West, and for almost two years it was erroneously believed that Faceplate was the winner. In fact, it was the delta, which had already been selected before the Tushino display.

As the first Mach 2 aircraft to reach the operational stage in the Soviet Union, the development of the MiG-21 was protracted, wiping out some of the lead established in 1956. The first service version (Fishbed A) was built in only small numbers, and did not enter Soviet air force (Voenno-Vozdushnye Sily, V-VS) service until the late autumn of 1959.

It was an extremely basic aircraft, though a clean and aerodynamically attractive one. The engine was a Tumansky R-11 afterburning turbojet, with maximum rating of 5100 kg (11 245 lb), internal fuel capacity 2340 litres (515 Imp gal), with provision for a 490-litre (108-Imp gal) drop tank, and sole armament two 30-mm (1.18-in) NR-30 cannon, staggered in the belly with ammunition boxes in tandem to leave space for the lower part of the engine air duct. The direct pitot nose intake was given a translating (axially sliding) centre-body to cause inclined shockwaves and thus improve efficiency, and provide

space for the simple gunsight ranging radar (almost certainly the X-band 'Scan Odd'). The most unexpected feature was the large one-piece blown canopy, hinged at the front to serve as a windshield to protect the pilot during ejection. Under it, fixed to the fuselage, was a thick bulletproof front screen.

Other features included Fowler flaps of rather small size, fully-powered flight controls including one-piece slab tailplanes used only for pitch, a long nose pitot boom hinged upwards to prevent damage on the ground, three airbrakes on the underside, two near the leading-edge roots and one ahead of the twin ventral fins, and a braking parachute housed under the rear fuselage.

Though limited in capability, this was the fastest aircraft in Soviet service, and it was popular with both pilots and ground crews. It formed a basis on which to build a family of combat aircraft whose diversity and numbers have no rival in the modern era (in both respects, paralleling the 90-odd variants and 15 000-odd production of the Ju 88).

The first sub-type to be built in large numbers was the MiG-21F *(forsirovannii,* boosted), which entered service in early 1960 with the Soviet air force's tactical air arm (Frontovaya Aviatsiya, or frontal aviation), and with selected Warsaw Pact forces; as the S-107 it was also made under licence in

Czechoslovakia. A similar version was supplied to China, where it was built in modest numbers as the F-8 without Soviet help. The 21F, called Fishbed C by NATO, has the uprated Tumansky R-11 of the type called Mk 37F, with maximum thrust of 5750 kg (12 676 lb). In most 21Fs the port cannon is removed, to save weight and provide space for the electronic pack serving two K-13A air-to-air missiles (AAMs), simple copies of Sidewinder called Atoll by NATO, carried on underwing rails.

As the -21F matured, the fin was increased in chord and the braking parachute moved to a cylindrical box at the base of the rudder, while various aerials betrayed the presence of such standardized electronics as the UHF/VHF in the fin cap, rear-warning radar (Sirena 3) and SRO-series SIF/IFF (called Odd Rods by NATO). The Czech version of the -21F had an opaque, instead of transparent, panel behind the ejection seat. Exports began in 1963 with the F-12 for Finland and F-13 for India (which called it Type 74) and Iraq.

In 1964 came the -21PF, the P signifying *perekhvatchik* (intercepter, ie all-weather). This was the first to have the fatter, less-tapered nose which made room for a search radar, the R1L, called Spin Scan A by NATO. The remaining gun was removed, and

Fishbed, MiG-21

the dorsal spine widened and deepened to reduce drag and increase internal fuel capacity to 2850 litres (627 Imp gal). In all except the first production blocks the engine was changed to the R-11-F2S-300, with maximum thrust of 6200 kg (13 700 lb), and the fin was made still broader; at some point in PF production the fuel capacity was once again increased, and the main wheels were increased in size, the low-pressure tyres requiring much-enlarged blister fairings above the wing root. The pitot boom was relocated above the inlet, the rear-view panel deleted, and avionics augmented. Provision is made for assisted takeoff (ATO) rockets just behind the main-gear bays, and some aircraft (called PFS or PF[SPS] from *sduva pogranichnovo sloya,* boundary-layer blowing) have plain flaps blown by compressor bleed air to give enhanced lift as in the F-104 and Phantom. This model, called Fishbed D, had appeared with a dummy metal radome at the 1961 Tushino show, and was made in very large numbers for many air forces. India calls it the Type 76.

Fishbed E is the NATO name for the C or D version with extra-broad fin, relocated brake chute and restored gun armament in the form of the GP-9 belly pack housing the GSh-23 twin-barrel 23-mm (0.90-in) gun, with predictor sight and simple radar ranging. The MiG-21FL, from *lokator* (locator), has the R2L (Spin Scan B) radar. Extra-broad fin and relocated chute are standard, as is the F2S-300 engine, but not SPS or ATO rockets. India calls this the Type 77, and it was the first version made under licence by Hindustan Aeronautics, some 100 being assembled from Soviet parts in 1966-70 and about another 96 with increasing Indian content in 1970-73.

The MiG-21PFM *(modifikatsirovannii)* combined all previous improvements, including ATO and SPS, with an even broader fin (with no small dorsal extension), a completely new conventional canopy hinged to the right, with fixed windshield, much larger

UHF/VHF fin cap and other changes, the NATO code being Fishbed F. From this stemmed a 1966 model, the PFMA (initials all explained previously), called Fishbed J. This was a supposed multi-role version with four underwing pylons, provision for a belly tank or GP-9 gunpack, either radar or infrared versions of K-13A and with three tank-fitted pylons to offset the reduced internal fuel capacity of 2600 litres (572 Imp gal), despite the new deep dorsal spine giving an almost straight line from canopy to fin. Other changes included a zero/zero seat (ejector seat usable at zero height and zero speed), improved weapon-aiming subsystem with alpha (angle of attack) sensor in a fairing on the left side of the nose, and pitot boom offset to the right.

The -21M was similar but had the GSh-23 gun mounted internally, with case chutes discharging on each side of the belly store. Called Type 88 in India, the M was produced by Hindustan Aeronautics in 1973-78. Another related variant is the -21R (Fishbed H) tactical-reconnaissance model with a large centreline pod housing fuel, multiple cameras, IR linescan and electronic countermeasures (ECM). Extra avionics are fitted inside the aircraft, and wingtip pods with ECM equipment (jammers or dispensers) are optional.

The MiG-21MF (still called Fishbed J) was the first to have the Tumansky R-13-300 engine, with maximum thrust of 6600 kg (14 550 lb). Small additional improvements include debris deflectors protecting the spring-loaded suction-relief doors below the root fairings and a streamlined rear-view mirror above the canopy. The MF entered service in 1970, and as the Type 96 is also coming into production at Hindustan Aeronautics. The RF (Fishbed H) is the corresponding reconnaissance version. The SMT (Fishbed K) has an even deeper dorsal spine giving greater internal fuel capacity, believed to be about 3180 litres (700 Imp gal). Tip pods for ECM are common on this

version, which is the latest issued to most Warsaw Pact air forces.

In 1973 it gradually became evident that a completely new MiG-21 was in wide service with Frontal Aviation, and this was called Fishbed L. It is often called MiG-21*bis,* though this is hardly likely to be a Soviet designation. The differences are subtle, and indicate a complete and thorough reengineering of the airframe to give greater structural and operational efficiency. In other words, instead of being the end-result of 20 years of inevitably haphazard development, the *bis* is an optimized design. Externally the only obvious changes are the even wider and deeper dorsal fairing and the major revision in electronics. This in turn has now led to what must surely be the final operational MiG-21, the Fishbed N, also rather weakly called MiG-21*bis.* The main changes are the completely new engine and a new weapon-delivery and fire-control subsystem with a long instrument boom carrying angle of attack and yaw transducers to provide precise air-data information. The engine, about which little is yet known, is the Tumansky R-25, with a maximum rating of 7500 kg (16 535 lb).

This completes the long story of the development of MiG-21 combat versions. North Korea is said to be starting production, presumably with Soviet help, while small numbers of older F-8 versions continue to be built in China alongside the generally superior derivatives of the F-6 (MiG-19). Several thousand MiG-21s of many kinds are in front-line service, and Britain has concluded several important contracts to update and refurbish several outdated versions for some customers. Rolls-Royce are overhauling the R-11 and R-13 engines (the much more powerful Spey could be substituted but only with difficulty), while Ferranti is updating the sighting and weapon-control subsystems with ISIS (integrated strike and interception system) and possibly even with a HUD (head-up display).

Among the many users of the MiG-21 are Afghanistan, Albania, Algeria, Angola, Bangladesh, Bulgaria, China, Cuba, Czechoslovakia, East Germany, Egypt, Finland, Hungary, India, Iraq, Mongolia, Mozambique, Nigeria, North Korea, North Yemen, Poland, Romania, Somalia, South Yemen, Soviet Union, Sudan, Syria, Tanzania, Uganda, Vietnam and Yugoslavia. Ethiopia is now probably also a major MiG-

Two Sukhoi Su-11 (Fishpot-B) all-weather intercepters, introduced into service in 1961

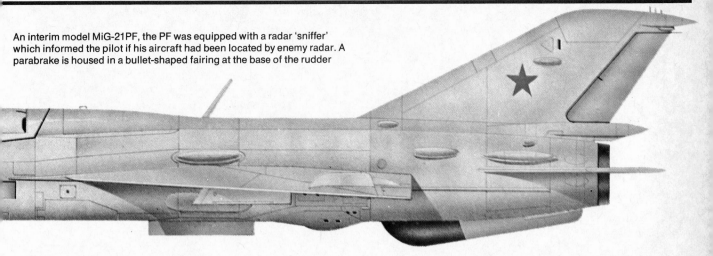

An interim model MiG-21PF, the PF was equipped with a radar 'sniffer' which informed the pilot if his aircraft had been located by enemy radar. A parabrake is housed in a bullet-shaped fairing at the base of the rudder

21 user, so similar aircraft probably fought on both sides in the war in the Horn of Africa.

There are also many non-combatant versions of the MiG-21, although they are not called Fishbed by NATO. Tandem-seat training versions, with the codename Mongol, are the MiG-21U, broadly equivalent to the -21F, the -21US with SPS flaps and a periscope for the instructor, and the UM with R-13 engine and four underwing pylons, the last two models being called Mongol B. Among many special versions are: the E-33 for women's records; E-66 (basically an F) used to set the first Soviet world speed record of 2388 km/h (1484 mph) in the hands of Georgii Mossolov on October 31, 1959; E-66A, with GRD U-2 rocket pack (not the same as on the original Ye-50) to set a world height record of 34 714 m (113 897 ft) on April 28, 1961; E-66B for women's time-to-height records; E-76, apparently standard squadron PFs used for several women's closed-circuit records; a STOL version (called Fishbed G) with two lift jets installed in a lengthened and widened fuselage (the only example seen, in 1967, having non-retractable landing gear); and the Analog, a PF rebuilt at the Tupolev bureau with a scaled wing of the Tu-144 (with no horizontal tail) to prove the aerodynamics and handling of the SST before the Tu-144 was completed. The Analog formated with the first Tu-144 on its maiden flight in 1968.

Span: 71.15 m (233 ft 5½ in) *Length:* (late models, including boom) 15.76 m (51 ft 8½ in) *Gross weight:* (F) 6900 kg (15 210 lb); (PF) 7575 kg (16 700 lb); (MF) 9400 kg (20 724 lb); (*bis*) about 11 000 kg (24 250 lb) *Maximum speed:* (all) about 2230 km/h (1386 mph, Mach 2.1) at altitude 11 000 m (36 000 ft)

Fishpot, Sukhoi Su-9/Su-11

Soviet jet fighter. A great deal of confusion exists in the West about the designations and codenames of the aircraft in this series. The 1956 Soviet Aviation Day at Tushino revealed three new Sukhoi types with similar fuselages and tails; one had a swept wing (the Su-7) and was codenamed Fitter by NATO's Air Standards Coordinating Committee, while the two with delta wings were both allocated the name Fishpot. One of these, Fishpot-A, had a fire-control radar mounted above the engine intake and was fitted with wing-root cannon. The other—Fishpot-B—had the radar antenna installed, as was usual for

Soviet fighters, in the centre of the annular intake and had provision for four AA-1 Alkali air-to-air missiles. Some sources maintain that Fishpot-A was designated Su-9 and that Fishpot-B was Su-11; others state that both were variants of the Su-9.

The Tushino air day in 1961 introduced further modifications. A Fishpot variant appeared with a less tapered nose and a larger central cone housing the radar aerial, together with an uprated engine and two AA-3 Anab missiles in place of the four AA-1s. This was certainly allocated the initial codename Fishpot-C, but whether it was the first true Su-11 or merely an improved version of the 1956 'Su-11' (Fishpot-B) is a matter of conjecture. The 1967 display at Domodedovo caused more headaches. Minor modifications were incorporated in the latest Su-11s; some observers say that the type had been changed sufficiently to merit the name Fishpot-D, while others are happy with Fishpot-C. For the sake of simplicity, therefore, all the variants described here are referred to merely as 'Fishpots'.

The Fishpot and Fitter series were developed in parallel, the latter having a swept wing and being optimized for ground-attack work while the former was an all-weather 'big brother' to the clear-weather MiG-21 fighter. Fishpot was a simpler design than the Mikoyan aircraft and was probably easier and cheaper to build. Fishpot has a 57° delta wing and entered service with the Soviet air force (VVS) in 1959, early aircraft being powered by a Lyulka AL-7 producing some 6500 kg (14 330 lb) of dry thrust and 10 000 kg (22 045 lb) with afterburning.

The initial aircraft were armed with four radar-guided AA-1 missiles carried on underwing pylons fitted outside the main undercarriage legs. The associated S-band Spin Scan search and fire-control radar had a maximum effective range of some 20 km (12 miles). The radar was later upgraded and AA-3 missiles replaced the AA-1s. Front-line deployment of the Fishpot series probably peaked at about 750 aircraft out of the total of 2500 intercepters operated by the Soviet air force. The type has mainly been replaced by the Su-15 Flagon. A tandem two-seat trainer version was assigned the NATO reporting name Maiden.

Span: 8.25 m (27 ft) *Length:* 17.4 m (57 ft) including probe *Gross weight:* 13 600 kg (30 000 lb) *Maximum speed:* Mach 1.8

Fitter, Sukhoi Su-7/Su-17/Su-20

Soviet jet ground-attack fighter. The basic Su-7 Fitter-A was the Soviet air force's standard close-support aircraft from the late 1950s until it began to be replaced by the MiG-27 Flogger-D in the mid-1970s. The Su-20 Fitter-C and its export equivalent, the Su-17, were developed from the Su-7 by the addition of variable-sweep wings.

The Su-7 was revealed to Western eyes in 1956, when the reestablishment of the Sukhoi design bureau was confirmed by the appearance of two new types at the Soviet Aviation Day, held at Tushino. The swept-wing Su-7 closely resembled the delta-wing Su-9/Su-11 Fishpot, also making its debut, and shared many major assemblies with the intercepter variants. The highly swept (62°) wing of the Su-7 allows higher lift coefficients to be developed without buffet at subsonic speeds than would be possible with a delta planform, but is by no means the ideal layout in other respects. Payload/range performance is unimpressive by Western standards, although Fitter is a stable weapon platform and carries a reasonable gun armament.

The Su-7 entered service with the Soviet air force in 1959, the variant produced in largest numbers being the Su-7BM powered by a Lyulka AL-7F turbojet producing 7000 kg (15 430 lb) of dry thrust and 10 000 kg (22 045 lb) with afterburning. A pair of 30-mm (1.18-in) NR-30 cannon with 70 rounds per gun are built into the wing roots and external stores can be carried on four pylons, two side by side under the belly and one outboard of each main undercarriage well. Each pylon can carry a 250-kg (550-lb) or 500-kg (1100-lb) bomb, a 240-mm (9.45-in) S-24 rocket or a UV-16-57 pod containing 16 55-mm (2.16-in) S-5 rockets. Some late production aircraft, notably those in Polish service, have two additional pylons.

The internal fuel capacity of some 4150 litres (913 Imp gal) can be supplemented by auxiliary tanks accommodating 600 litres (132 Imp gal) on each pylon. Fitter needs all the fuel that it can get, since the Indian air force has found that the AL-7F in its Su-7BMKs burns 2.2 kg/kg/h (4.85 lb/lb/h) at sea level in full afterburning, giving an endurance of little more than eight minutes on full internal fuel if reheat is maintained. The specific fuel consumption in maximum dry thrust at low level is a more sensible 0.817 kg/kg/h (1.80

F.K.3, Armstrong Whitworth

The final version of the Armstrong Whitworth F.K.8 two-seat reconnaissance bomber. It was known affectionately as 'Big Ack' by its crews

lb/lb/h), but maximum speed without after-burner engaged is 870 km/h (540 mph).

The Su-7 is fitted with a large gyro gunsight complemented by a ranging radar in the bullet at the centre of the intake; vanes on the pitot boom provide yaw and angle-of-attack information. The tailplane gearing is automatically adjusted according to height and speed, and Fitter is very manoeuvrable near the ground. Later models carry twin ribbon braking parachutes housed in a clamshell fairing at the base of the fin; these can be streamed while the aircraft is still airborne, allowing it to stop in only 300 m (984 ft) of runway. Pneumatic brakes are fitted to all three wheels, and an antiskid system is incorporated. The Indian air force's 150 Su-7BMKs have improved short-field capability, with provision for rocket assistance at takeoff and with low-pressure tyres.

A variable-geometry development, Fitter-C, was revealed to the West in 1967; the aircraft is designated Su-17 in service with the Soviet air force, export variants being known as Su-20. The Su-17, which entered service in 1972, is a minimum-change development of the Su-7 in an attempt to improve all-round performance. The outer 4 m (13 ft 1½ in) of each wing are pivoted, the junction with the fixed section being marked by a large fence which incorporates the outer stores pylon. The wingtip fences found on the Su-7 are deleted. The uprated Lyulka AL-21F-3 turbojet produces 7800 kg (17 200 lb) of thrust dry and 11 200 kg (24 700 lb) in afterburner. Fuel capacity is raised slightly, to 4550 litres (1000 Imperial gallons), by adoption of the deep spine which first appeared on the two-seat Su-7 Moujik trainer to compensate for space lost when the second crew position was added.

The adoption of variable sweep improves field performance and raises maximum payload greatly, while taking advantage of most existing Su-7 tooling and support facilities. The basic Su-7 is operated by several countries in the Warsaw Pact and the Middle East, together with India, and the Su-20 is being supplied to Peru under the

reported (but probably spurious) designation of Su-22. Poland, Egypt and possibily Syria have also received Su-20s. The Su-20 has a lower-rated engine and less-advanced electronics.

(Su-7BMK) *Span:* 8.93 m (29 ft 3½ in) *Length:* 17.37 m (57 ft) including probe *Gross weight:* 13 425 kg (29 600 lb) *Maximum speed:* Mach 1.8

(Su-20) *Span:* as Su-7 at maximum sweep *Length:* as Su-7 *Gross weight:* 17 700 kg (39 020 lb) *Maximum speed:* Mach 2

FJ, North American US Navy jet fighter aircraft See **Fury**

F.K.3, Armstrong Whitworth

British two-seat trainer aircraft. When the firm of W G Armstrong, Whitworth & Co received a contract in 1914 to build B.E.2 aircraft for the Royal Flying Corps and the Royal New Zealand Air Service, it offered to design and build a simpler but equally efficient aircraft instead. With official approval, Frederik Koolhoven designed the F.K.3, and construction started in August 1915. The resulting design was similar in configuration to the B.E. in its initial state, with separated cockpits for pilot and observer; but production versions incorporated a tandem crew cockpit—with the pilot seated forward—and a more efficient tail design. The prototype F.K.3 had a 120-hp Austro-Daimler engine, but most production models had the 90-hp RAF 1a, while a few had the 105-hp RAF 1b.

Approximately 500 F.K.3s were ordered for RFC use, the bulk of which were allotted to training units where they gave steady service until the end of hostilities. Pleasant to fly, with no vices in handling, the F.K.3—known as the 'Little Ack' to its crews—was an almost ideal instructional machine; virtually foolproof even in the inexperienced hands of raw pupils. Only one RFC squadron used F.K.3s operationally; 47 Squadron in

Macedonia, where the 'Little Ack' became a bomber and general reconnaissance machine from late 1916 until the Armistice. On October 31, 1918, the RAF had a total of 62 F.K.3s still on charge. At least four of these went onto the post-1918 Civil Register as G-EABY, G-EABZ, G-EAEU and G-EALK (ex-B9629, B9518, B9612 and B9603 respectively).

Span: 12.2 m (40 ft) *Length:* 8.8 m (29 ft) *Height:* 3.6 m (11 ft 10¾ in) *Maximum speed:* 142 km/h (88 mph) at 1980 m (6500 ft) *Service ceiling:* 3962 m (13 000 ft)

F.K.8, Armstrong Whitworth

British two-seat bomber/reconnaissance aircraft. One of the lesser-known aircraft of 1914-18, the F.K.8—or 'Big Ack' as it was dubbed affectionately by its crews—gave excellent service to the RFC and later the RAF in 1917-18. At least 1596 machines were built and delivered for service use. Designed by Frederik Koolhoven, the F.K.8 prototype first flew in May 1916, and bore a distinct family resemblance to its predecessor, the F.K.3. Of typical contemporary construction, the F.K.8 was strong and relatively easy to fly, making it popular with its crews. Standard production versions were powered by a 120-hp Beardmore engine, though later machines were fitted with a 160-hp Beardmore. All were fitted with a form of dual control so that the rear cockpit observer could partially fly the machine if his pilot was incapacitated. This was obviously an important feature in those days when air crews were not issued with parachutes.

The first RFC unit to receive F.K.8s was 35 Squadron, which flew fully-equipped to France on January 24, 1917. Then 2 Squadron began reequipment in April 1917; 10 Squadron in July; 8 Squadron in August, and 82 Squadron, fully equipped with the type, arrived in France in November 1917. In the Middle East zone of operations, 17 and 47 Squadrons in Macedonia, and 142 Squadron in Palestine were equipped with F.K.8s by

1918, and continued to operate them until the end of the war. In England, several home defence units were partly equipped with the F.K.8, and one belonging to 50 Squadron was responsible for shooting down a Gotha bomber on July 7, 1917.

The F.K.8 first came into prominence during the German spring offensive of March 1918, being used primarily in a tactical low-level bombing and strafing role against German infantry. It was during this period of action, on March 27, that a young Canadian pilot, Second Lieutenant Alan McLeod, earned the first of two Victoria Crosses awarded to F.K.8 crew members, when his aircraft was attacked by Fokker D.1 triplanes.

The second recipient was Captain F M F West, MC, of 8 Squadron, RAF, who gained the award on August 10, 1918, when his F.K.8, engaged in bombing a German gun position, was attacked by six or so enemy fighters.

Elsewhere along the Western Front, F.K.8s performed well until the Armistice. Apart from their routine duties of bombing and reconnaissance, the F.K.8s of 35 Squadron were given an unusual role on October 8, 1918—that of maintaining a two-hour smoke screen in front of an advancing British infantry corps. Other F.K.8s played an important part in low-level resupply patrols, dropping fresh ammunition and supplies to forward, isolated Allied infantry positions during the final Allied ground advances. In Macedonia and Palestine, F.K.8s bombed and strafed retreating enemy troops and air bases, blasting a path forward for the advancing Allied infantry and cavalry formations. By October 31, 1918, a total of 694 F.K.8s were still on RAF charge, but at the end of 1919 few examples remained. Eight found their way onto the Civil Register, and two went to Australia where they helped to pioneer air travel from late 1922 onwards.

Span: 13.26 m (43 ft 6 in) *Length:* 9.45 m (31 ft) *Height:* 3.35 m (11 ft) *Maximum speed:* 158 km/h (98.4 mph) *Service ceiling:* 3962 m (13 000 ft) *Armament:* 1 fixed, forward Vickers .303-in (7.7-mm) mg; 1/2 Lewis .303-in (7.7-mm) mg in rear cockpit; Approx 181.4-kg (400-lb) bombload

F.K.10, Armstrong Whitworth

British two-seat fighter/reconnaissance aircraft. Frederik Koolhoven's final designs for Armstrong Whitworth were several quadruplanes in early 1916. The first, the F.K.9, was tested at Upavon in November 1916. Test pilots' reports were critical of the machine and its poor performance. In spite of this, a batch of 50 improved versions, later designated F.K.10, was ordered on December 30, 1916, although only 11 such machines received official serial identities. After many minor modifications and part redesigning the F.K.10 still failed to reach a satisfactory performance, and the type was never put into service use operationally. A more bizarre multi-wing project was mooted in 1916, the so-called F.K.11, which proposed the use of no less than 15 narrow-chord mainplanes, on an F.K.10-type fuselage. Fortunately perhaps for those who would have flown the machine, this project did not proceed beyond the drawing-board stage.

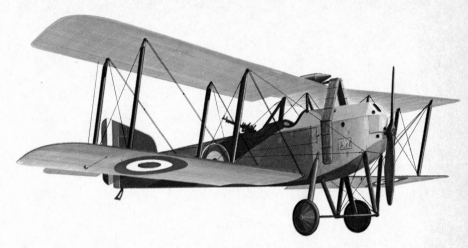

An Armstrong Whitworth F.K.8 with the early type of cowling fitted to its Beardmore engine. The 'Big Ack' served from July 1917 to the end of the First World War with RFC units on the Western Front, Mediterranean and Middle East. F.K.8s of No 47 Squadron operating over Macedonia attacked the Bulgarian army at Kosturino Pass on September 21, 1918, dropping 2250 kg (5000 lb) of high-explosive and firing 1200 rounds into the retreating enemy. On the same day in Palestine, Australian Bristol fighters hit the Turks as they withdrew

Span (all wings): 8.61 m (28 ft 3 in) *Length:* 7.8 m (25 ft 6 in) *Height:* 3.5 m (11 ft 6 in) *Maximum speed:* 169 km/h (105 mph) at ground level *Service ceiling:* Approx 3660 m (12 000 ft) *Engine:* 130-hp Clerget rotary *Armament:* 1 Lewis .303-in (7.7-mm) mg

F.K.31, Koolhoven

Dutch fighter/reconnaissance aircraft. This little-known biplane was designed by Frederik Koolhoven in the early 1920s for the NV (Nationale Vliegtuigindustrie, national aircraft industry), a small number being produced in 1924-25. Powered by a 400-hp Bristol Jupiter radial engine, it seated a pilot and observer/gunner in tandem open cockpits, operating respectively two fixed, forward-firing machine-guns and two ring-mounted.

Reconnaissance versions sometimes carried a fifth gun, firing downward through the floor of the rear cockpit. Performance was not up to LVA (Luchtvaartafdeling, army air service) requirements, but the F.K.31 was used until about 1930 by the Netherlands East Indies army air service as a fighter trainer. The Finnish air force operated 12 over a similar period, four of them built in Finland under licence. Louis de Monge in France also built a few, with Gnome-Rhône (Bristol) Jupiter engines.

Span and Length: not known *Gross weight:* 1760 kg (3880 lb) *Maximum speed:* 235 km/h (146 mph)

F.K.51, Koolhoven

Dutch advanced trainer/observation aircraft. First flown in 1937, this two-seat biplane had

One of only 11 Armstrong Whitworth F.K.10 two-seater fighter/reconnaissance aircraft

F.K.52, Koolhoven

Novosti

Sukhoi Su-15 Flagon intercepters armed with AA-6-2 advanced Anab AAM, guided by Skip Spin X-band radar with a range up to 40 km (25 miles)

tandem open cockpits, with dual controls; it was armed with two 7.7-mm (0.303-in) forward-firing machine-guns in the upper wing, a third movable 7.7-mm (0.303-in) gun in the rear cockpit, and provision for under-fuselage bomb racks. A vertical camera was mounted in the floor of the rear cockpit. Usual powerplant was a 350-hp Armstrong Siddeley Cheetah IX radial engine, but some F.K.51s had 270-hp Cheetah V, 450-hp Pratt & Whitney Wasp, or (those for Spain) 400-hp Armstrong Siddeley Jaguar engines; the F.K.51 *bis* (for Spain) had a 450-hp Wright Whirlwind.

The LVA (Dutch army air service) ordered 53 in 1937, later increasing its order. In all, some 130-140 F.K.51s were built, of which 28 F.K.51/51*bis* were supplied to Spain during the civil war. When Holland was invaded in May 1940, the 2nd Air Regiment possessed 16 observation F.K.51s. Others were used by the Dutch East Indies army air service for reconnaissance and coastal/maritime patrol during 1941-42.

Span: 9 m (29 ft 6¼ in) *Length:* 7.85 m (25 ft 9 in) *Gross weight:* 1600 kg (3530 lb) *Maximum speed:* 253 km/h (157 mph)

F.K.52, Koolhoven

Dutch fighter-bomber/reconnaissance aircraft. Of similar appearance to the British Gladiator, the F.K.52 biplane had a fully-transparent framed canopy over the two cockpits, and a Bristol Mercury radial engine driving a three-blade wooden propeller. It was intended as a multi-purpose successor to the Fokker C.V-D, but no Dutch production orders were forthcoming.

The prototype flew on February 9, 1937, with a 645-hp Mercury VIS, but subsequent aircraft (four or five others were built) had an 840-hp Mercury VIII. Two 20-mm (0.79-in) cannon were mounted in the upper wing, one or two 7.7-mm (0.303-in) machine-guns could be fired from the openable rear cockpit windows, and up to 115 kg (253.5 lb) of bombs could be carried under the fuselage.

Four F.K.52s were in Holland when the country was invaded on May 10, 1940, of which two were broken up during that year. The other two were supplied to the Finnish air force in January 1940, with whose TLeLv 36 (Ground Liaison Squadron 36) they served as trainer/observation aircraft during the Winter War of 1940-41 and its 'continuation' in 1941-43.

Span: 9.80 m (32 ft 1¾ in) *Length:* 8.35 m (27 ft 4½ in) *Gross weight:* 2500 kg (5510 lb) *Maximum speed:* 370 km/h (230 mph)

F.K.58, Koolhoven

Dutch single-seat fighter aircraft. The NV Koolhoven Vliegtuigen of Waalhaven, near Rotterdam, built the prototype F.K.58 within two months of completion of the design, and it flew for the first time on July 17, 1938, bearing the civil registration PH-ATO. Designed by Dr Erich Schatzki, formerly of Fokker, to meet a French requirement, the F.K.58 had plywood-covered wooden wings and fixed tail surfaces; a metal- and fabric-covered steel-tube fuselage; and metal-framed fabric-covered wing and tail control surfaces. A total of 450 litres (99 Imperial gallons) of fuel was carried internally, and the 1080-hp Hispano-Suiza 14Aa 14-cylinder two-row radial engine gave it a top speed of 483 km/h (300 mph).

This prototype was demonstrated to the French authorities at the Centre d'Essais du Matériel Aérien at Villacoublay on October 10, 1938, and an order for 50 aircraft followed in January 1939. Intended for use by the Armée de l'Air in French Indo-China, they were to be powered by 1030-hp Gnome-Rhône 14N39 14-cylinder radials and designated F.K.58A. Deliveries began in mid-June 1939, and 17 were delivered within the next three months, of which the first four retained the Hispano-Suiza powerplant, the other 13 being F.K.58As. However, due to inadequate production facilities, the small Koolhoven factory was not able to complete the French order. The construction of 10 French

F.K.58As was sub-contracted to SABCA in Belgium, but although the airframes had been completed when Germany invaded that country in 1940, their Gnome-Rhône engines had not been delivered from France.

Following the first flight of a second Hispano-powered prototype (PH-AVA) on February 14, 1939, the Netherlands government in the following month ordered 36 F.K.58s, to be powered by 1080-hp Bristol Taurus III engines; but here again engine supply problems intervened, and Koolhoven was unable to complete any of the order for the Luchtvaartafdeling (Dutch air force). The production line and the second prototype were destroyed in a Luftwaffe air attack, the first prototype having already been lost in a crash in January 1940.

Thus the only operational F.K.58s were those supplied to the Armée de l'Air. Armed with four 7.5-mm (0.29-in) FN-Browning machine-guns, in two underwing fairings outboard of the main undercarriage legs, most of them were deployed by *patrouilles de protection* in May 1940, in defence of such towns as Aulnat, Caen, Clermont-Ferrand, Cognac and La Rochelle. For a short time, they were among the Luftwaffe's most cosmopolitan opponents, for these Dutch fighters with French engines and Belgian guns were often flown by Polish pilots.

(F.K.58A) *Span:* 10.97 m (36 ft) *Length:* 8.68 m (28 ft 5¾ in) *Gross weight:* 2750 kg (6065 lb) *Maximum speed:* 475 km/h (295 mph)

Flagon, Sukhoi Su-15

Soviet jet intercepter. The Su-15 is a single-seat all-weather intercepter developed to replace the Su-11 Fishpot, on which it is based. The first prototype made its maiden flight in 1964 or 1965 and Flagon was revealed to Western observers at the 1967 Domodedovo aviation day, when ten flew past. The original Flagon-A has a mid-mounted delta wing, swept back by 57° at the leading edge and closely resembling that of the Su-9/Su-11 Fishpots. Twin Lyulka AL-

1F-3 turbojets each producing 7800 kg (17 200 lb) of dry thrust and 11 200 kg (24 700 lb) with afterburning, are mounted side by side in the rear fuselage, being fed from ram-type intakes with splitter plates mounted on the fuselage sides. Variable-area nozzles are used. The undercarriage and tail are also similar to those of the Su-11, but restressed for greater loads.

Standard armament is a pair of AA-3 Anab air-to-air missiles, one fitted with an infrared seeker and the other employing semi-active radar guidance; the missile pylons are mounted beneath each outer wing panel. Twin side-by-side fuselage pylons are provided for 600 litres (132 Imp gal) auxiliary fuel tanks and some aircraft carry twin 23-mm (0.90-in) GSh-23 cannon forward of these pylons. Fire control and illumination for the radar-guided AA-3 are provided by an X-band Skip Spin radar, with an effective range of 40 km (25 miles), mounted in the Su-15's nose. Later versions may be fitted with the AA-6 Acrid or AA-7 Apex air-to-air missiles, possibly in conjunction with a derivative of the MiG-25's Fox Fire radar.

Flagon entered service in 1969 and 600 or more were deployed by the mid-1970s. Flagon-B was an experimental derivative exhibited at Domodedovo in 1967, but not seen since. Three lift-jets mounted in the centre fuselage conferred STOL (short take-off and landing) performance, and the outer 40% of each wing was of reduced sweep, thereby increasing area without extending the tips. Flagon-C is a two-seat trainer with secondary combat capability. Flagon-D and -E have compound-sweep wings similar to those adopted for Flagon-B, and Flagon-E —which has been in service since the second half of 1973—additionally has more powerful engines and uprated avionics. The larger radar dish results in an original nose radome.

Span: 9.5 m (31 ft 2 in) *Length:* 21.5 m (70 ft 6 in) *Gross weight:* 20 000 kg (44 000 lb) *Maximum speed:* Mach 2.5

Flamant

French sloop. Although she was laid down at Rochefort dockyard in 1913 as a patrol sloop, work on the *Flamant* was continually delayed during the First World War to enable other more urgent naval construction to be completed. She was finally launched in 1916, but was not eventually completed for another two years. Four months after completion she was renamed *Quentin Roosevelt* in memory of one of President Theodore Roosevelt's sons who died in action on July 14, 1918, while flying with the French air force.

After the war, the *Quentin Roosevelt* was relegated to the role of a fishery protection vessel. The French navy was then in the process of commissioning a large class of fast, well-armed, turbine-propelled patrol sloops, capable of carrying out antisubmarine duties and the *Quentin Roosevelt* no longer met the stringent requirements for patrol vessels shown necessary by war experience. She remained on fishery protection duties until the Second World War.

When France surrendered in June 1940, the *Quentin Roosevelt* escaped to a British port and was seized by the Royal Navy on June 3, 1940. During the early part of the war she served with the Royal Navy as an antisubmarine training ship. In January 1943, she was relegated to the role of training ship and served as such until June 1945, when she was returned to the French navy. There she resumed her duties as a fishery protection vessel and remained in service until 1955 when she was scrapped.

Displacement: 585 tons (normal) *Length:* 50 m (164 ft) oa *Beam:* 8.4 m (27 ft 6¾ in) *Draught:* 5.8 m (19 ft) *Machinery:* 1-shaft reciprocating engine, 2 cylindrical boilers, 1200 ihp= 14½ knots *Radius:* 1930 km (1200 miles) at 10 knots *Armament:* 1 76-mm (3-in); 1 47-mm (1.85-in) *Crew:* 53

Flamant, Dassault

French transport, utility and trainer aircraft. When Marcel Dassault (the prewar Marcel Bloch) recovered from his wartime experience in Buchenwald concentration camp, he set up in the aircraft business with a factory at Talence and a scheme for this universal twin-engined machine. Civil markets proved elusive, but the Armée de l'Air bought considerable numbers.

The prototype, designated MD.303, flew on February 10, 1947. Engines were two 580-hp SNECMA 12S-201 inverted-V-12 air-cooled, previously known as the Renault 12S and before that the German Argus As 410. The first production version was the MD.315 Flamant light transport and 'Type Coloniale' utility machine with a crew of two and up to ten passengers or a tonne of freight. The production run totalled 137 during 1949-52.

The MD.312 was furnished for only six VIP passengers and 142 of these were built. The MD.311, 39 of which were delivered, was a crew trainer, with glazed nose for visual bombing. Most Flamants could be equipped as casevac stretcher (litter) ambulances. A few were still in use in 1978.

Span: 20.67 m (67 ft 10 in) *Length:* 12.6 m (41 ft 4 in) *Gross weight:* (typical) 6000 kg (13 230 lb) *Max speed:* 390 km/h (242 mph)

Flamethrower

Universal flame projector. The flamethrower originated in the German army in 1914. According to legend, it was first devised during an exercise in prewar years when a fortress commander, at his wits' end, deployed the garrison fire brigade to drench the attackers. When asked by Kaiser Wilhelm II what military value this tactic was supposed to have, the commander, with great presence of mind, said that in war he would have used an inflammable liquid and ignited it. The Kaiser, intrigued with the idea, gave orders for the possibilities to be examined, and a practical flamethrower was the result. It was used in one or two isolated instances against the French late in 1914, but the first major employment was against the British Army at Hooge in July 1915.

The original model consisted of a steel cylindrical tank divided internally into two compartments, the lower containing compressed gas and the upper an inflammable coal-tar liquid. By releasing a valve, the gas forced the liquid out of the tank, through a

British troops watch a spectacular demonstration of a heavy pump flamethrower in 1944

Flashlight

rubber hose and ejected it from a long steel nozzle. On the end of the nozzle was an igniting device containing a spring-loaded pin, detonator, gun-cotton and a paraffin-soaked wick. As the fluid passed through this device, it tripped the spring-loaded pin which fired the detonator and ignited, in turn, the guncotton, the wick and then the fluid. The resulting jet of flame reached for about 23 m (75 ft) and the flame could be emitted continuously for about a minute and a half. One drawback to the device was that every shot had to have a fresh igniter unit fitted to the nozzle.

Once adopted by the Germans, it was copied to a lesser extent by the French and British. The British Army, in particular, expended much effort in attempting to develop large static flamethrowers for defensive purposes, but with little success. After the war it was quickly discarded, since most armies considered it to have been a specialized device for the peculiar conditions obtaining in the trench warfare in Flanders. It reappeared in Italian hands in the Abyssinian campaign of 1935, when a tank-mounted flamethrower was employed, and also in small numbers in the Spanish Civil War, in both manpack and tank-mounted versions.

During the Second World War, the German army used flamethrowers in the Polish campaign and also in the advance into France and Belgium in 1940, particularly against the Belgian forts such as Eben Emael. After this, they saw little use since they did not fit in with the tactics of open war. The British Army, on the other hand, began development later in the war with the intention of using flame during assault operations against the coast of Europe.

Much British work was done in 1940 on developing hasty defensive devices; flame guns for Home Guard use, flame traps, and flamethrowers shooting flame into the sky to attack troop-carrying aircraft during their landing runs were all developed to varying degrees of efficiency. More serious work went into the development of tank-mounted flamethrowers, the Crocodile and Wasp being the principal models, and these were used to good effect in north-west Europe in 1944-45. A manpack model, known as the 'Ack Pack' was produced, though this was largely intended for operations in the Far East, particularly against Japanese pillboxes and bunkers where the defenders were willing to fight to the death.

The Ack Pack consisted of a ring-shaped container, similar to a lifebuoy, carrying 18 litres (4 Imp gal) of fuel; in the centre of the ring was a spherical gas container holding gas at 140.6 kg/sq cm (2000 lb/sq in) pressure. From the bottom of the fuel tank a hose ran to a nozzle unit which had two pistol grips and a firing trigger. Around the nozzle was a revolving cylinder with ten chambers, each holding a special ignition cartridge. On pressing the trigger, a valve released fuel under pressure, and an ignition cartridge was fired, igniting the fuel which then gave a jet to about 36 m (120 ft) range.

In 1940, the US Army began developing a manpack thrower, which was standardized in late 1941. The first combat use in American hands was on Guadalcanal in January 1943, when the 2nd Marine and 25th Infantry divisions used them to deal with Japanese

German pioneers with a Klief type flamethrower attack a bunker during the Second World War

pillboxes. Later operations were to have varied results, some successful and others disastrous. This was due to equipment malfunctioning; much of which was caused by the rapid effects of heat and damp experienced in the Pacific. Difficulty also arose over the fuel, and it was not until rigorous maintenance was insisted upon and a new fuel, based on napalm, was adopted, that flamethrower operations began to succeed.

Eventually the flamethrower became one of the most valued weapons in the Pacific, although one lesson which was soon learned was the need to protect the flame operator and give covering and diversionary fire to allow him to get close to his target. These techniques were soon perfected, and in November 1943 the flamethrower proved to be invaluable in the taking of Tarawa. In the European theatre, US troops used flame very much less, and although ample manpack units and numbers of tank-mounted units were available, they were not enthusiastically received and were rarely employed in action.

Since 1945, the flamethrower has, once again, vanished from sight. The US Marines deployed one or two tank-mounted throwers in Vietnam, but at present no NATO army has a flamethrower on its inventory, and the only Soviet thrower known to the West is an elderly manpack unit, the LPO-50.

Generally speaking, records tend to show that the flamethrower is a mixed blessing. To obtain results it demands a high state of specialized training, not only of the thrower operator but of his supporting squad, and this training is difficult to arrange when other, more basic, skills appear to be more vital. Since flame is used only occasionally, the tendency is for the trained team to be dispersed and used in other tasks when things are slack. When flame is suddenly needed, the trained squad is absent and an inexperienced team is hurriedly assembled. They usually fail, the failure is blamed on the flame device, which takes another drop in esteem. It was noticeable that where trained flame operators were in frequent use, as with the US Marines and infantry in the Pacific and the British 79th Armoured Division in north-west Europe, flame gave excellent results and commanders were willing to employ it. Where commanders were not used to it, they tended to shy away; there were several instances in Europe in 1945 where it might

have been used to good effect but where conventional weapons were used instead.

Flashlight, Yakovlev Yak-25/Yak-27

Soviet jet intercepter. The Yak-25 was the first Russian-designed true all-weather intercepter, being developed to meet a requirement issued in November 1951 for a twin-engined, two-seat aircraft carrying a comparatively long-range search radar—the X-band Scan Three, which employs a very high pulse-repetition frequency. The Yak-25 faced competition from the Mikoyan/Gurevich I-320 (R) and Lavochkin La-200, but was selected in preference to these types, reputedly because the Yakovlev intercepter was judged to have greater development potential.

The Yak-25 made its maiden flight in 1953 and entered production the following year. A contemporary of the French Sud-Ouest Vautour, which had a similar appearance, the Yak-25 was relatively conventional in layout, but had a number of unusual features. The combination of bulbous fuselage and small underwing nacelles posed problems for the undercarriage designer, these being solved by adoption of a zero-track landing gear; the Yakovlev design bureau had made the same decision for a number of previous aircraft, such as the Yak-50. The untapered wings were swept back by 45° and carried some 3° of anhedral. The initial powerplant comprised a pair of Mikulin AM-5 turbojets producing 2200 kg (4850 lb) of thrust each. From 1957 these were replaced in the definitive Yak-25F by Tumansky RD-9s of 2600 kg (5730 lb) thrust, thereby increasing the maximum speed.

The intercepter was codenamed Flashlight-A by NATO's Air Standards Coordinating Committee, Flashlight-B being a reconnaissance variant developed concurrently for service with the Soviet air force's frontal aviation or tactical air arm. The Yak-25R carried the second crew member in a pointed glazed nose instead of behind the pilot, and armament was reduced from the intercepter's pair of 37-mm (1.46-in) NR-37 cannon to a single 23-mm (0.90-in) weapon in the right-hand side of the forward fuselage.

The RD-9 turbojet had been installed in a separate development, the Yak-27P, before it

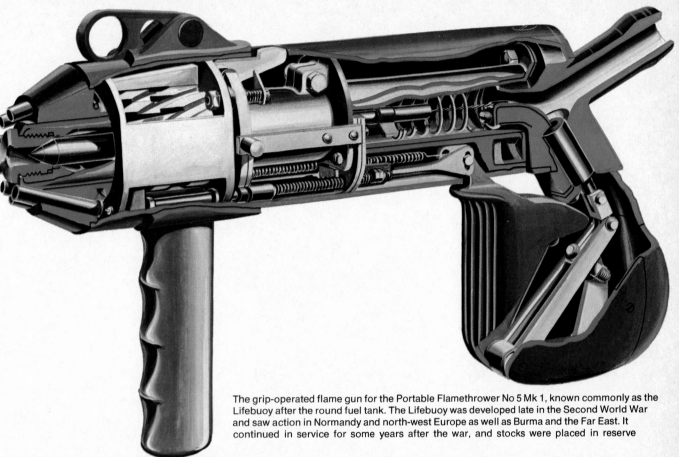

The grip-operated flame gun for the Portable Flamethrower No 5 Mk 1, known commonly as the Lifebuoy after the round fuel tank. The Lifebuoy was developed late in the Second World War and saw action in Normandy and north-west Europe as well as Burma and the Far East. It continued in service for some years after the war, and stocks were placed in reserve

Italian troops with a flamethrower during the Second World War

The harness for the No 5 Mk 1 Flamethrower, with armoured hose

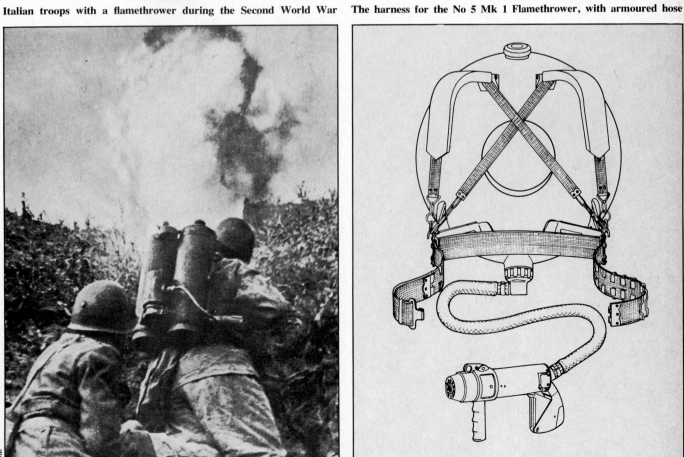

Fleet Shadower

The ungainly Airspeed Fleet Shadower was designed to give a crew of three (pilot, observer and radio operator) comfortable accommodation for patrols of up to 11 hours. Two prototypes flew at the beginning of the Second World War, but development was suspended in 1940

was adopted for the Yak-25F. The Yak-27P was dubbed Flashlight-C on its appearance at the Tushino Soviet Aviation Day in 1956. The adoption of afterburning for the RD-9 increased the maximum thrust to 3300 kg (7275 lb) per engine and necessitated some aerodynamic modifications to the airframe. A pointed radome replaced the unusually blunt nose of the Yak-25, thus reducing drag and rain erosion, and the wing leading edge was modified to increase the critical Mach number. The Yak-27P entered limited production, but it offered only a limited improvement over the Yak-25 and the Yakovlev bureau was already preparing for a much more radical development, the Yak-28 Brewer/Firebar series. However, the Mangrove reconnaissance version of the Yak-27 did serve with the Soviet air force in appreciable numbers. The Mandrake high-altitude reconnaissance aircraft, possibly designated Yak-26, also uses many Yak-25 components.

Span: 11 m (36 ft 1 in) *Length:* 15.6 m (51 ft 2 in)
Gross weight: In excess of 9000 kg (19 840 lb)
Maximum speed: Mach 0.95

Fleet Shadower, Airspeed/G.A.L.

British reconnaissance aircraft. In 1937 the British Admiralty issued a requirement for a novel type of aircraft to shadow enemy fleets, especially by night. The Air Ministry issued Specification S.22/37 calling for an aircraft compatible with aircraft carriers which would provide comfortable accommodation for a pilot, observer and radio operator, outstanding all-round view and the ability to cruise at 40 knots for 11 hours. Two prototypes were built, the Airspeed A.S.39 (serial N1323) and the General Aircraft G.A.L.38 (P1758). These flew after the outbreak of the Second World War.

Both were high-wing aircraft with extensive slats, flaps and drooping ailerons all in the slipstream of four 130-hp Pobjoy Niagara V radials driving fixed-pitch propellers. The G.A. aircraft was all-wood, but the Airspeed had a metal fuselage; the former had a nose-wheel and tall single fin, while the Airspeed had a tail-wheel and three small fins. Each seated the observer in a panoramic nose, the pilot high and behind and the radio operator further aft. Both aircraft met the requirement but the Admiralty changed their minds about the desirability of such an aircraft and scrapped this interesting programme in 1940.

(A.S.39) *Span:* 16.25 m (53 ft 4 in) *Length:* 12.19 m (40 ft) *Gross weight:* 3148 kg (6940 lb) *Maximum speed:* 201 km/h (125 mph)

(G.A.L.38) *Span:* 17.02 m (55 ft 10 in) *Length:* 11 m (36 ft 1 in) *Gross weight:* 3897 kg (8590 lb) *Maximum speed:* 185 km/h (115 mph)

The Airspeed Fleet Shadower was an all-metal construction. Both the Airspeed and G.A.L. types were powered by 130-hp Pobjoy Niagara V radials

Bildstelle der Marine

Destroyer *Z.4*, the ex-US *Fletcher* Class destroyer *Claxton* (DD.571). Six of these ships were transferred to the Federal German Navy in 1958-60

Fletcher

US destroyer class, built 1940-45. Under the provisions of the disarmament treaties, the US Navy was inhibited from designing to maximum dimensions to match the Japanese 'Special type', the *Fubuki* Class, and so the original basis for the design of the *Fletcher* was a 1500-ton ship with the same armament as the previous *Benson* and *Bristol* Classes. The emphasis on endurance led to an addition of some 500 tons, but this extra displacement was used to enhance the antiaircraft battery, and not the surface armament.

Only 24 of the class were in hand at the time of Pearl Harbor, but another 100 were immediately ordered, plus two experimental variants.

The Class comprised: DD.445 *Fletcher*; DD.446 *Radford*; DD.447 *Jenkins*; DD.448 *La Vallette*; DD.449 *Nicholas*; DD.450 *O'Bannon*; DD.451 *Chevalier* (ex-*Pringle*); DD.452 *Percival*; DD.465 *Saufley*; DD.466 *Waller*; DD.467 *Strong*; DD.468 *Taylor*; DD.469 *De Haven*; DD.470 *Bache*; DD.471 *Beale*; DD.472 *Guest*; DD.473 *Bennett*; DD.474 *Fullam*; DD.475 *Hudson*; DD.476 *Hutchins*; DD.477 *Pringle*; DD.478 *Stanly*; DD.480 *Stevens*; DD.481 *Leutze*; DD.482 *Watson*; DD.498 *Philip*; DD.499 *Renshaw*; DD.500 *Ringgold*; DD.501 *Schroeder*; DD.502 *Sigsbee*; DD.503 *Stevenson*; DD.504 *Stockton*; DD.505 *Thorn*; DD.506 *Turner*; DD.507 *Conway*; DD.508 *Cony*; DD.509 *Converse*; DD.510 *Eaton*; DD.511 *Foote*; DD.512 *Spence*; DD.513 *Thatcher*; DD.515 *Anthony*; DD.516 *Wadsworth*; DD.517 *Walker*; DD.518 *Brownson*; DD.519 *Daly*; DD.520 *Isherwood*; DD.521 *Kimberly*; DD.522 *Luce*; DD.523 unnamed; DD.524 unnamed; DD.525 unnamed; DD.526 *Abner Read*; DD.527 *Ammen*; DD.528 *Mullany* (ex-*Beatty*); DD.529 *Bush*; DD.530 *Trathen*; DD.531 *Hazelwood*; DD.532 *Heermann*; DD.533 *Hoel*; DD.534 *McCord*; DD.535 *Miller*; DD.536 *Owen*; DD.537 *The Sullivans* (ex-*Putnam*); DD.538 *Stephen Potter*; DD.539 *Tingey*; DD.540 *Twining*; DD.541 *Yarnell*; DD.542 unnamed; DD.543 unnamed; DD.544 *Boyd*; DD.545 *Bradford*; DD.546 *Brown*; DD.547 *Cowell*; DD.548 unnamed; DD.549 unnamed; DD.550 *Capps*; DD.551 *David W Taylor*; DD.552 *Evans*; DD.553 *John D Henley*; DD.554 *Franks*; DD.555 *Haggard*; DD.556 *Hailey*; DD.557 *Johnston*; DD.558 *Laws*; DD.559 *Longshaw*; DD.560 *Morrison*; DD.561 *Prichett*; DD.562 *Robinson*; DD.563 *Ross*; DD.564 *Rowe*; DD.565 *Smalley*; DD.566 *Stoddard*; DD.567 *Watts*; DD.568 *Wern*; DD.569 *Aulick*; DD.570 *Charles Ausburn*; DD.571 *Claxton*; DD.572 *Dyson*; DD.573 *Harrison*; DD.574 *John Rodgers*; DD. 575 *McKee*; DD.576 *Murray*; DD.577 *Sproston*; DD.578 *Wickes*; DD.579 *William D Porter*; DD.580 *Young*; DD.581 *Charrette*; DD.582 *Conner*; DD.583 *Hall*; DD.584 *Halligan*; DD.585 *Haraden*; DD.586 *Newcomb*; DD.587 *Bell*; DD.588 *Burns*; DD.589 *Izard*; DD.590 *Paul Hamilton*; DD.591 *Twiggs*; DD.592 *Howorth*; DD.593 *Killen*; DD.594 *Hart* (ex-*Mansfield*); DD.595 *Metcalf*; DD.596 *Shields*; DD. 597 *Wiley*.

DD.445-448, DD.465-466 and DD.498-502 were ordered from Federal shipbuilding, Kearny; DD.449-451 and DD.507-517 from Bath Ironworks; DD.470-471 and DD.518-522 from Bethlehem, Staten Island; DD.472-476 and DD.581-586 from Boston navy yard; DD.477-481 and DD.587-591 from Charleston navy yard; DD.523-541 from Bethlehem, San Francisco; DD.544-549 from Bethlehem, San Pedro; DD.550-553 from Gulf shipbuilding, Chickasaw; DD.554-568 from Seattle-Tacoma shipbuilding; DD.569-580 from Consolidated Steel corporation, Orange; DD.592-597 from Puget Sound navy yard, Bremerton. DD.503-506 and DD.542-543 were not allocated.

Several ships were cancelled. Five unnamed vessels, DD.523-525 and DD.542-543, were cancelled in December 1940 before being awarded to individual yards, and *Stevenson*, *Stockton*, *Thorn* and *Turner* (DD.503-506) were cancelled in February 1941. The *Percival* (DD.452) and *Watson* (DD.482) were basically similar to the general design, but were experimental prototypes to test advanced machinery. The *Percival* was to have high-pressure boilers, while the *Watson* was to have 32-cylinder General Motors diesels; neither unit was laid down, and they were suspended for the duration of the war, and finally cancelled in January 1946.

Six units, *Hutchins*, *Pringle*, *Stanly*, *Stevens*, *Halford* and *Leutze* (DD.476-481), were earmarked to carry a floatplane and catapult in place of the after bank of torpedo tubes—an attempt to copy the Dutch practice of extending the range of destroyers beyond the horizon. The Kingfisher floatplane was to be handled by a derrick stepped from a samson post abaft the second funnel. Trials with the first three, *Halford*, *Pringle* and *Stevens*, showed that operating a floatplane was not feasible in a small warship, and they reverted to the standard armament. The other three, *Hutchins*, *Stanly* and *Leutze*, were not converted.

The antiaircraft armament was soon

Blanco Encalada, ex-USS *Wadleigh* (DD.689), one of two *Fletcher* Class destroyers transferred to the Chilean navy in 1963

Name	transfer
Taylor	Italy *Lanciere* (1951)
Walker	Italy *Fante* (1969)
Prichett	Italy *Geniere* (1969)
Guest	Brazil *Para* (1959)
Bennett	Brazil *Paraiba* (1959)
Hailey	Brazil *Pernambuco* (1961)
Lewis Hancock	Brazil *Piaui* (1967)
Irwin	Brazil *Santa Catarina* (1968)
Cushing	Brazil *Parana* (1961)
Ringgold	West Germany *Z.2* (1959)
Anthony	West Germany *Z.1* (1958)
Wadsworth	West Germany *Z.3* (1959)
Charles Ausburn	West Germany *Z.6* (1960)
Claxton	West Germany *Z.4* (1959)
Dyson	West Germany *Z.5* (1960)
Jarvis	Spain *Alcala Galiano* (1960)
McGowan	Spain *Jorge Juan* (1960)
Converse	Spain *Almirante Valdez* (1959)
Capps	Spain *Lepanto* (1957)
David W Taylor	Spain *Almirante Ferrandiz* (1957)
Isherwood	Peru *Guise* (1960)
Benham	Peru *Villar* (1961)
Kimberly	Taiwan *An Yang* (1967)
Yarnall	Taiwan *Kun Yang* (1968)
Heerman	Argentina *Brown* (1961)

Name	transfer
Stembel	Argentina *Rosales* (1961)
Dortch	Argentina *Espora* (1961)
Boyd	Turkey *Iskenderun* (1969)
Cogswell	Turkey *Izmit* (1967)
Van Valkenburgh	Turkey *Izmir* (1967)
Clarence K Bronson	Turkey *Istanbul* (1967)
Preston	Turkey *Icel* (1969)
Bradford	Greece *Thyella* (1962)
Brown	Greece *Navarinon* (1962)
Aulick	Greece *Sfendoni* (1959)
Charrette	Greece *Velos* (1959)
Conner	Greece *Aspis* (1959)
Hall	Greece *Lonchi* (1960)
Erben	South Korea *Chung Ma* (1963)
Wickox	South Korea *Pusan* (1968)
Halsey Powell	South Korea *Seoul* (1968)
Hale	Colombia *Antioquia* (1960)
Heywood L Edwards	Japan *Ariake* (1959)
Richard P Leary	Japan *Yugure* (1959)
Wadleigh	Chile *Blanco Encalada* (1963)
Rooks	Chile *Cochrane* (1962)
John Rodgers	Mexico *Cuitlahauc* (1970)
Harrison	Mexico *Cauahtemoc* (1970)

Brazilian Navy

Para (D.27), ex-USS *Guest* (DD.472), one of six *Fletcher* Class destroyers transferred on loan to the Brazilian navy between 1959-61

augmented, and the quadruple 1.1-in (28-mm) mounting between No 3 and No 4 5-in (127-mm) guns was replaced by a twin 40-mm (1.57-in) Bofors, while the 20-mm (0.79-in) Oerlikons were in some cases reduced to four, or increased to a maximum of 11 singles. As more Bofors guns became available a second twin mounting was added aft, with a total of four or six 20-mm (0.79-in) guns. The fourth configuration, towards the end of the war, was three twin 40-mm (1.57-in) mountings and 10 or 11 Oerlikons, but under the threat of kamikaze attacks many finished the war with no fewer than five twin 40-mm (1.57-in), backed up by seven 20-mm (0.79-in) singles. This was achieved without sacrificing torpedo tubes, a remarkable testimony to the margin of stability of the original design. The flush-decked hull proved to be very tough, and a great improvement over the previous *Bristol* design, and the *Fletchers* can claim to be the finest all-round class of destroyers to serve in the Second World War.

Orders were placed in 1942 for a further 56, known as the 'Later *Fletchers*'. They were identical in design, but had a lower bridge and director control tower. Most were completed with heavy AA armament approved for the original *Fletchers* by 1943-44—five twin 40-mm (1.57-in) and 7 20-mm (0.79-in) guns although some. had fewer 40-mm (1.57-in) guns.

The 'Later *Fletchers*' comprised: DD.629 *Abbot*; DD.630 *Braine*; DD.631 *Erben*; DD.642 *Hale*; DD.643 *Sigourney*; DD.644 *Stembel*; DD.649 *Albert W Grant*; DD.650 *Caperton*; DD.651 *Cogswell*; DD.652 *Ingersoll*; DD.653 *Knapp*; DD.654 *Bearss*; DD.655 *John Hood*; DD.656 *Van Valkenburgh*; DD.657 *Charles J Badger*; DD.658

Colaham; DD.659 *Dashiel*; DD.660 *Bullard*; DD.661 *Kidd*; DD.662 *Bennion*; DD.663 *Heywood L Edwards*; DD.664 *Richard P Leary*; DD.665 *Bryant*; DD.666 *Black*; DD.667 *Chauncey*; DD.668 *Clarence K Bronson*; DD.669 *Cotton*; DD.670 *Dortch*; DD.671 *Gatling*; DD.672 *Healy*; DD.673 *Hickox*; DD.674 *Hunt*; DD.675 *Lewis Hancock*; DD.676 *Marshall*; DD.677 *McDermut*; DD.678 *McGowan*; DD.679 *McNair*; DD.680 *Melvin*; DD.681 *Hopewell*; DD.682 *Porterfield*; DD.683 *Stockham*; DD.684 *Wedderburn*; DD.685 *Picking*; DD.686 *Halsey Powell*; DD.687 *Uhlmann*; DD.688 *Remey*; DD.689 *Wadleigh*; DD.690 *Mertz*; DD.792 *Callaghan*; DD.793 *Cassin Young*; DD.794 *Irwin*; DD.795 *Preston*; DD.796 *Benham*; DD.797 *Cushing*; DD.798 *Monssen*; DD.799 *Jarvis*; DD.800 *Porter*; DD.801 *Colhoun*; DD.802 *Gregory*; DD.803 *Little*; DD.804 *Rooks*.

DD.629-644, DD.650-653 and DD.688-690 were ordered from Bath Ironworks; DD.649-653 and DD.665 from Charleston navy yard; DD.654-656 from Gulf shipbuilding, Chickasaw; DD.657-658, DD.685-687 and DD.796-798 from Bethlehem, Staten Island; DD.659-661 and DD.666-680 from Federal shipbuilding, Kearny; DD.662-664 from Boston navy yard; DD.681-682 and DD.792-795 from Bethlehem, San Pedro; DD.683-684 from Bethlehem, San Francisco; DD.799-804 from Todd Pacific, Seattle.

The *Fletcher* Class received its baptism of fire in the Solomons, and *Chevalier*, *Strong*, *De Haven* and *Brownson* were lost in the confused actions which followed the landings on Guadalcanal. Two, the *Hoel* and *Johnston*, were sunk during the tremendous fight against heavy odds between Admiral

Sprague's escort carriers and the Japanese fleet off Samar in October 1944, while the *Spence* and *Abner Read* were sunk by air attack during the landings in Leyte Gulf. The worst losses were suffered during the assault on Okinawa, when kamikazes and gunfire accounted for the *Hutchins*, *Pringle*, *Leutze*, *Thatcher*, *Luce*, *Bush*, *Evans*, *Haggard*, *Longshaw*, *Morrison*, *William D Porter*, *Bell*, *Twiggs*, *Callaghan*, *Halligan*, *Colhoun* and *Little*. The majority of these were not sunk outright, but were so badly damaged that they were written off as not worth repair.

The *Fletchers* formed the backbone of the postwar destroyer-strength of the US Navy, although more than half remained in mothballs. Those on the active list were gradually modernized in the 1950s, with a heavy tripod foremast to carry new radar arrays, the forward bank of 21-in (53-cm) torpedo tubes removed, and the third 5-in (127-mm) gun removed. This allowed the provision of three twin 3-in (76-mm) automatic gun-mountings, one firing over the after 5-in (127-mm) and two sponsoned between the funnels.

Under the 1948 Programme, nine were converted to escort destroyers (DDEs), with a view to improving their antisubmarine armament for use as convoy escorts. All torpedo tubes were removed and the antisubmarine rocket-projector known as Weapon Able/Alfa was installed in B position in some, although others had two trainable Hedgehogs. Three more were converted under the 1949 Programme, and six under the 1950 Programme, but the conversion of *Anthony* (DD.515) and *Charles Ausburn* (DD.570) were cancelled. *Saufley* was rerated as EDDE.465 but the others became DDE.445, 446, 447, 449, 450, 466, 468, 470,

Fliegerfaust

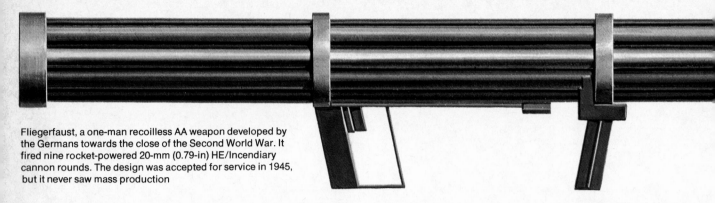

Fliegerfaust, a one-man recoilless AA weapon developed by the Germans towards the close of the Second World War. It fired nine rocket-powered 20-mm (0.79-in) HE/Incendiary cannon rounds. The design was accepted for service in 1945, but it never saw mass production

471, 498, 499, 507, 508, 510, 517, 576, and 577. In 1962 they all reverted to DDs.

Over the years many were transferred to allied navies.

The massive Fleet Rehabilitation and Modernization (FRAM) programme resulted in the reconstruction of many of the *Fletchers*, and details will be found elsewhere. The remainder started to be stricken for disposal from 1965 onwards, and by 1975 the last of these magnificent destroyers had gone, although strenuous efforts have been made to preserve the *Sullivans* as a destroyer-museum. Several were expended as targets. The *Ammen* was badly damaged in collision with the *Collett* off Newport Beach in 1960 and was subsequently scrapped, while the *Monssen* was wrecked while on tow off Beach Haven Inlet in 1962.

See also FRAM.

Displacement: 2050-2100 tons (standard), 2940 tons (full load) *Length:* 114.6 m to 114.76 m (376 ft to 376 ft 6 in) *Beam:* 11.96 m-12.19 m (39 ft 3 in-40 ft) *Draught:* 5.41 m (17 ft 9 in) maximum *Machinery:* 2-shaft geared steam turbines, 60 000 shp=37 knots (maximum on standard displacement), 31 knots (sea speed) *Armament:* (As built) 5 5-in (127-mm)/38-cal DP (5×1); 4 1.1-in (28-mm) AA (1×4); 6 20-mm (0.79-in) AA (6×1); 10 21-in (53-cm) torpedo tubes (2×5); (As modernized) 4 5-in (127-mm)/38-cal (4×1); 6 3-in (76-mm)/50-cal AA (3×2); 5 21-in (53-cm) torpedo tubes (1×5) *Crew:* 319-336

Fliegerfaust

German hand-held antiaircraft rocket launcher. Developed in 1944-45 Fliegerfaust consisted of nine 20-mm (0.79-in) barrels arranged in a ring and provided with a shoulder-rest and pistol grip and a simple open sight. The projectile was the standard 20-mm (0.79-in) HE/Incendiary cannon shell with impact fuze, attached to a steel tube containing a single stick of nitrocellulose propellant. The base of the tube was pierced by four venturi jets, offset at a slight angle to provide spin stabilization as well as forward thrust. The firing trigger incorporated a magneto assembly and the rockets were furnished in a prepared clip matching the layout of the barrels and wired up to an electric igniter in each rocket motor. The firing circuit had a built-in delay so that when the trigger was pressed five rockets were fired immediately and then, after a tenth of a second pause, the other four were fired; this prevented adjacent rockets from upsetting each other by exhaust blast during launch.

The design was accepted for service in early 1945 and several thousand projectors and their ammunition were ordered in March, but very few were ever made and it is doubtful if any were used in combat.

Weight of rocket: 240 gm (8.5 oz) *Muzzle velocity:* 310 m/sec (1017 ft/sec) *Effective AA range:* 500 m (1640 ft)

Flogger, Mikoyan MiG-23/MiG-27

Soviet jet fighter and fighter-bomber. The Flogger family constitutes an extremely important part of the Soviet air force's front-line combat strength, both in terms of numbers deployed and of capabilities. The MiG-23 variants have a primary air-to-air role, while MiG-27 is optimized for air-to-surface operations; they are replacing the MiG-21 Fishbed and Su-7 Fitter respectively, with a probable total requirement exceeding 5000.

A prototype Flogger-A was revealed to the West at the 1967 Soviet Aviation Day, the type probably having flown for the first time the previous summer. A number of modifications were introduced before the definitive MiG-23S Flogger-B entered service with the Soviet air force's frontal aviation or tactical air arm in 1971-72. Flogger was the first Soviet variable-geometry aircraft to enter service, and flight trials evidently revealed centre-of-gravity problems. All tail surfaces except the ventral fin are positioned further to the rear on the fuselages of production aircraft, increasing the gap between the wing trailing edge and the tailplane. The exhaust nozzle no longer projects beyond the tail, and a more powerful engine is installed than was available for initial flight-testing. The area of the dorsal fin at its base has also been increased to improve stability in yaw.

The production MiG-23 additionally incorporates extensions on the wing leading edge which increase the chord. The sweepback angle of 16° with the wings fully forward increases to 72° as they move to the fully aft position, a process which took four seconds on the prototype demonstrated in 1967. An intermediate dogfighting setting of 47° is also available. Leading-edge flaps extend along the outer two-thirds of the wings and these, combined with the full-span single-slotted trailing-edge flaps, provide the maximum lift to give short takeoffs and slow approaches leading to short landing runs. Flogger can also loiter for extended periods while airborne, the wings being in the forward position and the engine throttled back to conserve fuel while waiting for a target to be allocated.

Roll control with the wings forward is provided by spoilers which are fitted to the upper surface of the wings over the inner two-thirds of the moving sections. The differential tailplanes assume control at wing sweep angles greater than some 45°, there being no ailerons. The single engine is thought to be either a Tumansky turbofan or the Lyulka AL-21F-8 turbojet, the latter being a derivative of the powerplant in the Su-15 Flagon and also fitted to the Su-17 Fitter-C. Estimates of installed thrust range from 6350 kg (14 000 lb) to 8000 kg (17 640 lb) dry and 10 900 kg (24 030 lb) to 12 000 kg (26 455 lb) with afterburning. Thrust-to-weight ratio at typical combat weight is thus about 0.8:1.

The primary sensor in the MiG-23S Flogger-B is a High Lark J-band pulse-Doppler

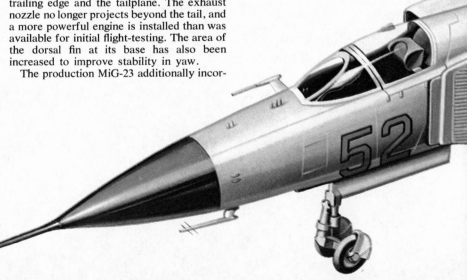

search and fire-control radar with, according to the US Air Force, a performance similar to that of the Westinghouse AWG-10 equipment fitted to F-4J Phantoms. The AWG-10 has a detection range of about 80 km (50 miles) against a fighter-size target and provides track information for infrared and semiactive radar-guided missiles, in addition to supplying continuous-wave illumination for the latter. A retractable laser range-finder is fitted under the nose in the MiG-23S.

Flogger-B is armed with a GSh-23 twin-barrelled 23-mm (0.90-in) cannon mounted under the fuselage and normally carries four air-to-air missiles: two medium-range AA-7 Apex, one employing infrared guidance and the other semiactive radar homing, on the glove pylons and a pair of short-range AA-8 Aphid. Air-to-surface weapons include the AS-7 Kerry missile, four of which can be carried, unguided rockets, or up to 4000 kg (8820 lb) of bombs. Pylon-mounted electronic

countermeasures (ECM) pods have also been seen on Flogger, and an auxiliary fuel tank can be carried on the centreline pylon.

Each MiG-23 unit is allocated a small number of two-seat MiG-23U Flogger-Cs used for continuation training and as ECM escorts; this variant may additionally equip specialized ECM units and second-line combat squadrons. The two-seater is fitted with a slightly less powerful engine than Flogger-B and carries a different fire-control radar, possibly Spin Scan.

Flogger-B was developed to overcome the deficiencies of the MiG-21: short range, small payload, inability to carry a powerful fire-control radar, and use of a heavy, slow-firing cannon. The basic aircraft has also been adapted as a replacement for the Su-7 Fitter in its Flogger-D variant, originally thought to be designated MiG-23B (*Bombardirovshchik*, bomber). The generally accepted designation is now MiG-27. The structure forward of the wing is substantially altered, with a slimmer nose reminiscent of that on the Anglo-French Jaguar fighter-bomber. The upper surface slopes down more acutely ahead of the armoured cockpit and this, combined with deeper glazing, gives the pilot a clear and uninterrupted view which he needs for visual operations against surface targets and for dogfighting over the battlefield.

The fire-control radar is removed, although a small ranging radar may be installed in its place, and Flogger-D carries a laser ranger/designator. Simple fixed air intakes and exhaust nozzle are fitted in place of the MiG-23's variable units, and an engine of increased dry thrust but reduced augmentation is installed; these modifications combine to reduce top speed. Rocket-assisted takeoff (RATO) units can be fitted on the rear fuselage to reduce takeoff distance, and low-pressure tyres are used to allow operations from semi-prepared strips; the undercarriage doors are bulged to accommodate the larger-diameter tyres. Terrain-avoidance radar may be fitted.

The MiG-27's armament is optimized for the ground-attack role and includes a new six-barrel Gatling-type gun of 30-mm (1.18-in) or, more probably, 23-mm (0.90-in) calibre. The five stores pylons can carry guided missiles, rockets or bombs, including tactical nuclear weapons. Two auxiliary fuel tanks of 530 litres (116 Imp gal) each can be carried on fixed pylons under the outer wing panels, the pylons and tanks being jettisoned before the wings are swept. Guided weapons can include the AS-7 Kerry and up to four of the new-generation AS-8, AS-9 and AS-10.

A probable combination of missiles would be an electro-optically guided AS-10 under

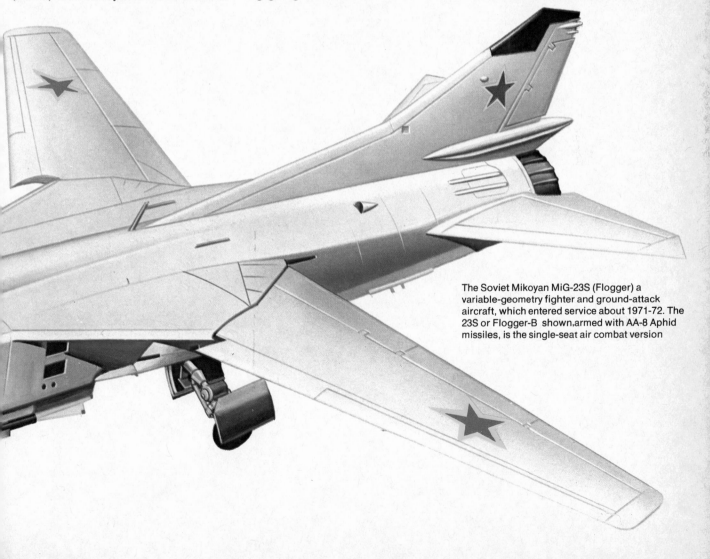

The Soviet Mikoyan MiG-23S (Flogger) a variable-geometry fighter and ground-attack aircraft, which entered service about 1971-72. The 23S or Flogger-B shown, armed with AA-8 Aphid missiles, is the single-seat air combat version

Flora, Yakovlev Yak-23

USS *Florida* after her 1924-26 refit, when she was equipped with an aircraft catapult, converted from coal to oil and had her aft cage mast removed

the port wing glove and an antiradiation AS-8 on the starboard side. The pylons in these positions include pods which appear to contain a television camera for target recognition/missile guidance (left) and possibly a passive radiation seeker (right), both being used to detect and classify targets and provide initial aiming information for the weapons.

Bulges on each side of the nose may contain continuous-wave illuminators for missile guidance in the secondary air-to-air role, or they might house jammers. The standard Sirena III passive warning system uses antennas in the ventral and dorsal fins plus the notches on the wing leading edges. Jamming equipment is thought to be installed at the base of the fin to counter Sparrow air-to-air missiles, with other units in the gloves and/or fuselage parrying surface-to-air threats.

The export equivalent of the MiG-23S Flogger-B is the Flogger-E, which does not carry some of the more advanced equipment fitted to the Soviet air force's aircraft. The High Lark radar is replaced by a unit with a smaller antenna—possibly the MiG-21 Fishbeds' Spin Scan. The older AA-2 Atoll air-to-air missile is carried in place of the new generation of weapons, and the laser range-finder and Doppler radar are also omitted. A lower-power variant of the Flogger-B engine may be installed. Flogger-E has been supplied to Libya and Egypt, and possibly to Syria and Iraq (although the two last-named may have received Flogger-Ds instead).

A hybrid version, the MiG-23MB Flogger-F, has also been introduced in the Middle East. This variant has the variable inlets and nozzle, plus the GSh-23 gun of the MiG-23S, combined with the nose profile, armoured cockpit and RATO attachment points of the MiG-27. Flogger-F has also been observed in Russian service and may have been a development aircraft for the MiG-27.

(MiG-23S Flogger-B) *Span:* 14.02 m (46 ft) *Maximum length:* 17.05 m (55 ft 11¼ in) *Gross weight:* 20 400 kg (44 975 lb) *Maximum speed:* Mach 2.3

(MiG-27 Flogger-D) *Span:* 14.02 m (46 ft) *Maximum length:* 15.69 m (51 ft 5½ in) *Gross weight:* 20 400 kg (44 975 lb) *Maximum speed:* Mach 1.6

Flora, Yakovlev Yak-23

Soviet jet fighter. The Yak-23 was an interim design intended to offer all-round improvements over the first-generation MiG-9 Fargo and Yak-17 Feather, and also to act as a back-up in case the more advanced MiG-15 and La-15 failed to live up to expectations. Flora had its roots in the Yak-19, originally designed around the Kolesov RD-10A copy of the Junkers Jumo 004, but the supply of 30 Rolls-Royce Derwent turbojets in 1947 led to a rapid change of powerplant. The second prototype Yak-19 was modified to accommodate the fatter Derwent, with its large centrifugal compressor requiring the engine to be shifted rearwards into the widest section of the fuselage.

The Derwent-powered Yak-19 paved the way for the Yak-23 Flora and Yak-25, which embodied new fuselages and tail assemblies. Both made their maiden flights in 1947 and each had its advantages; the Yak-23 lost out on top speed and pilot's view but had the edge in other areas, and was accordingly selected for production in 1948. The fighter entered service with the Soviet air force later that year, the initial NII-1 pre-production Derwent copy soon being replaced by the RD-500 of 1590 kg (3505 lb) thrust.

Flora carried a pair of 23-mm (0.90-in) NS-23 cannon, each supplied with 90 rounds, which were later replaced by NR-23 revolver cannon. The fighter could also be fitted with up to 60 kg (132 lb) of bombs or rockets under the wings in place of the tip tanks. Production totalled 310 Floras, 12 each being supplied to the Polish and Czech air arms, carrying the designation S.101 in the latter case. Deliveries were also made to other friendly air forces, and one Yak-23UTI two-seater was evaluated. Flora was outclassed by the MiG-15 but achieved its niche in history by being the first Soviet production aircraft fitted with an ejection seat, albeit a crude device, which afforded no protection to the occupant during ejection and which must have made the pilots thankful for the Derwent's reliability.

Span: 8.73 m (28 ft 7¾ in) *Length:* 8.16 m (26 ft 9¼ in) *Gross weight:* 3384 kg (7460 lb) *Maximum speed:* 950 km/h (590 mph)

Florida

US battleship class, authorized by Congress in May 1908 and built 1909-11. They were an improved edition of the *Delaware* Class, with two additional 5-in (127-mm) guns, and the principal external difference was the regrouping of masts and funnels, with both funnels set between the two cage masts.

The first to be completed was the *Utah,* in August 1911, and she spent the next two years in the Atlantic Fleet. In February 1914 she was sent to Vera Cruz to safeguard US interests in the dispute with Mexico, and took part in the landings in April. After the entry of the United States into the First World War she was sent to Chesapeake Bay as a gunnery training ship and also trained engineers. She did not take an active part in the war until August 30, 1918, when she sailed for Great Britain as the flagship of Vice Admiral Henry T Mayo, C-in-C of the Atlantic Fleet. *Utah* served at Bantry Bay as the flagship of Battleship Division 6 until December the same year, when she returned to New York.

After an overhaul lasting until mid-1921 *Utah* became the European Flagship and visited several foreign ports, and the following year she joined the Scouting Fleet. In 1926-28 she was modernized at Boston Navy Yard, was converted from coal to oil, and had her cage main mast removed. In the summer of 1930 she was decommissioned and demilitarized as she was surplus to the numbers allowed under the terms of the recently signed London Naval Treaty. Her 12-in (305-mm) guns were removed and she was converted to a radio-controlled target-ship; her classification changed from *BB.31* to *AG.16* with effect from July 1, 1931, and she recommissioned the following April.

Utah was mistaken for an aircraft carrier by Japanese pilots at Pearl Harbor on

Name and No	launched	builder
Florida (BB.30)	3/1909	New York navy yard
Utah (BB.31)	12/1909	New York shipbuilding

USS *Florida* at Rosyth in 1918, in which year she attended the German naval surrender

December 7, 1941, and took two torpedo hits which caused 58 casualties. Although some AA guns were recovered, the salvage work proved difficult and the wreck was eventually abandoned. The ship was officially stricken in November 1944 and her hull remains there to this day.

Florida commissioned in September 1911, and her early career resembled her sister's in many respects. In April 1917 she formed part of Battleship Division 9 and left Lynhaven Roads, Virginia, on November 25 for the British Isles. She arrived at Scapa Flow with her division on December 7, and became part of the new 6th Battle Squadron of the Grand Fleet. On the night of November 20-21, 1918, she was one of the battleships sent to meet the German High Seas Fleet steaming across the North Sea to surrender, and returned to New York on Christmas Day.

The ship underwent a similar modernization to the *Utah* during 1924-26 and then served in the Scouting Fleet. She was decommissioned in February 1931 and two months later was stricken to comply with the London Naval Treaty and sold for scrap.

In 1917-18 the ships underwent minor modifications, principally the siting of long rangefinders on No 2 and No 4 turrets and the provision of 3-in (76-mm) AA guns on platforms at the top of the derrick-posts amidships. The modernization between 1924 and 1928 totally altered the appearance of the two ships, and they emerged with a single tall funnel and a short pole mast between No 3 and No 4 turrets. The forward 5-in (127-mm) guns were also blanked off. As a target-ship the *Utah* merely had the 12-in (305-mm) guns taken out of the turrets, and had the light guns removed as well. An aircraft catapult and antitorpedo bulges were also fitted to both ships.

Displacement: 21 825 tons (normal), 23 400 tons (full load) *Length:* 159 m (521 ft 6 in) oa *Beam:* 26.9 m (88 ft 2 in) *Draught:* 8.7 m (28 ft 7 in) *Machinery:* 4-shaft steam turbines, 44 000 shp = 20.75 knots *Protection:* 280 mm (11 in) belt; 254 mm (10 in) bulkheads; 76 mm (3 in) decks; 305 mm (12 in) conning tower *Armament:* (As built) 10 12-in (305-mm)/45-cal (5×2); 16 5-in (127-mm)/51-cal (16×1); 2 3-in (76-mm) AA (2×1), added 1917; 2 21-in (53-cm) torpedo tubes (beam, submerged); (After modernization) 10 12-in (305-mm); 12 5-in (127-mm); 8 3-in (76-mm) AA (8×1) *Aircraft:* 3 floatplanes, 1 catapult (after 1926-28) *Crew:* 1000

'Flower' Generic name for British corvette class   See **Gladiolus**

'Flower'

British sloop class. These ships originated the idea of designing warships with merchant ship-type hulls and machinery to utilize the capacity of firms without previous warship-building experience. The concept was again used with great success in the Second World War with the design of the 'Flower' Class corvette, which were escort vessels, whereas their First World War counterparts were intended to make up for a deficiency in fleet minesweepers.

The design, drawn up in 1914/15, was made as simple as possible so they could be built quickly, the average construction time being six months. They were two-funnelled ships, with a short forecastle, shallow draught and a reinforced bow as protection against mine damage. They had good sea-keeping qualities, but were difficult to handle, particularly in heavy weather, mainly because of the single screw. They proved to be very adaptable and were employed extensively as convoy escort and patrol vessels for which purpose the armament was strengthened.

Twenty-four of the class (the *Acacia* type) were ordered in January 1915 and another 12 (the *Azalea* type) in May 1915. The main armament of the latter vessels was changed from two 12-pdr to two 4.7-in (120-mm) guns while they were under construction as the earlier group was being rearmed with two 4.7-in (120-mm) guns after completion, the two types were otherwise identical.

The third group (the *Arabis* type) ordered in July 1915, were slightly larger than the earlier ships and while the majority of this type carried two 4.7-in (120-mm) guns, six ships (the *Berberus, Lobelia, Lupin, Pansy, Snapdragon* and *Wisteria*) mounted two 4-in (102-mm) guns. In the last two groups (*Aubrietia* and *Anchusa* types) the design was modified to make them suitable for service as convoy escort vessels. The principal feature of this change being the alteration of their appearance to resemble merchant vessels so that while operating with a convoy or on A/S patrol their true identity would not be apparent.

The idea was adapted from the successful use of old merchant ships with a hidden armament as decoy vessels (Q-ships) to trap enemy submarines. The builders were given a free hand in the design of the superstructure and there were a considerable number of variations in appearance. Six of the *Aubrietia* type were ordered in January 1916 and a further six in December 1916. They had a single funnel, more powerful engines than the earlier ships, carried a depth charge armament and mounted 4-in (102-mm) instead of 4.7-in (120-mm) guns. The *Anchusa* type

Name	fate
Arabis	Sunk by German torpedo boats off Dogger Bank 2/1916
Primula	Torpedoed by *U 35* in Mediterranean 3/1916
Nasturtium	Mined off Malta 4/1916
Genista	Torpedoed by *U 57* in Atlantic 10/1916
Mignonette	Mined south of Ireland 3/1917
Alyssum	Mined south of Ireland 3/1917
Tulip	Torpedoed by *U 62* in Atlantic 4/1917
Lavender	Torpedoed by *U 62* in Atlantic 5/1917
Salvia	Torpedoed in Mediterranean 6/1917
Aster	Mined in Mediterranean 7/1917
Bergamot	Torpedoed by *U 84* in Atlantic 8/1917
Begonia	Sunk after colliding with *U 151* 10/1917
Candytuft	Torpedoed and beached near Bougie, North Africa, 11/1917
Arbutus	Torpedoed by *UB 65* in St George's Channel 12/1917
Gaillardia	Mined in northern barrage 3/1918
Cowslip	Torpedoed by *UB 105* off Cape Spartel 4/1918
Rhodo-dendron	Torpedoed by *U 70* in North Sea 5/1918
Anchusa	Torpedoed by *U 54* off Irish west coast 7/1918
Myrtle	Mined in Gulf of Finland 7/1918
Gentian	Mined in Gulf of Finland 7/1918

'Flower'

were ordered in January and February 1917 and were generally similar to the previous group except that they were of slightly greater displacement and carried a heavier armament. In addition to the above vessels, six ships of the *Arabis* type and the *Andromeda* of the *Aubrietia* type were transferred to the French navy, the latter vessel being renamed *Andromede* (later *Ville d'ys*).

During the war, the 'Flower' Class served mainly in home waters and the Mediterranean and were employed extensively for convoy escort in those theatres. Twenty of the class were lost, seven being sunk by mines, 12 by submarines and one by torpedo boat. The *Begonia* was converted to a decoy ship during repairs after mine damage and had the unusual distinction of being sunk in collision with the German submarine *U 151*, which survived. The *Bluebell* was the ship that intercepted and captured the German vessel *Libau*, which was disguised as a Norwegian merchantman and was carrying a cargo of rifles to Ireland for the Easter Rising of 1916. During 1917-18, ships of the class sank ten U-Boats but only two of these went to vessels of the decoy type.

During 1919-22, 19 were sold into merchant service, the *Zinnia* was sold to the Belgian navy and the *Lychnis* and *Ceonothis* transferred to the Royal Indian marine as *Cornwallis* and *Elphinstone* respectively. Three of the class were wrecked, the *Marjoram* in 1921, the *Elphinstone* in 1925 and the *Valerian* in 1926. Thirty-four were sold for scrap during 1921-23, two more in 1927, and 23 between 1930 and 1939. The *Saxifrage* was transferred to the RNVR in 1921 and the *Chrysanthemum* in 1938, the former vessel being renamed *President*. Both vessels were moored in the Thames at the Embankment, London, and are still in service. The remaining six vessels, *Foxglove*, *Laburnum*, *Cornflower*, *Lupin*, *Rosemary* and *Lychnis* served during the Second World War. The *Cornflower* (which was sold and then repurchased in 1940) was lost at the fall of Hong Kong in December 1941, and the *Laburnum* at the fall of Singapore in February 1942. The other four vessels were sold for scrap during 1946-47.

U-Boats sunk by 'Flower' Class ships during the First World War were: *U 88* by *Stonecrop* in Bay of Biscay, April 1917; *U 99* by *Valerian* off Ireland, June 1917; *U 87* by *Buttercup* and *PC 56* in Irish Sea, December 1917; *UB 69* by *Cyclamen* off Sicily, January 1918; *UB 66* by *Campanula* in Mediterranean, January 1918; *U 104* by *Jessamine* in Atlantic, April 1918; *UB 85* by *Coreopsis* in Irish Sea, April 1918; *U 32* by *Wallflower* in Mediterranean, May 1918; *U 64* by *Lychnis* and trawler in Mediterranean, June 1918; *UB 68* by *Snapdragon* and trawler in Ionian Sea, October 1918.

Group I fleet minesweeping sloops (*Acacia* type): *Acacia*, *Anemone* (built by Swan Hunter); *Aster* (built by Earle); *Bluebell*, *Daffodil*, *Magnolia* (built by Scotts); *Dahlia*, *Daphne*, *Foxglove*, *Hollyhock*, *Lily*, *Mallow* (built by Barclay Curle); *Honeysuckle*, *Iris* (built by Lobnitz); *Jonquil*, *Laburnum* (built by Connell); *Larkspur* (built by Napier and Miller); *Lavender* (built by McMillan); *Lilac* (built by Greenock and Grangemouth); *Marigold*, *Mimosa* (built by Bow McLachlan); *Primrose* (built by Simons); *Sunflower* (built by Henderson); *Veronica* (built by Dunlop Bremner).

Group II (*Azalea* type): *Azalea*, *Begonia* (built by Barclay Curle); *Camelia* (built by Bow McLachlan); *Carnation*, *Clematis* (built by Greenock and Grangemouth); *Heliotrope*, *Myrtle* (built by Lobnitz); *Jessamine*, *Zinnia* (built by Swan Hunter); *Narcissus* (built by Napier and Miller); *Peony*, *Snowdrop* (built by McMillan).

Group III (*Arabis* type): *Alyssum*, *Amaryllis* (built by Earle); *Arabis*, *Asphodel*, *Berberis* (built by Henderson); *Buttercup*, *Campanula*, *Celandine*, *Cornflower* (built by Barclay Curle); *Crocus*, *Cyclamen* (built by Lobnitz); *Delphinium*, *Genista* (built by Napier and Miller); *Gentian*, *Geranium* (built by Greenock and Grangemouth); *Gladiolus*, *Godetia*, *Hydrangea* (built by Connell); *Lobelia*, *Lupin* (built by Simons); *Marguerite*, *Mignonette* (built by Dunlop Bremner); *Myosotis* (built by Bow McLachlan); *Nasturtium* (built by McMillan); *Nigella*, *Pansy* (built by Hamilton); *Pentstemon*, *Petunia* (built by Workman Clark); *Poppy*, *Primula* (built by Swan Hunter); *Rosemary* (built by Richardson); *Snapdragon* (built by Ropner); *Verbena* (built by Blyth); *Wallflower*, *Wistaria* (built by Irvine); *Valerian* (built by Rennoldson).

Group IV convoy sloops/decoy ships (*Aubrietia* type): *Aubrietia*, *Gaillardia* (built by Blyth); *Heather*, *Hibiscus* (built by Greenock and Grangemouth); *Salvia*, *Montbretia* (built by Irvine); *Tamarisk*, *Polyanthus* (built by Lobnitz); *Tulip* (built by Richardson); *Viola* (built by Ropner); *Andromeda* (built by Swan Hunter); *Lychnis* (built by Hamilton).

Group V (*Anchusa* type): *Anchusa*, *Bergamot*, *Candytuft*, *Ceonothus*, *Arbutus*, *Auricula*, *Bryony*, *Chrysanthemum* (built by Armstrong); *Convolvulus*, *Eglantine*, *Coreopsis*, *Cowslip*, *Dianthus*, *Gardenia*, *Gilia*, *Harebell* (built by Barclay Curle); *Spiraea*, *Silene* (built by Simons); *Syringa*, *Windflower* (built by Workman Clark); *Ivy* (built by Blyth); *Marjoram*, *Mistletoe* (built by Greenock and Grangemouth); *Pelargonium* (built by Hamilton); *Rhododendron* (built by Irvine); *Saxifrage* (built by Lobnitz);

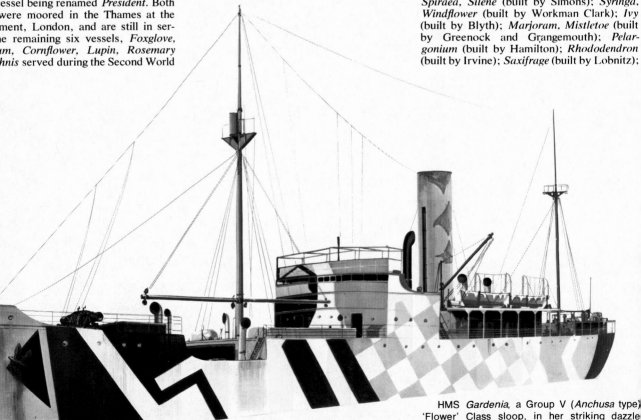

HMS *Gardenia*, a Group V (*Anchusa* type) 'Flower' Class sloop, in her striking dazzle camouflage developed during the First World War

Flutto, one of a class of 12 ocean-going submarines completed by the Italians before 1943

Sweetbriar, Tuberose (built by Swan Hunter).

French vessels: *Altair, Antares* (built by Hamilton); *Bellatrix, Rigel* (built by Henderson); *Cassiope, Regulus* (built by Barclay Curle).

Displacement: (Group I and II) 1200 tons; (Group III and IV) 1250 tons; (Group V) 1290 tons *Length:* 80 m (262 ft 6 in); (Group III and IV) 81.69 m (268 ft) *Beam:* (Group I and II) 10.06 m (33 ft); (Group III and IV) 10.21 m (33 ft 6 in); (Group V) 3.35 m (11 ft) *Draught:* 3.35 m (11 ft) *Machinery:* (Group I and II) 1-shaft, triple expansion engines, 1800 ihp= 16.5 knots; (Group III) 2000 ihp= 16 knots; (Group IV) 2500 ihp= 17.5 knots; (Group V) 2500 ihp= 16.5 knots *Armament:* (Group I) 2 12-pdr (2×1), 2 3-pdr AA (2×1); (Group II and III) 2 4.7-in (120-mm) (2×1), 2 3-pdr AA (2×1); (Group IV) 2 4-in (102-mm) (2×1), 1 3-pdr AA; (Group V) 2 4-in (102-mm) (2×1), 2 12-pdr (2×1) *Crew:* 80 to 100

Flutto

Italian submarine class. This was the last class of seagoing submarine to be designed and built for the Italian navy before the Armistice of 1943. A total of 48 boats in three groups was planned with construction commencing in May 1941, all boats to have been completed by 1944. By the time of Italy's surrender in September 1943, only 27 boats of the first and second groups had been laid down and only eight completed.

The design of the partial double hull was developed from the preceeding seagoing types with dimensions slightly increased to improve underwater trim. Previous experience had shown the Italians that they had tended to design submarines with too large a conning tower, giving rise to instability and poor underwater performance.

In this design a smaller conning tower was fitted and the internal layout improved, allowing space for the carriage of an extra four reload torpedoes. War experience in the Mediterranean had also given rise to misgivings over the hull strength of earlier designs and this was to some extent improved in this class, although Italy still suffered from an acute shortage of specialized materials for warship construction. Noise was greatly reduced, another vital factor when running silent while under attack from sonar-equipped surface ships. The threat from the air led to the mounting of a much more powerful antiaircraft armament, while more powerful diesels improved the surface speed by about two knots. The final advance in

design was the greatly-improved layout and the smaller conning tower which enabled a highly-trained crew to crash-dive the submarines in about 30 seconds.

While they were fitting out, *Grongo* and *Murena* were fitted with four watertight cylinders on saddle tanks amidships for the transport of the small assault craft *Maiale*—a piloted torpedo known in the Royal Navy as a 'Chariot'.

Of the 12 first group vessels laid down, eight were completed and *Flutto, Gorgo* and *Tritone* were sunk in action, while *Marea* and *Vortice* were surrendered to the British. *Vortice* was returned to the Italian navy and served until 1967, while *Marea* was handed over to Russia as war reparation. *Murena, Nautilo* and *Sparide* were captured and served in the German navy, finally being sunk in air raids on Italian ports. The remainder of the first group, together with 15 of the 24 boats of the second group which had been laid down, were captured on the slips and broken up by the Germans. *Bario* was later salvaged, rebuilt and served as *Pietro Calvi* in the postwar Italian navy. The *Nautilo* was also salvaged and commissioned into the Yugoslav navy as *Sava* after the war.

Displacement: 905-928/1068-1131 tons (surfaced/submerged) *Length:* 63.15 m (207 ft 2¼ in) (first group); 64.19 m (210 ft 7 in) (second and third groups) oa *Beam:* 6.98 m (22 ft 11 in) *Draught:* 4.9 m (16 ft) *Machinery:* (surfaced) 2-shaft diesels, 2400 bhp= 16 knots; (submerged) electric motors, 800 hp= 7 knots *Radius:* 8690 km (5400 miles) at 8 knots (surfaced), 128 km (80 miles) at 4 knots (submerged) *Armament:* 1 100-mm (3.9-in); 4 13.2-mm (0.52-in) AA; 2 20-mm (0.79-in) AA in second group; 6 53-cm (21-in) torpedo tubes (12 torpedoes carried) *Crew:* 49

Flycatcher, Fairey

British naval fighter aircraft. One of two biplane designs conforming to Specification 6/22 (the other was the Parnall Plover), the Flycatcher prototype (N163) was designed by F Duncanson. It was first flown in 1922 with a 400-hp Jaguar III 14-cylinder radial engine. It had a metal and wooden fuselage, and equal-span wings with two sets of full-span flaps. Steel-jaw-type arrester gear was fitted for trials on board HMS *Argus* in February 1923, and remained standard until fore-and-aft arrester wires were discontinued in 1926. *Argus* was the first aircraft carrier with a large hangar and full-length flight deck when completed in 1918.

The first prototype Flycatcher was later fitted with a Bristol Jupiter engine, as was the third (amphibian) prototype N165, but the second prototype (N164, a twin-float seaplane) and all production Flycatchers were powered by the Jaguar III or IV. The short wingspan made it unnecessary for the Flycatcher's wings to fold, but the aircraft's construction was such that no component was more than 4.1 m (13 ft 6 in) long, so that it could be dismantled easily for stowage. Armament comprised two 0.303-in (7.7-mm) Vickers machine-guns, mounted one on each side of the fuselage and firing forward through the propeller disc; both guns were accessible from the cockpit. The very strong airframe of the Flycatcher enabled it to be used also as a dive-bomber, and four 9-kg (20-lb) bombs could be carried on racks beneath the lower mainplanes. The Flycatcher was highly manoeuvrable, and an easy aircraft to fly; it was much liked by its pilots, in spite of its somewhat ungainly appearance.

The initial order was for nine aircraft only, but later contracts brought the total number built (including prototypes) to 192 aircraft by June 1930. The first production Flycatcher amphibian was flown on February 19, 1924, and the floatplane variant started catapult

A British Fairey Flycatcher floatplane. One of its two Vickers guns is visible on the fuselage side

Flying Boxcar, Fairchild

Fairey Flycatcher I, the first postwar quantity production naval fighter to serve with the Fleet Air Arm. It was a compact, tough aircraft which began its deck trials on the *Argus* in 1923 and flew until the early 1930s. Its capacity to survive rough handling from FAA pilots earned it the nickname 'Unbreakable'

trials in the aircraft carrier *Vindictive* (originally designed as the cruiser *Cavendish*) in 1925. Deliveries from the Fairey factory at Hayes, Middlesex, began in late 1923, to No 402 Flight. Flycatchers were in service with the Fleet Air Arm for 11 years, serving in such carriers as *Argus, Courageous, Eagle, Furious, Glorious* and *Hermes*; from platforms on other capital ships; and from shore stations in the UK, the Mediterranean and China. In the China theatre, seaplanes of No 403 Flight were in action against local pirates raiding coastal shipping around Hong Kong. A much-valued aircraft during its long career, the Flycatcher was out of first-line service by 1934 and declared obsolete in April 1935.

Span: 8.84 m (29 ft) *Length:* 7.01 m (23 ft) *Gross weight:* 1351 kg (2980 lb) *Maximum speed:* 215 km/h (133.5 mph)

Flying Boxcar, Fairchild

US transport and interdictor gunship aircraft. This diverse family has for 35 years been one of the most important military transports and boasts a remarkable assortment of names, including Packet, Boxcar, Night Gunship, Shadow—and even 'Dollar-Nineteen'.

In 1941, before Pearl Harbor drew the United States into the Second World War, the US Army Air Corps issued a requirement for a purpose-designed cargo transport. This was the first time a completely new aircraft had been designed in the United States as a military transport; in fact, it could claim to be the first in the world, apart from the contemporary Me 321 Gigant (which later became the Me 323). Fairchild had the mock-up approved in mid-1942, but did not fly the first XC-82 Packet until September 10, 1944, and the type missed the war. At VJ-Day, production by North American was cancelled, and Fairchild's contract was cut by 80%, from 1000 to 200.

Powered by two 2100-hp Pratt & Whitney R-2800-22 Double Wasp engines, the original C-82 was noteworthy in having twin tail-

booms so that the rear of the central cargo nacelle could be made in the form of left and right doors, opened on the ground to give easy loading at truck-bed height over the full cross-section of the interior. Construction was all-metal stressed skin, except for fabric-covered control surfaces, and the flight deck was above the forward fuselage although the nose was not designed to open.

In 1945 North American delivered three C-82N Packets before cancellation, while Fairchild made 220 (20 on a repeat order) ending in September 1948. These had R-2800-85 engines and carried up to 42 troops or 5900 kg (13 000 lb) of cargo; in a casevac role 34 stretcher (litter) patients could be accommodated. All went to the newly-formed USAF Tactical Air Command or Military Air Transport Service.

In November 1947, Fairchild flew the first XC-82B, a C-82 rebuilt with a flight deck relocated in the nose to give a better forward view and improved cargo space, as well as 3250-hp Pratt & Whitney R-4360-20 Wasp Major engines. In December 1949, deliveries began to the USAF of the C-119B and to the US Navy of the R4Q-1, both named Flying Boxcar. This was a refined XC-82B with fuselage 356 mm (14 in) wider, stronger wings permitting a great increase in weight and many other changes.

Production ceased at 1087 aircraft in 1955, 946 going to US forces and 141 being supplied under the Mutual Defense Assistance Program to Italy, Belgium and India. Most were built as C-119F or G with the Wright Duplex Cyclone engine, the F type having the 3250-hp R-3350-85WA and the G type the 3700-hp R-3350-89B Turbo-Compound. Many were rebuilt in various ways; for example, the J type had a beaver-tail rear ramp/door openable in flight, while Indian models were fitted by Hindustan Aeronautics with a Steward-Davis jet-pack booster above the fuselage, initially with the Westinghouse J34 and later with the Indian-built Bristol Orpheus. Italian Flying Boxcars were refurbished and three were rebuilt as ECM platforms, while in

Vietnam there were many minor and major modifications. Other second-hand machines went to Brazil, Ethiopia, Taiwan and Morocco. Electronic-warfare rebuilds for the USAF were designated RC-119 series.

In February 1967 Fairchild flew a YC-119K boosted by two General Electric J85 jet pods, each housing a J85-17 rated at 1293 kg (2850 lb) thrust. At about the same time, the concept of the large armed gunship for the war in Southeast Asia led to various AC-119 armed versions. By various rebuild programmes Fairchild and USAF bases produced the jet-boosted C-119K, the armed AC-119G Night Gunship and the jet-boosted and armed AC-119K.

All AC models were fully equipped with night sensors including FLIR (forward-looking infrared), image intensifiers and target-illumination systems, as well as special communications and navigation systems. The AC-119G was usually fitted with four 7.62-mm (0.30-in) Miniguns, with over 100 000 rounds of ammunition, while the K had two 20-mm (0.79-in) T-171 cannon in addition. These Shadow aircraft saw extensive action in Vietnam, orbiting targets at night and putting down withering fire and often working in partnership with an FAC or F-4 'fast-mover FAC', the latter acting as a back-up sensor and often suppressing fire from the ground while the Shadow destroyed the targets. Surviving Shadows were handed over to the Vietnamese air force.

Always colloquially known as the 'dollar-nineteen', the Flying Boxcar was a tough and reliable performer that saw arduous service in all parts of the world. Capable of accommodating 62 equipped troops or up to 9070 kg (20 000 lb) of cargo, it was still in use in several countries during the late 1970s. Engine-out performance was marginal, though much improved with the jet booster pods of the G and K models.

(C-119K) Span: 33.3 m (109 ft 3 in) *Length:* 26.36 m (86 ft 6 in) *Gross weight:* 34 927 kg (77 000 lb) *Maximum speed:* 391 km/h (243 mph)

A Boeing B-17C Flying Fortress, one of a batch of 20 supplied to the RAF in May 1941 under the Lend-Lease agreement

Flying Fortress, Boeing B-17

US four-engined day bomber, first flown 1935. Although technically inferior in terms of all-round performance and bombload capacity when compared with several of its Allied contemporaries during the Second World War, the Boeing B-17 Flying Fortress has come to be recognized as one of the truly classic bombers of all time. Its ability to absorb catastrophic battle damage, its exceptionally heavy defensive armament in its later variants, and an excellent high-altitude performance all combined to give the aircraft an enviable fighting reputation amongst its operational crews. In the years 1942-44 the B-17 became virtually a symbol of the USAAF's daylight strategic bombing policies, and its continuous modification over the years exemplified the increasing responsibility the crews bore in their determination to pursue that policy.

The development of the B-17 was lengthy, beginning in August 1934 when Boeing commenced construction of its Model 299, an all-metal, four-engined, long-range bomber intended as an entrant for that year's US Army Air Corps multi-engined bomber competition. First flown on July 28, 1935, the Model 299, progenitor of all Flying Fortresses, was a graceful, clean monoplane design. Carrying a crew of eight, the B-299 (as it was officially designated) had four hand-operated machine-guns mounted in defensive blisters, and could carry a bombload of up to 2177 kg (4800 lb) on internal racks. Powered by four 750-hp Hornet radial engines, with a wingspan of 31.62 m (103 ft 9 in), and an all-up weight of 19 504 kg (43 000 lb), the prototype demonstrated its capability of achieving a maximum speed of almost 402 km/h (250 mph), with a ceiling of 7620 m (25 000 ft). On October 31, 1935, however, the bomber crashed just after takeoff and burned out

because the elevator control locks had been left in place. But the promise of this bomber was such that an evaluation batch was ordered in 1936. By August 1937, these 12 Y1B-17s equipped the 2nd Bombardment Group, which had the task of developing operational techniques with the new design.

Interservice wrangling between the US Army and Navy chiefs over tactical and strategic policies for the future use of aircraft slowed down substantial production of the B-17, which in the interim continued to be modified and improved by the designers and makers. When the war in Europe began in September 1939, the US Army Air Corps had just 23 B-17s in service. A further 53 were delivered in 1940, and in early 1941, 20 B-17C variants were given to the RAF under the Lease-Lend agreement. These equipped 91 Squadron RAF in May 1941, and commenced operational service on July 8, 1941. High casualties during the following few months quickly caused these aircraft to be withdrawn from daylight bombing sorties, and transferred to RAF Coastal Command where they were operated by 206 and 220 Squadrons.

Flying Fortress casualties in the opening months of the US war with Japan proved only too clearly that the aircraft was weak in defensive armament, and hasty revision and modification led to the B-17E version. There was now an extended fin, a deeper rear fuselage section, and a tail turret installed at the extremity. Additional 0.5-in (12.7-mm) machine-gun positions were incorporated at various points, including the now-famous Sperry ball-turret under the belly. The crews now numbered up to 10 men, and the all-up weight was 54 000 lb (24 494 kg), with a possible maximum speed of 317 mph (510 km/h), fully loaded. Most B-17E variants were sent to the Pacific theatre of war, but a small number were flown to England—the first arriving on July 1, 1942—to inaugurate

the US Army Air Forces daylight bombing contribution to the Allied air offensive against Germany. They flew their initial operational sorties on August 17, 1942. A total of 45 other B-17Es were allocated to RAF Coastal Command in the summer of that year, to assist in the vital antisubmarine war in the Atlantic. Known to the RAF as the Fortress IIa, the type entered service with 59 Squadron in August 1942. Eventually about 200 Fortress II, IIa and III variants were delivered to the RAF—all going to Coastal Command—although in February 1944 a few Fortress IIIs were allotted to Bomber Command, where they flew with 100 Group on radio-countermeasures sorties.

The Fortress III was the RAF's designation for the next major variant of the Boeing Fortress—the B-17G. The chief modification externally on the G-version was the addition of a Bendix chin turret, mounting twin 0.5-in (12.7-mm) machine-guns, under the nose, to counter the mounting casualties suffered by the USAAF's Eighth Air Force from head-on attacks by Luftwaffe fighters in the continuing daylight bombing offensive across Germany. This turret brought the 17G's defensive armament up to a total of 13 0.5-in (12.7-mm) machine-guns; and the G-version first entered operational service with the Eighth and Fifteenth Air Forces, USAAF in late 1943. In the event, over 4000 B-17Gs were built, making the version the most extensively built variant. The 17G was powered by four 1200-hp Wright Cyclone GR-1820-97 nine-cylinder radial engines and had a maximum speed of 483 km/h (300 mph) at 9144 m (30 000 ft). Service ceiling was 10 668 m (35 000 ft). Armament varied, but normally consisted of 13 0.5-in (12.7-mm) Browning machine-guns, manual and turreted. The maximum short-range bombload was 7983 kg (17 600 lb) with a normal long-range load of approximately 1814 kg (4000 lb).

Flying Fortress

Cutaway of a B-17F Flying Fortress. Developed from the B-17E, the B-17F had a new one-piece Plexiglass nose housing the bomb-sight and a mounting for a single machine-gun in the tip in place of the greenhouse canopy of the E. Total armament was increased to six .5-in Brownings in the power-operated tail, dorsal and ventral turrets, with a further six or seven hand-held guns in the nose, waist and radio-operator's mid-upper fuselage position. Internal modifications included self-sealing fuel tanks, wing fuel cells for greater range and improved brakes and oxygen system. To meet the orders placed for the type a consortium was formed between Boeing, Douglas and Lockheed-Vega, and starting in May 1942 a total of 3400 were built, including 600 by Douglas and 500 by Lockheed-Vega, though only 19 of this variant went to the RAF. The increase in the armament reflected aggressive Luftwaffe tactics which included diving down to attack the bombers head on where earlier marks had the least guns. Despite this it was not until long-range escorts became available that bombers were fully protected. The box formations which they had hoped would give interlocking fire in fact made them vulnerable to flak and air-to-air rockets. Some enterprising Luftwaffe pilots even used antipersonnel bombs on parachutes which floated down among the close packed bombers

Flying Fortress

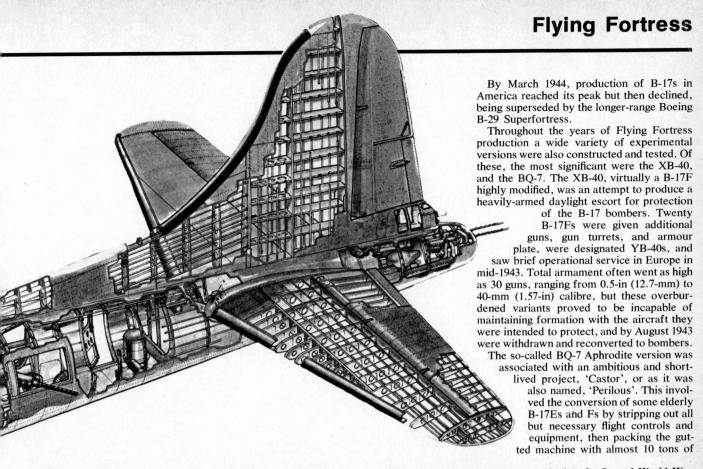

By March 1944, production of B-17s in America reached its peak but then declined, being superseded by the longer-range Boeing B-29 Superfortress.

Throughout the years of Flying Fortress production a wide variety of experimental versions were also constructed and tested. Of these, the most significant were the XB-40, and the BQ-7. The XB-40, virtually a B-17F highly modified, was an attempt to produce a heavily-armed daylight escort for protection of the B-17 bombers. Twenty B-17Fs were given additional guns, gun turrets, and armour plate, were designated YB-40s, and saw brief operational service in Europe in mid-1943. Total armament often went as high as 30 guns, ranging from 0.5-in (12.7-mm) to 40-mm (1.57-in) calibre, but these overburdened variants proved to be incapable of maintaining formation with the aircraft they were intended to protect, and by August 1943 were withdrawn and reconverted to bombers.

The so-called BQ-7 Aphrodite version was associated with an ambitious and short-lived project, 'Castor', or as it was also named, 'Perilous'. This involved the conversion of some elderly B-17Es and Fs by stripping out all but necessary flight controls and equipment, then packing the gutted machine with almost 10 tons of

Flying Fortresses drop part of the total of 640 000 US tons of bombs carried by B-17s to targets in Europe during the Second World War

Flying Fortress

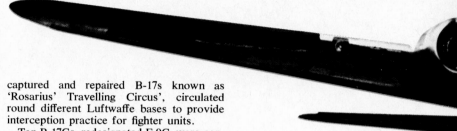

Torpex explosive. The crew comprised one pilot and a radio operator, whose task was to take off from an English airfield, set the controls and arm the explosive load, then bale out prior to reaching the English coastline. Once bereft of its two-man crew, the pilotless 'flying bomb' was radio-controlled from an accompanying Flying Fortress which, theoretically, then directed it onto a precise target. Two dozen Flying Fortresses were converted for use in this way by the 3rd Air Division.

Flying Fortresses were also utilized by the Luftwaffe, when several captured and refurbished examples, bearing German markings, were flown by a special unit, I/KG 200. Given a cover designation of Dornier Do 200, these aircraft were employed on ferrying and supply for secret agents, and on long-range operations, particularly across the Western Desert of North Africa as late as 1944, using fuel dumps and maintenance landing grounds set up secretly. It is claimed that captured B-17s infiltrated bomber formations as they were leaving England, or during the course of a raid, and reported back on the course, speed and altitude of the attackers. There are also stories of these aircraft opening fire on American bombers. Such reports are unconfirmed. It has been established that a group of

captured and repaired B-17s known as 'Rosarius' Travelling Circus', circulated round different Luftwaffe bases to provide interception practice for fighter units.

Ten B-17Gs, redesignated F-9C, were converted to high-level photo-reconnaissance aircraft, and 40 machines were transferred to the US Navy and fitted out with the first APS-20 radar installations for the new airborne early warning surveillance role under the new designation of PB-1W. Yet another 130 were converted to B-17H and TB-17H versions, for search and rescue duties, carrying an airborne lifeboat in place of a bombload.

The main reputation of the B-17 was, however, built on its prodigious operational record against Germany from English airfields. From the early, costly days of 1942-43, when the stubborn policy of unescorted daylight bombing by the pioneer Eighth Air Force had resulted in high casualty rates each sortie, until the final months of the war in early 1945 when Fortresses and Consolidated

Liberators dominated the waking hours over Germany, the B-17 was responsible in large part for the final aerial destruction of Hitler's 'Thousand Year Reich'. In total, Flying Fortresses released no less than 640 000 US tons of bombs on enemy targets in Europe in three years of unceasing operational effort. B-17 gunners also claimed twice as many aerial victories as all the American fighter pilots, although post-1945 research shows that this contemporary calculation was greatly exaggerated in the heat of combat. The B-17's ability to sustain alarming battle damage and still bring its crew back to base became a legend. Although the normal USAAF tour of operations for individual crew members was 25 sorties, many Fortresses eventually

The Boeing B-17D (above) and the B-17E (right) included features suggested by the RAF who had flown B-17Cs during high-altitude raids over Germany in 1941. The D had self-sealing tanks, and an armament of six 0.50-in (12.7-mm) machine-guns and one 0.30-in (7.62-mm) machine-gun. This comparatively light armament allowed the D to carry a bombload of 4750 kg (10 500 lb) which was reduced in later marks

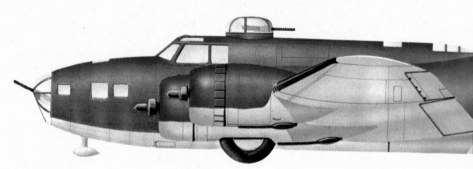

The B-17E had a dramatically reduced bombload of 1814 kg (4000 lb) but increased armament of up to 12 machine-guns some of which were mounted in the tail, ventral and front upper turrets. Though capable of repelling attacks from the rear or beam, the E was vulnerable to frontal attacks. The increased range of 5300 km (3300 miles) enabled it to be sent deeper into Germany, where it encountered attacks on the way to and from the target. On August 17, 1942, 12 B-17Es became the first USAAF Flying Fortresses to attack targets in Europe when they hit Rouen in France

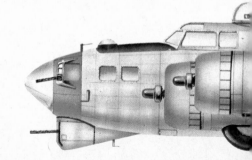

The B-17G featured a chin turret which was well received by air crew in Europe. Only the sight and remote firing control were inside the nose; guns, recoil dampers and gun chargers were housed in the turret, which gave an uncluttered view to the front and a good field of fire. The G also featured enclosed waist positions which were staggered to give the gunners more space in action. Though the G was slower and heavier than the F some Gs had remarkable records. 'Hi Ho Silver' of the 91st Bomb Group survived 130 missions while 'Nine-O-Nine', which flew 140, was described by a crewman as 'a big, dumb, tired aircraft which performed normally'

Boeing

A B-17G comes in to land. It was hard on the belly gunner if the undercarriage failed through battle damage—he had no chance to enter the fuselage from his cramped and uncomfortable perch aft of the bomb bay and inevitably became a casualty

achieved more than 100 bombing missions over Germany before being rested.

With the end of the European and Pacific wars, B-17s continued, in much smaller numbers, to give service in a variety of experimental and more mundane roles with the American air services. When the Korean War began, the 3rd Air Rescue Squadron was equipped with the type. Other nations used Fortresses during the late 1940s and 1950s, including the original Israeli air force of 1948-49, the Brazilian air force, and—in civil guise—Sweden. The swansong of the B-17 came in June 1960, when a USAF QB-17 'drone' took off from Cape Canaveral, and was destroyed in the air by a Boeing IM-99

Bomarc missile. Several examples of the Flying Fortress, preserved and refurbished, can be seen in various countries.

(B-17G) *Span:* 31.64 m (103 ft 9½ in) *Length:* 22.66 m (74 ft 4 in) *Height:* 5.82 m (19 ft 1 in) *Weight:* (empty) 14 841 kg (32 720 lb); (normal load) 24 948 kg (55 000 lb); (max overload) 32 659 kg (72 000 lb) *Maximum speed:* 483 km/h (300 mph)

FN

Belgian arms manufacturer. The Fabrique Nationale Herstal SA, of Herstal, Belgium (formerly known as Fabrique National d'Armes de Guerre) was formed in 1889 by a consortium which included Ludwig Lowe of Berlin, an affiliate of Mauser. The primary purpose of the company was the manufacture of M1889 Mauser rifles for the Belgian army. This was the rifle which introduced the box magazine fed by a 5-round charger, one of the basic features of all Mauser rifles thereafter.

Production of the weapon, and its carbine version, left the company underemployed, and in 1896 H O Berg, the factory manager, began acquiring some of John M Browning's pistol patents and then persuaded Browning to come and work for the company, where he remained until his death. Using the Browning

FN

Below: Belgian troops in September 1917. They are cleaning their Fusil d'Infanterie Modele 1889 rifles, a weapon built by Fabrique National d'Armes de Guerre of Herstal. The Mle 89 fired a 7.65-mm (0.301-in) round and was recognizable by the prominent barrel jacket which protected the muzzle

patents and name, FN began making the long line of automatic pistols, currently represented by the GP35 model. The company then went into the manufacture of sporting arms, and the most notable of these was the automatic shotgun designed by Browning.

After 1919 the company continued to make Mauser rifles for the international sporting and military markets which Mauser had served prior to 1914. The postwar rifles differ in minor details from the M1889 type, but are still recognizably Mauser and were always sold as FN-Mauser arms. During the same period, the company acquired rights to the

Browning automatic rifle (BAR) outside the US, and made it for the Belgian army and for foreign sale. The FN-built BAR can always be distinguished from the US model by its pistol grip, finned barrel, and domed gas regulator beneath the barrel. Some were made with quick-change barrels, while others were furnished with tripods to convert them into sustained-fire machine-guns.

During the 1930s, Dieudonne Saive, the FN designer, began developing a gas-operated automatic rifle to meet a Belgian army specification. Work on this came to a halt with the German invasion in 1940, and

The L1A1 SLR (self loading rifle), the British version of the FN FAL rifle adopted by more than 70 countries. A gas-operated automatic or semi-automatic weapon it has a standard 20-round box magazine and though a rigid butt is normally fitted there is a folding skeleton version used by Belgian airborne forces. A 30-round magazine with a heavier barrel and folding bipod is fitted to the LMG version

British troops with an L7A1 7.62-mm GPMG, the modified version of the FN MAG. Each British gun bears the information 'FN Design' on the left-hand side of the main body. The gun is gas operated, air cooled and fires a disintegrating link belt which is compatible with the US M60 GPMG. The L8A1 is fitted to Chieftain tanks and has a bore evacuator to keep the tanks' interior free from cordite fumes

MOD

The FN FAL squad automatic. Its heavy barrel allows the weapon to be fired on full automatic without excessive overheating. The FAL is in service with the Belgian army

British troops with a GPMG in the sustained-fire role. In this role the gun has a heavier barrel and the butt is replaced by a small butt piece to allow the gunner access to the sights

Saive fled to England with some of his staff, and continued work at the Royal Small Arms Factory. During the war the FN factory in Belgium was operated under German supervision, manufacturing GP35 pistols and Mauser rifles for the German army.

After 1945, Saive and his staff returned to Belgium and in 1949 introduced the semi-automatic rifle as the SAFN (semi-automatic FN) for overseas sale, or as the ABL (Automatique Belgique Légère) for issue to the Belgian army. The rifle was of conventional, full-stocked form, was gas operated, and used a bolt which locked by tipping down against a locking bar in the receiver.

In 1948 Saive took the basic mechanism and built it into a rifle of more advanced form, with a large removable box magazine, pistol grip and prominent handguard. After extensive tests it became the FAL (Fusil Automatique Légère) and was adopted throughout the world, achieving probably the widest distribution of any non-Soviet weapon in postwar years. With the introduction of the .223 (5.56-mm) cartridge, it was first proposed to scale down the FAL to make a light assault rifle, but this was found not to work

well and, while the basic outline was preserved, the operation was changed to have a rotating bolt instead of a tipping one. This became the CAL (Carabin Automatique Légère), but by 1978 had not achieved the overall success of the larger rifle.

The postwar machine-gun market was first catered for by the BAR Type D, an improved version of the prewar weapon. It featured a quick-change barrel, a rate reducer which allowed two rates of fire, and a greatly improved method of dismantling. Nevertheless, it was still basically the old BAR and still had many of the BAR's disadvantages.

Aware of this, Ernest Vervier, a senior FN designer, set out to eliminate the BAR's weak spots while keeping the advantages of its reliability and simplicity. The result was the MAG (Mitrailleur à Gaz) machine-gun, introduced in the early 1950s. The basic gas piston and bolt mechanism is the same as that of the BAR, although the bolt moves down to lock instead of moving up. The feed, however, is by means of a belt, and the feed mechanism owes a great deal of its inspiration to the wartime German MG 42. The barrel is quickly changed and the whole weapon easily

dismantled in the field. It has been widely adopted as a general-purpose machine-gun throughout the world and, most recently, has been taken into US army service as a tank machine-gun.

The calibres and data given below refer to the standard Belgian army versions. Other calibres were available for commercial sale, and the dimensions differed slightly.

See also Browning, CAL, FAL.

(M1889 Mauser rifle) *Calibre:* 7.65-mm (.301-in) *Weight:* 4.02 kg (8.86 lb) *Length:* 127 cm (50 in) *Barrel length:* 78 cm (30.7 in) *Feed:* 5-round box *Rate of fire:* Single shot *Muzzle velocity:* 610 m/sec (2000 ft/sec)

(M1889 Mauser carbine) *Calibre:* 7.65-mm (.301-in) *Weight:* 3.51 kg (7.74 lb) *Length:* 104.5 cm (41.1 in) *Barrel length:* 55 cm (21.7 in) *Feed:* 5-round box *Rate of fire:* Single shot *Muzzle velocity:* 580 m/sec (1900 ft/sec)

(SAFN) *Calibre:* 7.65-mm (.301-in) *Weight:* 4.31 kg (9.5 lb) *Length:* 111 cm (43.7 in) *Barrel length:* 59 cm (23.2 in) *Feed:* 10-round box *Rate of fire:* Single shot *Muzzle velocity:* 610 m/sec (2000 ft/sec)

(BAR Type D) *Calibre:* 7.92-mm (.312-in) *Weight:* 9.21 kg (20.3 lb) *Length:* 114.5 cm (45.1 in) *Barrel length:* 50 cm (19.7 in) *Feed:* 20-round box *Rate of fire:* 400 or 700 rds/min *Muzzle velocity:* 850 m/sec (2790 ft/sec)

(MAG) *Calibre:* 7.62-mm (.30-in) *Weight:* 10.84 kg (23.9 lb) *Length:* 125 cm (49.2 in) *Barrel length:* 54.5 cm (21.5 in) *Feed:* Belt *Rate of fire:* 700-1000 rds/min *Muzzle velocity:* 850 m/sec (2790 ft/sec)

Foca

Italian submarine. Completed in 1909, this small coastal boat was only the third type of submarine to be built for the Italian navy. The first, the experimental *Delfino*, was built by Engineer Inspector Giacinto Pullino, based on principles developed by Thorsten Nordenfeldt. The second type to enter service was *Glauco*, designed by Italy's most successful submarine designer, Engineer Captain Cesare Laurenti. It was based on the double-hull principle of the French designer Maxime Laubeuf. The third type, *Foca*, was a private venture design engineered by the FIAT company of San Giorgio, La Spezia.

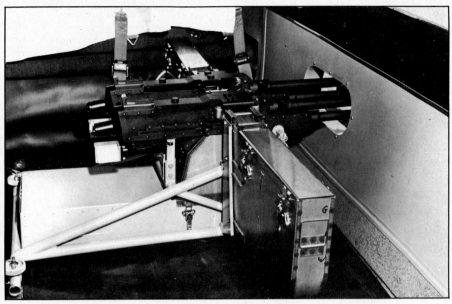

Two sideways-firing FN machine-guns installed in a Britten-Norman Defender

This firm subsequently became the principal suppliers of propulsion machinery for Italian submarines. However, the FIAT design was not a complete success and only one vessel was built. In an effort to improve the speed characteristics of submarines, FIAT incorporated a novel feature in *Foca*, three shafts driven by three petrol motors.

Foca was laid down in April 1907, launched in September 1908 and completed on February 15, 1909. Two months after completion, on April 26, 1909, a serious explosion occurred in *Foca*, caused by escaping petrol fumes. To prevent the subsequent fire completely destroying the boat, she was scuttled in Naples harbour. She was later salvaged and rebuilt, the central shaft and one of the petrol motors being removed. She continued in service and was finally withdrawn from service and scrapped in September 1916.

Displacement: 182/275 tons (surfaced/submerged) *Length:* 42.51 m (139 ft 5½ in) oa *Beam:* 4.28 m (14 ft) *Draught:* 2.61 m (8 ft 6¾ in) *Machinery:* 2-shaft Fiat petrol motors/electric motors, 600 bhp/160 ehp= 12 knots/6 knots (surfaced/submerged) *Armament:* 2 45-cm (17.7-in) torpedo tubes (4 torpedoes carried) *Crew:* 17

Foca

Italian submarine class, built 1937-39. The design of the three minelaying submarines of this class, *Foca, Atropo* and *Zoea*, was based upon the earlier *Pietro Micca* and were the last purpose-designed minelaying submarines to be built for the Italian navy.

Although slightly smaller than *Pietro Micca*, they were a vast improvement on the previous design. Despite the mounting of less powerful machinery, the lighter displacement and improvements in hull design enabled higher speed performances to be achieved. The reduction in size, however, and the extra space allocated to mine storage meant a reduction in the fuel capacity with consequent loss of radius of action. When submerged their underwater radius was superior to *Pietro Micca*, 170 km (106 miles) as opposed to 129 km (80 miles) at four knots.

In spite of the improvements to the machinery, they still suffered the disadvantages of other Italian submarines which had large conning towers. These created a certain instability and caused problems with the underwater trim, not to mention the grave disadvantage caused by such a large construction throwing underwater shadows in the clear waters of the Mediterranean.

Mine capacity in the *Foca* Class was practically double that of *Pietro Micca*. In addition to the midships 20-capacity cylindrical mine chamber (the same as in *Pietro Micca*) housed in the lower part of the pressurized partial double hull, two launching tubes holding eight mines apiece were built into the stern of the submarines.

When first completed, the 100-mm (3.9-in) gun was fitted in a revolving mount at the rear of the conning tower, but as in other submarines this was found to be an unsuitable position and in 1941 the two surviving boats, *Atropo* and *Zoea*, had their gun resited on the foredeck casing. The conning tower was then rebuilt to a smaller design, a modification which improved underwater manoeuvrability.

The boats carried out a number of minelaying missions in the Eastern Mediterranean during the early months of the war. On one of these *Foca* was lost off Haifa on October 13, 1940, either through the explosion of her own mines (*Atropo* subsequently suffered a similar experience while minelaying, but without such a disastrous result) or through striking a British mine.

Following the brief period of minelaying operations, the boats were almost entirely engaged on transport missions to North Africa, under similar conditions to those under which British minelaying submarines were used to transport supplies to Malta. In the summer of 1942, *Zoea* accidentally sank in harbour. She was raised immediately and put back into service. After Italy's surrender in September 1943, *Atropo* and *Zoea* were used to train Allied antisubmarine forces. The boats were finally sold for scrap in March 1947.

All three boats were built at the Tosi yard, Taranto. *Atropo* was laid down on July 10, 1937 and completed on February 14, 1939; *Foca* was laid down in January 1936, and

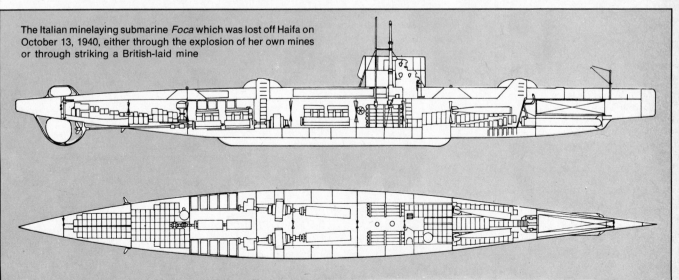

The Italian minelaying submarine *Foca* which was lost off Haifa on October 13, 1940, either through the explosion of her own mines or through striking a British-laid mine

Föhn

completed on November 6, 1937; *Zoea* was laid down in February 1936 and completed on February 12, 1938.

Displacement: 1318-1333/1647-1659 tons (surfaced/submerged) *Length:* 82.8 m (271 ft 9 in) oa *Beam:* 7.08 m (23 ft 3 in) *Draught:* 5.31 m (17 ft 5 in) *Machinery:* 2-shaft Fiat diesel engines/electric motors, 2880 bhp/1250 ehp= 15.25 knots/7.4 knots (surfaced/submerged) *Armament:* 1 100-mm (3.9-in); 4 13-mm (0.51-in) (2×2); 6 bow 53-cm (21-in) torpedo tubes (6 torpedoes carried); 36 mines *Crew:* 61

Focke Wulf German aircraft See **Condor, Fw 189, Fw 190, Ta 152, Ta 154**

Föhn

German unguided antiaircraft rocket developed in 1944. The rocket itself had been developed as the RZ-65 much earlier in the war, intended as an air-to-surface attack rocket. Work continued throughout the war on developing a suitable magazine-loading launcher, but without much success. In 1944, the Luftwaffe began considering the use of free rockets as an antiaircraft weapon, and since a large stock of RZ-65 rockets existed, a simple multibarrel launcher was devised. This consisted of a pedestal which could be either trailer-mounted or emplaced in concrete, and which carried a frame of 35 rocket launcher racks. A simple sight was fitted and electrical firing circuits discharged the rockets either singly or in salvos of five.

The rocket was spin-stabilized and looked more like a gun shell than a rocket. The warhead held 280 gm (10 oz) of RDX/TNT, with an impact fuze in the nose and a self-destroying igniter in the base. The motor compartment contained a single stick of smokeless powder propellant which exhausted through seven angled venturis to give spin, and seven straight venturis to give forward thrust.

Like so many German designs, Föhn appeared too late to be brought into production in any quantity, and few were actually deployed, though a Föhn projector was also proposed as an armament for the Bachem Natter rocket-powered intercepter.

Calibre: 73 mm (2.87 in) *Length:* 262 mm (10.31 in) *Weight:* 2.38 kg (5 lb 4 oz) *Velocity:* 275 m/sec (902 ft/sec) *Ceiling:* 1000 m (3280 ft) *Spin rate:* approximately 18 000 rpm

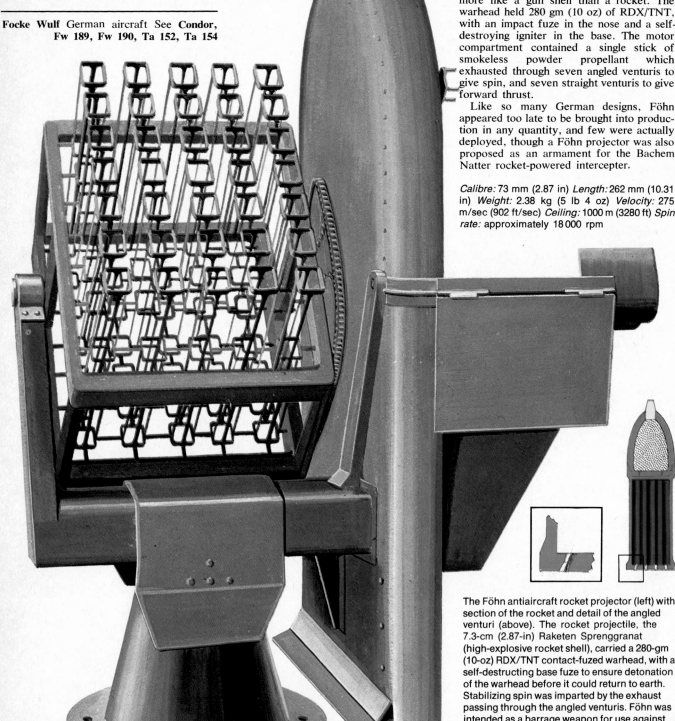

The Föhn antiaircraft rocket projector (left) with section of the rocket and detail of the angled venturi (above). The rocket projectile, the 7.3-cm (2.87-in) Raketen Sprenggranat (high-explosive rocket shell), carried a 280-gm (10-oz) RDX/TNT contact-fuzed warhead, with a self-destructing base fuze to ensure detonation of the warhead before it could return to earth. Stabilizing spin was imparted by the exhaust passing through the angled venturis. Föhn was intended as a barrage weapon for use against low-flying aircraft, though only a few were deployed by the end of the Second World War

Bur. Mar. Hist. v.d. Marinestaf

The prototype of the Dutch *Foka* Class torpedo boats, *Empong*, built by Yarrow in 1888

Foka

Dutch torpedo boat class, built in 1888. These small steel torpedo boats were developed from the Yarrow types built in Britain between 1882-86, but incorporated a number of differences. The principal change was to mount the forward torpedo tubes below the waterline in the bow, a position which caused a great deal of trouble in rough weather. A prototype, the *Empong* was built by Yarrow at Poplar in 1888, and in the same year the *Foka*, *Goentoer* and *Habang*, *Idjen* and *Krakatau* were built in Amsterdam.

These boats were obsolescent by about 1905 and could make less than 20 knots. They

were still in existence at the outbreak of the First World War but were scrapped shortly afterwards.

Displacement: 90 tons (normal) *Length:* 39 m (128 ft) between perpendiculars *Beam:* 4 m (13 ft 1½ in) *Draught:* 2 m (6 ft 6¾ in) mean *Machinery:* 2-shaft reciprocating, 750-1100 ihp=20.5-24 knots *Armament:* 2 37-mm (1.46-in) QF (2×1); 3 35.5-cm (14-in) torpedo tubes (2 forward submerged, 1 on deck aft) *Crew:* 16

Fokker Dutch aircraft See **C.IV, C.V, C.X, C.XI, D.XIII, D.XVI/XVII, D.XXI, DC.I, F.VIII, G.I, T.IV, T.V, T.VIII, T.IX**

Fokker D-Series

German single-seat biplane fighters. The relative success of the Fokker Eindecker monoplane scouts in 1915 was soon abated in early 1916 by the operational introduction of superior Allied designs. An immediate successor for the E-types was not readily available, but as an interim measure the Fokker firm produced its D.I. (D for *Doppeldecker*) biplane which was first tested in April 1916.

Derived from a series of M-class biplanes designed by Martin Kreutzer of Fokker's, the D.I. was quickly criticized for its mediocre performance and poor quality construction. However, as no other suitable fighter was available, a limited production order was given. Of about 80 D.Is actually delivered, only four were still in service in France by December 1916. In combat, the D.I. was slower and less manoeuvrable than its opposing French Nieuport and British de Havilland 2 scouts. German fighter pilots clearly preferred the new Albatros D.I. and Halberstadt D scouts then becoming available for operations.

The Fokker D.II, which actually slightly preceded the D.I. in testing and acceptance by German authorities, proved to be more manoeuvrable, but its performance profile was no better and its operational use in 1916 remained limited. A larger version of the D.II (Fokker M.19) soon followed, armed with

A Fokker D.VII in the lozenge wing camouflage and death's-head fuselage markings of Georg von Hantelman of Jasta 15 during the closing months of the First World War

Fokker D

A line-up of Fokker D.VIIs, the type with which most of Germany's Jagdstaffeln (fighter squadrons) were re-equipped in the summer of 1918

The Fokker D.V, which suffered from lack of power and was largely relegated to training duties

two LMG 08/15 machine-guns and powered by a 160-hp Oberursel U.3 twin-row rotary engine. On September 1, 1916, Hauptmann Oswald Boelcke, Germany's leading fighter ace and commander of the recently-formed elite Jagdstaffel 2, took over D.III,352/16 (the first operational example), and during the next two weeks scored six victories. Nevertheless, he considered the type to be inadequate for existing combat conditions, and changed to Albatros D.I and D.II aircraft for operational flying. At the same time he recommended the withdrawal of the D.III from front-line units. The type was then relegated to home defence units (Kampfeinsitzerstaffeln) in which it served until late 1917. Deliveries of D.IIIs to the army air services totalled 159, but less than half saw front-line use. In addition, a small number were supplied to the Austrian front.

Fokker's next product, the M.20, which was virtually an improved D.I. using a 160-hp Mercedes engine, underwent extensive army

testing in late 1916. This resulted in the D.IV (as it was redesignated) going into very small production—with a total of 30 machines —and entering operational service in early 1917. Its war career was brief, as it was inferior to contemporary German and Allied scouts. Fokker next redesigned the D.II and installed the only engine available to him, the 100-hp Oberursel rotary. The result was the D.V, undoubtedly the best Fokker scout produced to date; being easy to fly and highly manoeuvrable. Its low-powered engine had a natural effect on overall performance, but the design's promising potential led higher authority to recommend it for production in late 1916. Unfortunately, the D.V found little favour among front-line pilots, who still preferred the Albatros D.III, and the Fokker was almost wholly used as a fighter-trainer until the end of the war.

For much of 1917 the Fokker designers concentrated on a series of experimental monoplane aircraft, and the design and pro-

duction of the legendary Fokker Dr.1 Triplane; but by the end of the year construction was proceeding on yet another biplane scout, designated D.VI. A neat, rotary-engined craft, the D.VI employed N-type interplane strutting, later evident in the highly successful D.VII. Yet again, the lack of a sufficiently powerful engine—the few production machines usually had a 110-hp Le Rhône— condemned an otherwise potentially good fighter as unsuitable for combat conditions. The result was very limited first-line usage, and overall relegation to instructional roles.

Parallel with development of the D.VI, the Fokker firm also constructed their V.11 biplane, with a forthcoming fighter design competition at Adlershof uppermost in Anthony Fokker's mind. Powered by a 160-hp Mercedes engine, the V.11 was of clean outline, and incorporated the thick aerofoil upper wing, designed by Reinhold Platz, who had been responsible for most of the Fokker designs to see service. Interplane N-struts and tripod centre-section strutting were bare of inter-strut wire bracing, while the fuselage structure was mainly of welded steel tubing framework.

At the Adlershof competition in late January 1918, the V.11 was found to be directionally unstable in flight, with a strong tendency to veer in a dive. The first pilot to test the V.11 was the famous Manfred von Richthofen, whose comments led the Fokker team to modify the V.11 fuselage, extending it by some 40 cm (16 in). On its next test, the modified V.11 handled beautifully and earned almost unanimous approval of the operational pilots at Adlershof. As a result of such praise, the German authorities immediately promised Fokker a provisional production order for 400 V.11 machines. He was also informed that his great rivals, Albatros Werke and the AEG concern, were being

The parasol-wing Fokker E.V. monoplane, later redesignated D.VIII, was built in small numbers after winning an April 1918 competition for new fighter designs, having demonstrated fast takeoff and climb rate and good manoeuvrability

ordered to build the V.11 under licence. Swift development of the V.11, to bring it to operational requirements, was followed by fast production in the Albatros and Fokker works (in the event the AEG firm built no V.11s); and the first example of the new aircraft, now designated D.VII, to go to a front-line unit went to von Richthofen's Jagdgeschwader 1 in early April 1918.

During May, five more Jagdstaffeln (2, 3, 26, 27 and 36) were equipped with D.VIIs; and by July 1 a total of 407 D.VIIs were with first-line units on operations along the Western Front. D.VII pilots were delighted with their aircraft. It was strong, fully aerobatic, reliable, with an excellent handling performance at combat altitudes. By the late summer of 1918, at least 46 Jagdstaffeln were flying Fokker D.VIIs in combat, and the type was considered by most pilots, Allied and German, to be the best all-round single-seat fighter produced by Germany throughout the war. Such was the high regard for the D.VII by the Allies, that it was specially mentioned in the Armistice agreement designating war material to be surrendered: *'In erster Linie alle apparate D.VII'* (especially all first-line D.VII aircraft). After the war, D.VIIs were used by the air services of Holland, Belgium, Poland and the United States for several years.

(D.I) *Length:* 5.7 m (18 ft 8½ in) *Span:* 9.05 m (29 ft 8⅜ in) *Powerplant:* 120-hp Mercedes D II *Maximum speed:* 150 km/h (93 mph)

(D.II) *Length:* 6.4 m (21 ft) *Span:* 8.75 m (28 ft 8½ in) *Powerplant:* 100-hp Oberursel U I 9 *Maximum speed:* 150 km/h (93 mph)

(D.III) *Length:* 6.3 m (20 ft 8 in) *Span:* 9.05 m (29 ft 8⅜ in) *Powerplant:* 160-hp Oberursel U III *Maximum speed:* 160 km/h (100 mph)

(D.IV) *Length:* 6.3 m (20 ft 8 in) *Span:* 9.7 m (31 ft 10 in) *Powerplant:* 160-hp Mercedes D III *Maximum speed:* 160 km/h (100 mph)

(D.V) *Length:* 6.05 m (19 ft 10¼ in) *Span:* 8.75 m (28 ft 8½ in) *Powerplant:* 100-hp Oberursel U I 9 *Maximum speed:* 170 km/h (106 mph)

(D.VI) *Length:* 6.23 m (20 ft 5½ in) *Span:* 7.65 m (25 ft 1¼ in) *Powerplant:* 110-hp Oberursel U II 9 *Maximum speed:* 196 km/h (122 mph)

(D.VII) *Length:* 7 m (22 ft 11¾ in) *Span:* 8.9 m (29 ft 2½ in) *Powerplant:* 160-hp Mercedes D III, or 185-hp BMW *Maximum speed:* 186.5 km/h (116 mph)

Fokker E.I—E.IV

German single-seat fighters. In 1915, aerial combat over the Western Front in France took a new, deadly direction. In that year the first aeroplanes armed with fixed, synchronized, forward-firing machine-guns appeared. The first aircraft to introduce this latest form of mortal combat was a frail, single-seat monoplane designated the Fokker E.I. For nearly a year, the nimble Fokker and its variants created havoc with its aerial opponents, and gave birth to the phrase 'Fokker scourge'. The genesis of the Fokker Eindecker (monoplane) designs can be traced to a 1913 Morane Saulnier Type H monoplane purchased by Anthony Fokker for study and as a basis for his own ideas on light, manoeuvrable monoplanes for military reconnaissance duties. From his evaluation of the Morane Saulnier, Fokker produced drawings for a new aircraft, the Fokker M.5 single-seater. The M.5 differed in many technical features from its parent. It had a welded steel-tube structure in place of the Morane's conventional wooden construction, and a

more efficient wing aerofoil design. Initially, the M.5 was powered by a 50-hp Gnome rotary engine, but this was soon replaced by a German-built Oberursel 80-hp rotary.

Two prototype M.5s were constructed in early 1914—the M.5K and M.5L (short and long wing, respectively). The latter version became much sought after by German army pilots after the outbreak of war, but the M.5K became the true progenitor of the 1915-16 E-series of armed Fokker monoplanes. Used during the first 12 months of hostilities simply as fast reconnaissance scouts, the various Fokker designs gave sterling service. Then, during a bombing sortie against Courtail railroad station on April 18, 1915, a French pilot, Roland Garros, was forced down by ground fire and landed his Morane-Saulnier Type L Parasol aircraft intact near Ingelmunster, Belgium. His attempt to destroy his aircraft failed, and the Germans discovered that the Morane was fitted with a forward-firing machine-gun, which fired directly through the propeller arc. Its propeller blade was protected by two steel deflector wedges bolted to appropriate sections of the blade. With this device, Garros had destroyed three German aircraft in previous weeks.

Attempts by German engineers to copy the Garros device proved fruitless, so Fokker was sent for and permitted to take away Garros' propeller and a new Parabellum machine-gun, with instructions to produce efficient synchronizing gear to enable the gun to fire through a propeller arc without damaging the blades. At the Fokker works the problem was solved by three of the engineering staff who produced a simple linkage system of cams and rods between the engine and gun trigger—virtually making the engine operate the gun. A full gear was then installed in an M.5K monoplane (Factory No 216). After flight testing it was redesignated

Fokker E

M.5K/MG. Fokker himself then demonstrated the 'gun-fighter' at a gathering of staff officers, and the test aircraft later received a military designation as Fokker E.1/15. The first two Fokker fighters to go to the Western Front, E.2/15 and E.3/15, were fitted with the more reliable LMG.08 machine-gun, designed at the Spandau rifle factory (and thereafter mistakenly referred to as the 'Spandau gun').

Individual examples of the M5K, now officially titled E.I (Eindecker), began to reach first-line units, and they were employed initially as escorts to the two-seat reconnaissance machines. On July 1, 1915, Leutnant Kurt Wintgens flew an Eindecker over the lines and destroyed a French two-seater in the course of his patrol—the first Fokker victory. This example of the potential offensive role for the nimble Fokker was quickly taken up by other notable pilots like Oswald Boelcke, Parschau, Kastner Walz, von Buttlar, Hohndorf, and Max Immelmann. On August 1, Immelmann, who was serving with Boelcke in Flieger Abteilung Nr 62, brought down his first victim during an RFC bombing attack on Douai airfield. His victory confirmed higher authority's decision to inaugurate the first of several Kampf-Einsitzer Kommando (KEK), or single-seater fighting units, whereby two or three E.Is were grouped together to form purely offensive fighting units. From these tiny units came the later Jagdstaffeln, or independent fighting squadrons. In their new role, the Fokker pilots recorded an immediate string of suc-

Profile top plan, and front elevation of a 1915 Fokker E.III monoplane fighter

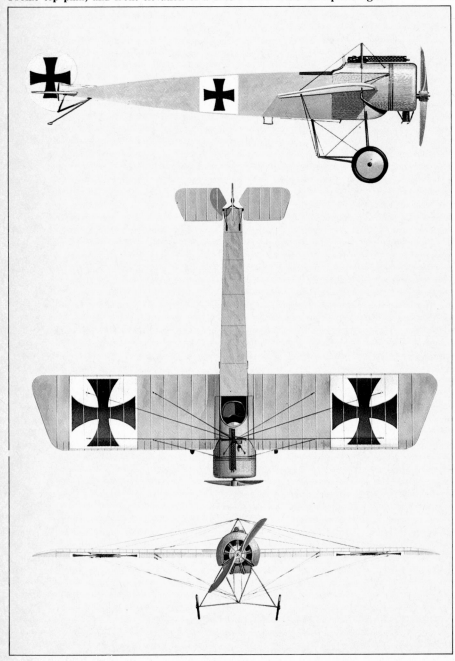

cesses against their Allied opponents, and by the end of 1915, Allied air losses were mounting swiftly. Across the skies of France the name Fokker came to be a dreaded symbol of swift death for the British and French reconnaissance and bomber crews. It was the birth of the 'Fokker scourge'.

Progressive modification and improvement of the E.I was put in hand quickly. By installing a more powerful 100-hp nine-cylinder Oberursel engine, with several minor structural alterations, the Fokker team produced the M.14, redesignated E.II. The first example reached a front-line unit in July 1915, and at least eight examples were operational by October. It proved to be little better than E.I, and Fokker decided to produce a further improved version with larger wingspan—the E.III, which became the most used and known variant of the Eindecker series. The first E.III reached an operational unit in August 1915, still armed with a single LMG.08 machine-gun but with a faster fire rate. Boelcke urged Fokker to produce examples carrying twin machine-guns, and many E.IIIs were soon in action with this doubled firepower, in spite of the effect of extra weight on performance.

Max Immelmann, who was becoming acknowledged as the chief exponent of the Eindecker, requested even heavier armament combined with better performance at higher altitudes. As a result, the E.IV monoplane was designed, carrying a battery of three machine-guns and a 160-hp engine. Immelmann's special E.IV, E.189/16, was ready by December 1915, and he took it over from the factory on January 16, 1916. Flying it in action, he had the guns set to tilt upward at a modest angle for under-tail attacks, but the

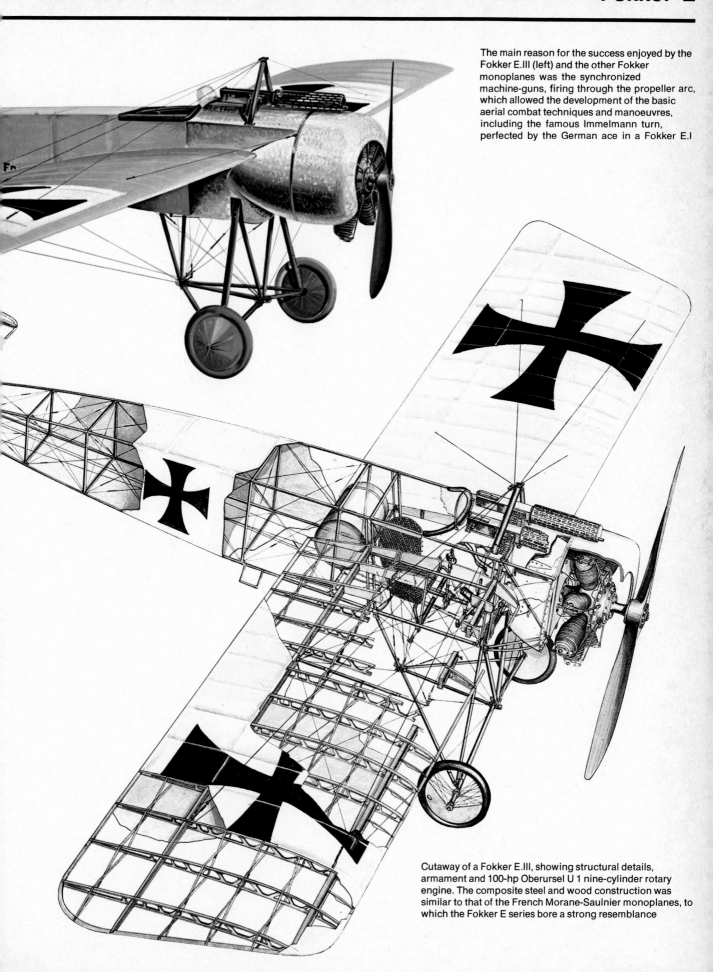

The main reason for the success enjoyed by the Fokker E.III (left) and the other Fokker monoplanes was the synchronized machine-guns, firing through the propeller arc, which allowed the development of the basic aerial combat techniques and manoeuvres, including the famous Immelmann turn, perfected by the German ace in a Fokker E.I

Cutaway of a Fokker E.III, showing structural details, armament and 100-hp Oberursel U 1 nine-cylinder rotary engine. The composite steel and wood construction was similar to that of the French Morane-Saulnier monoplanes, to which the Fokker E series bore a strong resemblance

Folder, Short

A captured Fokker E.III is examined by British airmen on an airfield in northern France

added complications of synchronizing a triple-gun installation soon produced problems, with Immelmann on at least one occasion shooting off his own propeller.

Boelcke also received an E.IV with triple guns, but soon suffered the same faulty synchronization troubles and shattered his propeller in flight. Gun problems apart, the heavily-loaded E.IV design failed to come up to the required performance profile, particularly in terms of rate of climb and manoeuvrability when compared with the French Nieuport Baby Scouts now opposing it in the air. By April 1916, the 'Fokker scourge' had been abated. Fresh Allied aircraft designs were demonstrating an obvious all-round superiority over the Fokkers, and the toll of Eindecker pilots in early 1916 emphasized the design's obsolescence. Of the first 15 pilots to operate Fokker monoplanes, none was destined to survive beyond 1916. Most of them became victims of the agile French Nieuports or of structural and gun synchronization failures in the air. On June 18, Max Immelmann, flying an E.III, took off in company with several other Fokkers to intercept a patrol of F.E.2bs from 25 Squadron, RFC, over German-occupied territory. Immelmann attacked one pair of FEs and shot one down. Then, passing across the nose of the second FE, he came under fire from Corporal J Waller, who poured a full drum of ammunition at the skidding Fokker. Immelmann's machine reared sharply, undulated wildly, then broke up in mid-air. German technicians examined the wreckage of the Eindecker and came to the unanimous conclusion that Immelmann's death was yet another caused by faulty gun-synchronization gear. One propeller blade had been sawn off, and the vibration of the unbalanced rotary engine had torn the monoplane apart.

Immelmann's death was also the end of the Fokker Eindecker on operations, and existing E monoplanes were immediately relegated to training purposes, or scrapped along the main Western Front. Looked at objectively, the Fokker was a mediocre design, of poor performance and indifferent structure, which had acquired an undeserved deadly reputation among its opponents. Nevertheless, it had one distinguishing feature—a synchronized machine-gun, firing along the line of flight. As such it inaugurated a new and lasting concept of aerial combat, a pioneer of man-to-man mortal conflict in the skies.

Span: (E.I) 8.95 m (29 ft 4½ in); (E.III) 9.52 m (31 ft 2¾ in) *Length:* 7.2 m (23 ft 7½ in) *Height:* 2.4 m (7 ft 10½ in) *Armament:* (E.I) 1 fixed LMG.08 mg; (E.II/E.III) 1 or 2 LMG.08 mg; (E.IV) 3 LMG.08 mg *Powerplant:* (M.5K) 50-hp Gnome; (E.I/E.II) 80-hp Oberursel; (E.II/E.III/E.IV) 100-hp Oberursel; (E.IV) 160-hp Le Rhône; (E.IV) 160-hp Oberursel; (E.III) 80-hp Le Rhône; (E.III) 100-hp Gorbel Goe I; (E.III) 90-hp Siemens-Halske Sh.I *Maximum speed:* (E.I/E.II) 130 km/h (81 mph); (E.III) 140 km/h (87 mph)

Folder, Short

British two-seat floatplane. In 1912, Horace Short made drawings of a wing-folding device, which he patented in 1913, and then constructed an aircraft to incorporate this innovation. The resulting floatplane was numbered 81 and was the first British aircraft to have folding wings, and which bore a strong family resemblance to the Short Improved S.41.

By 1914, at least eight examples had been delivered to the naval air service, including four to Calshot naval air station. Here Squadron Commander Arthur M Longmore flew No 121 on July 28, 1914, to make the first successful British torpedo air-drop of a 35.6-cm (14-in) 367-kg (810-lb) Whitehead torpedo. Immediately after war was declared, three Folders were allotted to the aircraft carrier *Engadine* for torpedo-dropping roles, although none saw any such action. However, on Christmas Day, 1914, two Folders (Nos 119 and 120) were among the naval aircraft despatched to bomb Cuxhaven. In March 1915, three Folders were sent to Africa as ancillaries to the naval force attempting to locate and destroy the German cruiser *Königsberg*, where they performed useful reconnaissances but took no part in the eventual destruction of the vessel. Two main types of Folder were built—two-bay and three-bay—but both variants were otherwise virtually identical.

Span: upper 17.07 m (56 ft) (2-bay) or 20.42 m (67 ft) (3-bay) lower 12.19 m (40 ft) (both variants) *Length:* 11.89 m (39 ft) *Powerplant:* 160-hp Gnome *Speed:* 125.5 km/h (78 mph)

Folgore

Italian antitank rocket-launcher. In 1978 Breda Meccanica Bresciana announced a new recoilless rocket-launcher which had been developed in conjunction with SNIA, for medium- and short-range antitank warfare. It comprises an 80-mm (3.15-in) recoilless rifle firing a hollow-charge round fitted with six stabilizing fins which open as it leaves the muzzle. It can penetrate up to 400 mm (16 in) of armour at 70° incidence.

The weapon comes in two versions, one with a bipod and simple optical sight, and one with a tripod and rangefinder. The optical sight is used for ranges up to 500 m (550 yards), while the rangefinder allows firing up to twice that distance.

Length: 1.85 m (6 ft) *Weight:* 17 kg (37 lb) bipod version; 28 kg (61 lb) tripod version *Projectile weight:* 3.1 kg (6.8 lb)

Folgore, Macchi C.202

Italian fighter aircraft. Breaking with the tendency of Italian aircraft designers towards bulky radial engines, engineer Mario Castoldi was given the task by the Macchi company of

A 160-hp le Rhône-powered Fokker E.IV armed with three air-cooled Maxim machine-guns

Demonstration of the Italian Folgore antitank weapon system, showing the tripod-mounted version with range-finder and optical sight

designing an aircraft around the Daimler-Benz DB 601 inverted-V engine, a specimen of which was acquired in 1940. The basic airframe was similar to that of the proven C.200 Saetta of 1938. An all-metal monoplane of semi-monocoque construction, the C.202 flew for the first time on August 10, 1940. Highly manoeuvrable, and with a rapid rate of climb, the aircraft quickly attracted the attention of the Ministero dell'Aeronautica and was ordered into series production immediately with the name Folgore (Thunderbolt).

Manufacture was undertaken by the Breda company and by Macchi's Varese factory. Supplies of the Daimler-Benz engine from Germany were slow to arrive, and only a few of the initial production batch were thus powered. The remainder utilized the licence-built version, the 1075-hp Alfa Romeo RA 1000 RC 41 Monsone (Monsoon). Armament at first comprised only two 12.7-mm (0.5-in) Breda-SAFAT machine-guns, with 360

rounds per gun, mounted in the upper engine cowling and synchronized to fire through the propeller arc. This armament deficiency was realized later, and a pair of 7.7-mm (0.303-in) machine-guns was installed in the wings, each with 500 rounds. (One Folgore was tested with two 20-mm [0.79-in] Mauser MG 151 cannon in underwing fairings, but this proved unsatisfactory.)

Deliveries to the Regia Aeronautica began in the summer of 1941, and by November of that year the 1° Stormo CT—Caccia Terrestre, land-based fighter—was fully equipped, trained and fighting in Libya during the last stages of the siege of Tobruk. Folgores also served on the home front, in the Mediterranean, in other parts of North Africa, and on the Eastern Front in Russia, from August 1941 until 1943. A total of about 1500 C.202s were built, including 392 by Macchi. Although produced in 11 different Series (I to XI), only minor alterations to structure and internal equipment were made during the three-year production period. Dust filters were fitted to Folgores in desert service, and these aircraft also had the designation suffix AS (Africa Settentrionale).

Towards the end of production, some Folgores were fitted with underwing attachment points for jettisonable fuel tanks or for two 50-kg (110-lb), 100-kg (220-lb) or 150-kg (330-lb) bombs as fighter-bombers.

The strongly-constructed fuselage and clean design enabled the Folgore to absorb heavy punishment and to perform intricate aerobatic manoeuvres. In spite of its light-weight armament, it was in some ways the most efficient fighter used by the Regia Aeronautica in the Second World War. It remained in production until the Italian armistice of 1943, although by that time only 53 serviceable Folgores were available in the whole of Italy.

In an effort to achieve better results against superior Allied aircraft, two advanced developments, the C.250N Orione and C.205V Veltro, were produced with more powerful Daimler-Benz engines; but only a few of these were built, arriving on the scene too late to assist the Italian war effort.

Span: 10.58 m (34 ft 8½ in) *Length:* 8.85 m (29 ft 0½ in) *Gross weight:* 2930 kg (6459 lb) *Maximum speed:* 595 km/h (370 mph)

A Macchi MC.202 AS (Africa Settentrionale, or North African) Folgore. Able to absorb a large amount of punishment, and highly manoeuvrable, the Folgore gave a good account of itself with the Italians in Libya

Food Machinery Corporation

A US Army Food Machinery Corporation M113A-1 fully-tracked armoured personnel carrier

Folland British aircraft   See **Gnat**

Food Machinery Corporation

US manufacturer of armoured personnel carriers. The FMC came into the armaments field during the Second World War, building amphibious tractors for the US Marine Corps and Army, their most notable development being the LVT-4. After the war, they were involved, together with International Harvester, in building a number of M75 armoured personnel carriers for the US Army. These, the first full-tracked APC, were based on components of the M41 light tank, and as a result they were not entirely successful. They were too high, too heavy, had no amphibious capability, and were far too expensive at $100000 per vehicle. The US Army issued a fresh specification and FMC developed a new design using aluminium-alloy armour, which went into service as the M113. Production began in 1960 at the FMC factory at San Jose, California, and upwards of 60000 have now been produced, in addition to several thousand more built under licence in Italy.

The FMC Northern Ordnance Division in Minneapolis produce the US Navy's new 8-in (203-mm)/55-cal Mark 71 'lightweight gun'. This is a completely automated installation in which a single seaman at a below-deck con-

trol station can load and fire the gun at a rate of 15 rds/min. A magazine of 75 rounds is carried below the mounting and the entire cycle, once the magazine has been hand-loaded, is mechanical.

Due to the light weight, small bulk, and reduced deck blow, this 8-in (203-mm) gun, firing a 121.5-kg (268-lb) shell to a range of over 24 km (15 miles), can be fitted and safely fired from destroyers and similar small warships which hitherto have been unable to mount armament of this calibre.

Forban

French torpedo boat built 1893-95. In the late nineteenth century the French were the great exponents of the torpedo boat. They hoped that it was a weapon with which to counter the British superiority in conventional warships. According to the doctrines of the *'Jeune Ecole'* held by many French naval officers, torpedo boats were to be complemented by commerce-raiding cruisers. The *Jeune Ecole,* an influential school of French naval strategic opinion, originated in the mid-1880s; its central tenet was a theory of commerce warfare directed against merchant fleets, primarily the British.

Though France had the world's biggest force of small torpedo boats by the late

1880s, these were too small to be of much use for more than local defence, so there was a requirement for larger and more powerful seagoing torpedo boats, or what the French called *torpilleurs de haute mer*. This requirement became even more obvious when Britain began building the logical counter—even larger torpedo boats, with heavier gun armament, called torpedo boat destroyers. France could either match these with similar vessels, which she did not do until much later, or attempt to make her high seas torpedo boats even faster, to evade rather than fight off the English boats.

When the French Ministry of Marine decided in February 1892 to order a new and even faster torpedo boat there was one obvious builder for her. The Le Havre firm of Normand had consistently produced faster, better and more seaworthy boats than any other French yard, and was the only French builder which could compare with the great British specialist torpedo boat builders. The new order was for a modified version of the *Ariel* Class, an earlier and successful Normand type, but *Ariel* was designed for 25 knots, while the top speed of the new boat, to be called *Forban,* was intended to be five knots more.

Forban, launched on July 25, 1895, was a typical Normand boat in appearance, with twin funnels, and a hull whose greatest breadth was well aft of midships. In plan view she resembled an elongated teardrop with the pointed end foremost. She had the rounded top to the hull typical of French torpedo boats, with a light slatted hurricane deck built above it, a combination which proved fairly seaworthy, as the waves could wash over the hull, while the crew still had dry and secure footing.

On trials in September and October 1895, this squat-looking vessel considerably exceeded expectations by making 31.03 knots, a world speed record. This impressive performance for so small a vessel produced an immediate effect on the other side of the Channel, making the British decide to order large numbers of 30-knot destroyers. Part of this excellent performance was due to her builders' skill as engineers. Her triple expansion engines, and two water tube boilers were both to Normand's special designs.

In spite of her initial success, the little

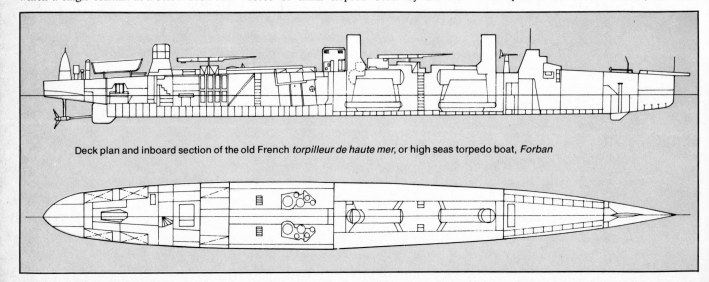

Deck plan and inboard section of the old French *torpilleur de haute mer,* or high seas torpedo boat, *Forban*

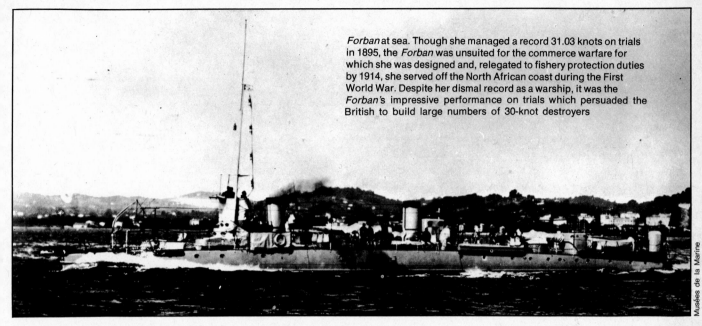

Forban at sea. Though she managed a record 31.03 knots on trials in 1895, the *Forban* was unsuited for the commerce warfare for which she was designed and, relegated to fishery protection duties by 1914, she served off the North African coast during the First World War. Despite her dismal record as a warship, it was the *Forban*'s impressive performance on trials which persuaded the British to build large numbers of 30-knot destroyers

Musées de la Marine

Forban represented a blind alley of naval development; the future lay with much larger, more seaworthy and more heavily armed ships, and it would be many years before the French caught up with the British lead in destroyers. The ship herself was out of front-line service by the time war broke out in 1914, and was serving as a fishery protection vessel at Algiers. The First World War was spent uneventfully patrolling the North African coast.

Forban was sold in 1920, ending a quarter of a century of service.

Displacement: 123.4 tonnes (normal), 152 tonnes (full load) *Length:* 44 m (144 ft 4¼ in) pp *Beam:* 4.64 m (15 ft 2¾ in) *Draught:* 1.4 m (4 ft 7 in) maximum *Machinery:* 2-shaft triple-expansion, 3775 ihp (trials)=30 knots *Armament:* 2 37-mm (1.46-in) QF (2×1); 2 35-cm (14-in) torpedoes (1×2); replaced by 2 45-cm (17.7-in) in 1907 *Crew:* 29

Ford Motor Company

US tank and armoured car manufacturer. As might be expected, Ford became involved in tank manufacture at a very early stage in the vehicle's history, principally because of their expertise in mass production. In 1918, the US Ordnance Department designed a three-ton tank which was primarily intended as an ammunition and machine-gun carrier for use by the infantry, though with planned modifications it could have been used to carry 680 kg (1500 lb) of cargo or a 75-mm (2.95-in) gun. The design was intended to utilize as many existing commercial parts as possible, the power unit, for example, being two Ford Model T engines. Prototypes were built, sent to France, tested and approved. In October 1918, a contract was given to Ford for 15015 tanks. The war ended during the following month, the contract was cancelled, and only 15 tanks were ever made.

Meanwhile, the Services of Supply branch of the US Army had asked for a slightly larger version which would allow a bigger gun to be mounted—the three-ton carried only a machine-gun—and the Ordnance Department

designed the Mark 1 three-man tank, virtually an enlargement of the three-ton with the addition of a turret for the third crew member and mounting a 37-mm (1.46-in) gun M1916. Ford took up the development of this vehicle, but since all the Ford engines were earmarked for the three-ton, the Mark 1 had to be fitted with a Hudson six-cylinder engine. Although 1000 of these tanks were to be built, they proved to be unsatisfactory when tested and the entire project was cancelled.

After this, Ford returned to its ordained task of putting the world on wheels and left the tank business alone. However, subsidiary companies in other parts of the world sometimes found themselves involved in military work—for example, the Russian Ford factory which produced chassis for the BA7 and BA32 armoured cars in the 1920s and 1930s.

In the Second World War, Ford production facilities were again called upon, but as far as tanks were concerned it was mainly a matter of producing Ordnance Corps designs, notably the M4 Sherman. The company developed a V-8 engine, the Model GAA, which became the standard tank engine, and produced Jeeps by the thousand.

In 1941, the British tank mission in the US, in conjunction with the US Ordnance Department, prepared specifications for an armoured car, which was to have all-wheel drive and carry a 37-mm (1.46-in) gun. Designs were invited from major companies, and Ford submitted a proposal for a six-wheel car which was accepted. Designated T17, the pilot model was successful in its trials and 2260 were ordered in January 1942. Ford laid down a production line in their factory in St Paul, Minnesota, and in June 1942 an additional 1500 were ordered. Unfortunately, the American armoured car programme had degenerated into a shambles by mid-1942, and in October a Special Armoured Vehicles Board (the 'Palmer Board') was convened, with carte blanche to bring some order on to the scene. One of the first victims was the T17, castigated as being too big and heavy, and its contract was cancelled. As a concession, and to keep the St Paul plant and workforce in being until another project was

ready, the company was allowed to complete 250 cars. These were offered to the British Army, but by that time the war in North Africa, for which they had been intended, was almost over and there was no role for them. Eventually they were disarmed and became military police patrol vehicles.

The other project was for a light armoured car, the T22. Prototypes had been made by several companies and after much testing and modification the Ford T22E2 model was standardized as the M8 in May 1942, with an order for 5000. By July this had been increased to more than 11000. Production took place at St Paul, and by April 30, 1945, when the contract ended, 11667 had been built. Known in British service as the Greyhound, the M8 was widely adopted by many other armies in postwar years and was one of the most successful armoured car designs ever built.

Forel

Russian submarine, built in 1903. The distinguished designer d'Equevilley left France in 1902 and went to work for Friedrich Krupp's Germania shipyard at Kiel. The company was anxious to get into the business of building submarines and, under d'Equevilley's supervision, an experimental boat was designed. Known for reasons of security as a lightbuoy, the boat was ordered in July 1902 and laid down the following February. She was 'launched' (actually lowered into the water by crane) on June 8, 1903, and ran trials during the next six months under the name *Forelle* (trout).

Forelle was not a startling advance over contemporary French designs, with a single electric motor providing motive power on the surface as well as below it. The armament was two 45-cm (17.7-in) torpedoes carried in tubes slung externally and a small conning tower was provided.

The Imperial Russian Navy offered to buy the little boat since their Pacific Fleet needed reinforcements to fight the Japanese. On May 6, 1904, she was renamed *Forel*, the Russian form of her German name, and was loaded

Forger, Yakovlev

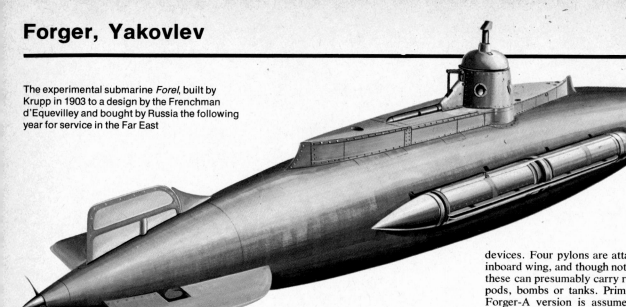

The experimental submarine *Forel*, built by Krupp in 1903 to a design by the Frenchman d'Equevilley and bought by Russia the following year for service in the Far East

onto a flat railcar for shipment to St Petersburg. After trials there she was transhipped to Vladivostok via the Trans-Siberian railway. Thereafter she disappeared into obscurity, and there is no record of her operational career. It is believed that she was scrapped in the Far East about 1911.

Displacement: 15.5 tons (surfaced) *Length:* 15 m (49.2 ft) *Beam:* 4.26 m (14 ft) *Draught:* not known *Machinery:* 1-shaft electric motor, 65 shp= 5.5 knots (submerged) *Armament:* 2 45-cm (17.7-in) torpedoes *Crew:* 5

Forger, Yakovlev Yak-36

Soviet shipboard VTOL aircraft. Existence of a VTOL jet-lift aircraft to be carried aboard the *Kuril* Class ships was predicted in 1973, and in July 1976 it was seen publicly for the first time when the first ship of this class, *Kiev*, passed through the Bosporus and into the Mediterranean. The customs statement to the Turkish authorities listed the aircraft as the Yak-36, and the same designation has been used by the US Department of Defense, the assigned ASCC reporting name being Forger. (Previously Yak-36 had been thought to be the designation of the experimental jet-lift aircraft called Freehand.)

As expected, the Yak-36 is a relatively small and limited strike and reconnaissance aircraft combining both vectored-thrust and direct lift jets and used primarily for training and development of operational techniques. Almost certainly it is incapable of being used in the STOL mode, as is the Harrier; thus, unlike the British aircraft, it cannot carry heavier loads in rolling or ski-jump takeoffs. The main engine is a single unaugmented turbojet (possibly a turbofan) said to be mounted below the arching bridge members of the wing, fed by two plain inlet ducts and discharging through left and right single swivelling nozzles. These nozzles curve round through roughly 90°, unlike the open nozzles of the Harrier which turn the jets by means of cascade vanes. The two lift jets are mounted in tandem and inclined downward to the rear, so that in the engine-supported mode the nozzles of the main engine are angled about 10° forward of vertical to balance the horizontal component of the lift-jet thrust.

This arrangement makes possible a smaller main engine than in a single-jet aircraft, such as the Harrier, but reduces reliability by having additional engines and inhibits STOL flight, or Viffing (vectoring of the main nozzles in forward flight to increase combat manoeuvrability). Thrust of the main engine is estimated at 7710 kg (17 000 lb), and of the lift jets 2540 kg (5600 lb) each. Installation of the lift jets appears to be similar to that in various MiG and Sukhoi VTOL prototypes displayed as long ago as 1967, with powered dorsal doors fitted with axial louvres. The main inlets are plain, without even splitter plates, though some Yak-36 aircraft have a row of auxiliary blow-in inlet doors as on the Harrier. Despite the simple intakes it is estimated that supersonic speed can just be achieved in level flight.

Most Yak-36 embarked on *Kiev*'s shakedown cruise were single-seaters (12 were seen). Features include a mid-high wing of small span and area, with a powered fold about half-way to the tip, the leading edges being fixed and the trailing edges having Fowler flaps inboard and ailerons outboard. Reaction control jets are visible at the tail and under each tip but not at the nose, which houses a small ranging radar. All the usual communications, IFF and navigation avionics are fitted, but no sensors or weapon

devices. Four pylons are attached under the inboard wing, and though not yet seen loaded these can presumably carry rocket pods, gun pods, bombs or tanks. Primary role of this Forger-A version is assumed to be operational indoctrination in shipboard VTOL flying, with elementary capability in attack and reconnaissance (using one or more external pods). The same aircraft could probably also carry EW (electronic-warfare) pods, and might possibly be modified to carry guidance equipment for naval missiles seeking over-the-horizon targets.

At least one aircraft on board *Kiev* was a two-seat (assumed dual-control trainer) version called Forger-B. This has a much longer drooping nose, though the tail is not enlarged; instead the rear fuselage is lengthened to balance the side areas ahead of and astern of the centre of gravity. Forger-B carried no ranging radar or pylons. A notable feature of the intensive flying conducted on *Kiev*'s first cruise was the absolute precision of all approaches on to the ship's deck. This was taken to indicate shipboard guidance (laser methods have been suggested), though the equipment on either the ship or aircraft has not been publicly identified.

Today's Yak-36 is judged to be an interim type. A larger and much more capable shipboard aircraft is anticipated.

Span: About 7 m (23 ft) *Length:* (Forger-A) about 15 m (49 ft 2½ in); (Forger-B) about 17.7 m (58 ft) *Gross weight:* about 10 000 kg (22 050 lb) *Maximum speed:* about 1380 km/h (860 mph, Mach 1.3 at height)

A Yak-36 Forger Soviet VTOL aircraft hovers over the flight deck of the aircraft carrier *Kiev*

Given US expertise in automotive engineering, it is not surprising that several hundred self-propelled designs have appeared since the first in 1917. Although many of these were interesting and ingenious designs, due to limitations of space only those which actually reached service status are dealt with here.

Self-propelled gun development in the US can be seen as having taken place in a number of distinct phases. Firstly, the 1917-24 period in which the initial enchantment with tracks was being worked out of the Ordnance Department system. This was followed by the 1940-42 period when 'tank destroyers' were all the rage and any gun capable of shooting was liable to find itself on some sort of self-propelled mounting. Next came the later war period when the move was toward marrying-up service guns with existing tank chassis. After the war the first reaction was to produce new designs to replace the wartime ones which were often too heavy and did not permit the full performance of the gun to be reached; this was the period in which 'families' of tanks and SP chassis were attempted. Then came the nuclear fallout hazard and a move to develop SP guns in which gun and crew were fully protected by a turret. Finally came the move toward lighter weapons in which less attention was paid to crew protection and more to air-portability.

The First World War period saw a few designs worked out, largely by private companies. Walter Christie, later famous for his tanks, produced a wheeled SP mount for a 3-in (76-mm) AA gun and tracked mounts for the 8-in (203-mm) howitzer, but neither were very successful. The Ordnance Department then adopted the French St Chamond designs and developed carriages for the 8-in howitzer, 155-

mm (6.1-in) gun and 240-mm (9.45-in) howitzer. Fifty 8-in, 50 155-mm and 250 240-mm were ordered, to be completed by February 1919, but the end of the war saw all these contracts cancelled. A handful of 8-in and 155-mm mounts were completed for tests but none reached service units. In the early 1920s several experimental mountings, including a 4.7-in (120-mm) AA gun mount by Christie, were made for tests, but shortage of funds put an end to this work by about 1925.

Nothing further was done until the summer of 1941 when, as a result of events in Europe, interest in SP guns revived. Three agencies, the Tank Destroyer Board, the Armored Board and the Ordnance Department, began looking at ideas and all produced designs, the TD Board being the most prolific and least practical of the three. The TD Board promoted a 75-mm (2.95-in) gun mounted in the back of a half-track personnel carrier; as a weapon it was of little use, but it served as a useful tactical training vehicle.

The Armored Board, concerned with artillery support for their armored divisions, devised a modified M3 tank into which a standard field artillery 105-mm (4.1-in) howitzer was fitted. They managed to interest the artillery in the idea and two pilots were built late in 1941. These were tested in March 1942, the modifications needed marked on the pilots in chalk, and they were sent off as the manufacturer's patterns. This appeared in service as the M7, and was shipped to the British Army in 1942 in time to be used at Alamein.

The Ordnance Department's idea was a much heavier weapon. They wanted to find a use for a number of obsolescent 155-mm (6.1-in) M1918 guns, and devised a mounting on

Above: A 75-mm Gun Motor Carriage M3 comes ashore during landings in New Britain. *Below:* A Mk X 155-mm SP gun, one of the experimental types developed in the 20s

top of a modified M3 tank chassis. The artillery showed no interest, so the Ordnance Department side-stepped them and went directly to the Adjutant-General for the authority. He gave immediate approval and pilots were tested early in 1942. One hundred were built, as the M12, by March 1943, but Army Ground Forces condemned the idea out of hand and restricted them to training use. Eventually, early in 1944, it was realized that there might be a place for them on the forthcoming invasion, and 76 M12s were refurbished and shipped to Europe where they were employed for the rest of the war.

The subsequent development of the various weapons is an involved story, therefore the designs are given in numerical order, with a brief recital of their particular features. Note that howitzers were called 'Howitzer Motor Carriages' or 'HMC' and guns were 'Gun Motor Carriages' or 'GMC'.

An M7 105-mm SP Howitzer, dubbed 'Priest' by the British because of the pulpit-like mounting for the 0.5-in (12.7-mm) AA machine-gun

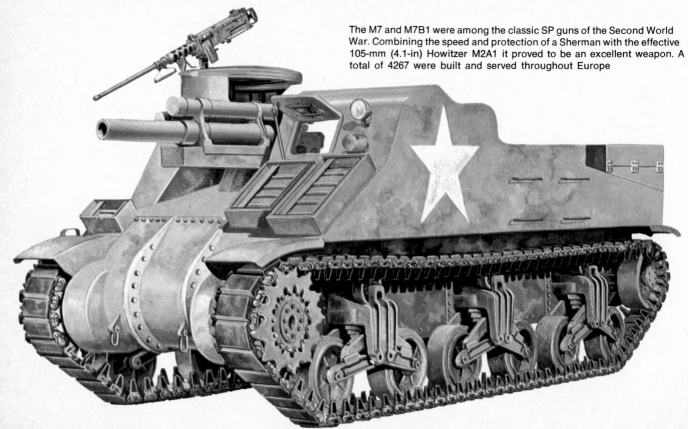

The M7 and M7B1 were among the classic SP guns of the Second World War. Combining the speed and protection of a Sherman with the effective 105-mm (4.1-in) Howitzer M2A1 it proved to be an excellent weapon. A total of 4267 were built and served throughout Europe

The M8 mounted a 75-mm howitzer on a modified M5 light tank chassis. It gave better protection for the crew and consequently was often used in a direct support role with tanks, rather than an indirect fire SP gun. The vehicle was standardized in April 1942 and some 1778 were completed

GMC M3

The first US SP equipment, standardized in November 1944 and consisting of the 75-mm (2.95-in) Gun M1897A4 mounted in the rear of a half-track personnel carrier and firing over the driver's head. Numbers were used in the Philippines and Tunisia between 1941-42.

GMC M5

A 3-in (76-mm) AA gun mounted on top of a Cleveland Tractor company 'Cletrac MG-2' tractor. The gun was on a turntable and protected by a light shield. Seats were provided for two gunlayers, but there was no room for the rest of the squad or the ammunition. Although standardized in 1942 it never went into production.

GMC M6

A 37-mm (1.46-in) antitank gun M3 Pedestal-mounted in the back of a Dodge 15-cwt weapons carrier. A thin armour shield gave some protection to the gunners. It was standardized in 1942, but saw little active use.

GMC M7

The standard 105-mm (4.1-in) howitzer on a carriage derived from the M3 tank. The superstructure was open-topped with the howitzer in the front plate, and alongside was a round barbette which mounted an AA machine-gun. Nicknamed 'Priest' in British service, a total of 4267 M7s and M7B1s (a variant which used the M4A3 tank chassis) were made.

HMC M8

Developed by the Armored Board as a close-support tank, this was the 75-mm (2.95-in) howitzer turret-mounted in a modified M5 light tank. Standardized in April 1942, 1778 were made. Although classed as an SP gun it was employed as a support tank.

Above: An M7 prepares to fire against German positions during the Ardennes offensive in 1944

Surrounded by a litter of shell cases and festooned with equipment, an M8 in action in 1944

Self-Propelled

An M10, the first fully-tracked tank destroyer

GMC M9

This was the 3-in (76-mm) Antitank gun M5 mounted on an M3 tank which had the hull opened up to resemble the M7. It was standardized in the hope that 50 M5 guns would be provided, but these never materialized and only 27 M1918 AA gun tubes were allotted, so production for service was cancelled.

GMC M10

One of the TD Board's more successful efforts, an M4A2 tank chassis with an open-topped turret mounting the 3-in (76-mm) gun M7. Standardized in November 1943, it was a good design but towards the end of the war the 3-in gun was no longer powerful enough. Numbers were used in British service as the 'Wolverine'. They were then modified by substituting the 17-pdr gun for the 3-in and became the 'Achilles'. The M10A1 used a petrol engine instead of a diesel.

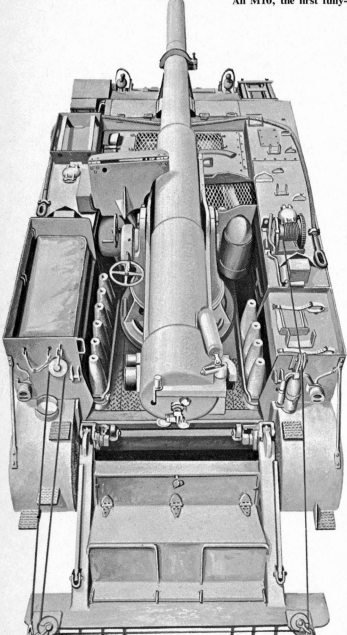

Above: The M12 mounted the M1917A1 or M1918A1 on an M3 chassis
Left: A 155-mm (6.1-in) GMC M12 showing the crew position and ammunition stowage. *Below:* An M12 in action

GMC M12

The 155-mm (6.1-in) Gun M1917A1 or M1918A1 on top of an M3 tank chassis. A recoil spade was placed at the rear to take the shock of discharge off the suspension, and a working platform surrounded the gun. There was no protection for the crew.

GMC M18

This was a tank destroyer unique among wartime SP guns for having been purpose-designed from the start. It originated as a light Christie-type chassis to mount a 37-mm (1.46-in) gun, but after much rethinking it emerged in January 1943 as a 76-mm (3-in) gun turret-mounted on a tracked chassis, fully armoured and resembling a tank. Christ-ened 'Hellcat', 1000 were ordered and it proved to be a very effective weapon. Two thousand five hundred and seven were eventually made and numbers still exist with the Nationalist Chinese, Venezuelan, South Korean and Yugoslavian armies.

GMC M19

Development of the M24 light tank led to the idea of a family of combat vehicles, the first of which was the M19. The tank chassis was modified by moving the engine forward to leave space at the rear, into which a powered turret mounting twin 40-mm (1.57-in) Bofors light AA guns was placed. Some 900 were ordered in August 1944, but final production was substantially less.

Below: An M10 showing its semi-open turret, main armament and AA mg. The hull sides had bosses to enable the crew to bolt extra armour plates over the basic armour

Above: **An M12 fires at German bunkers near Grossenich on the Westwall on November 16, 1944**

Above: **US officers inspect a new M12 with supports for a canvas cover over the crew position**

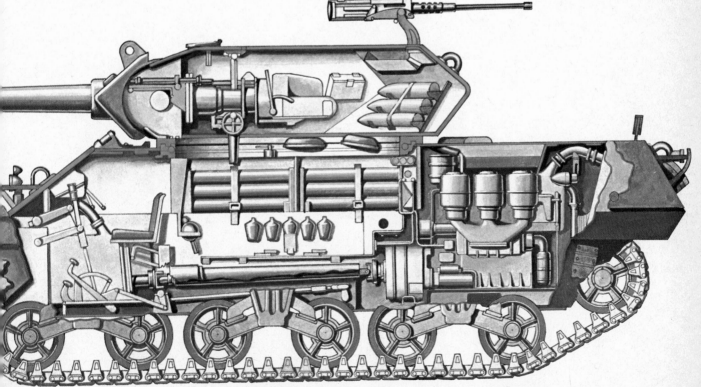

Self-Propelled

HMC T19

A 105-mm (4.1-in) Howitzer M2A1 mounted on a half-track, very like the GMC M3. Developed in 1942 it was never standardized but a small number were made and were used by US troops in the Tunisian campaign.

The T19 Howitzer Motor Carriage was a semi-experimental SP mount which was used in Tunisia in 1942-43. It was a good gun in a reliable vehicle, but it was also an exposed and thinly-armoured SP mount and was withdrawn following the introduction of the M7

GMC M36

By mid-1944 the M10 was outmatched by German tanks, and it was modified by fitting a new turret carrying the 90-mm (3.5-in) Gun M3. As the M36 it was adopted in June 1944. Known as 'Slugger' it proved to be a highly effective weapon and remained in service for some years after the war. Numbers were still used by the armies of Pakistan, South Korea, Turkey and Yugoslavia in 1978.

HMC M37

Standardized in January 1945 this replaced the M7, being lighter, more mobile, less expensive and allowing the gun to develop its full range. The armament and general layout were the same as the M7 but it was based on the M24 light tank chassis.

Above: A T19—a 105-mm howitzer mounted on a half-track chassis. The trailer carried stores

GMC M40

The M12 had used an obsolescent 155-mm (6.1-in) gun, and once the concept of SP medium artillery was accepted, a fresh design was begun, using the 155-mm gun M2, which had a much better performance. This was pedestal-mounted in a chassis based on the M4A3E8 tank. The engine was moved forward to leave a clear working space around the gun, and a heavy recoil spade was fitted. It was standardized in April 1945, but early models, known as the T83, were sent to Europe in time to see action. It was also adopted by the British Army, and it stayed in service until the mid-1950s. The HMC M43 was the partner to the M40 and consisted of the 8-in (203-mm) Howitzer M1 mounted on the same chassis in the same fashion.

HMC M41

This was the 155-mm (6.1-in) Howitzer M1 on the same M24 tank chassis developed for the M19. The rear end carried the gun, with a small working platform and a recoil spade. A total of 500 were authorized in July 1944 but final production was less than 100. Though tested by the British in 1947 it was not adopted, and was used by the US Army until the mid-1950s and by the French until the early 1960s.

The M37 replaced the M7; it was lighter, cheaper and could reach 56 km/h (35 mph) on roads. The 105-mm howitzer had a maximum range of 11 160 m (12 205 yards)

US M40 'Long Tom' 155-mm SP guns dug in during the fighting in Korea, 1952. The crew are digging individual fox holes around the gun

Above: An M40 Long Tom preserved at the Aberdeen Proving Ground.
Right: An M40 at the Rotunda Artillery Museum, Woolwich. This SP mount on a modified Sherman M4A3E8 chassis used the 155-mm Gun M2. The tank engine was mounted in the front to give the crew access to the breech and fighting compartment. Some early models saw action in Europe in 1945, but it was the Korean war that saw its full deployment. Its chief disadvantages were the lack of cover for the crew, particularly vulnerable if caught in counter-battery fire, and the lack of internal ammunition stowage. However it had a marked advantage in range over the M12, though it had a smaller radius of action

GMC M42

This was begun in 1951 to replace the ageing M19s which were rapidly wearing out in Korea. Original intentions were to produce one vehicle carrying guns and a companion vehicle with radar and predictor, but the project was simplified and resulted in another twin 40-mm (1.57-in) vehicle, this time based on the components of the M41 'Walker Bulldog' tank. The principal change was in the layout; in the M42 the engine stayed at the rear and the gun unit was central, taking the place of the original tank turret. Standardized in October 1953, 3700 were made. By 1978 a few were still in use with the US Army, plus those of West Germany, Austria, Japan, Jordan and the Lebanon.

A British M44 155-mm SP Howitzer in 1957; an SP 25-pdr is visible in the background

HMC M44

The 155-mm (6.1-in) Howitzer M41 was made in small numbers and not well received because it gave no protection to the crew and had little crew or stowage space. In 1949 work began on a new design based on components of the M41 tank. This had a large working area at the rear, armoured walls, full power operation area at the rear, armoured walls, full power operation of the gun, a mechanical rammer and the driver's controls set high up in the fighting compartment. It was adopted in 1952 by the US Army and in 1956 by the British. It was also used extensively by the West German army, and in 1978 was still in service with the armies of Italy, Japan, Spain, Turkey and Greece.

SPR M50

The 'Multiple SP Rifle M50' or 'Ontos' was a peculiar device which began development in 1951 as a lightweight tank destroyer. It finally took the form of a small tracked chassis with six 106-mm (4.17-in) recoilless rifles mounted externally. These could be fired singly, in pairs, or as a six-gun salvo. The drawback was that after firing, the crew had to get out and reload them in the open. A total of 297 were built and issued to the US Marine Corps. They were used in Vietnam and in the Dominican Republic before being withdrawn and scrapped in 1970.

HMC M52

With a view to standardization of chassis components, this SP 105-mm (4.1-in) Howitzer was developed during 1948-50 using components of the M41 tank. Innovations included the encasing of the gun plus crew and driver in an armoured turret with limited traverse. No longer in first-line US service, it was still in service with Greece, Japan and Jordan in 1978.

GMC T48

Developed in 1942, this consisted of the 57-mm (2.24-in) gun M1 on a half-track combat car. Originally intended for US and British use, the US Army abandoned the requirement and a small number were completed to British specification in 1943.

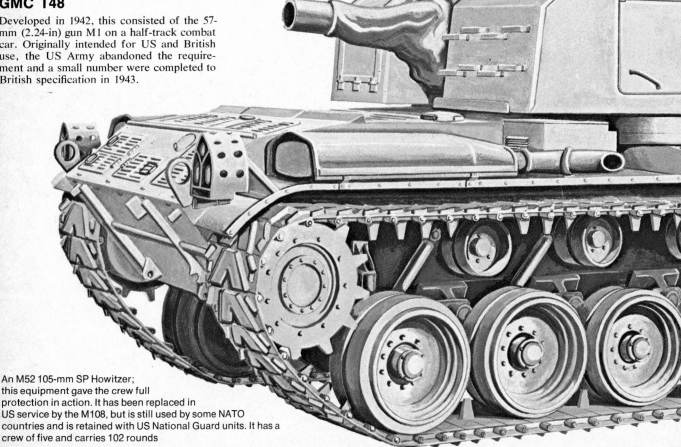

An M52 105-mm SP Howitzer; this equipment gave the crew full protection in action. It has been replaced in US service by the M108, but is still used by some NATO countries and is retained with US National Guard units. It has a crew of five and carries 102 rounds

Above: A US M42 'Twin 40' SP AA

'Claymore', a British-crewed US M107 175-mm (6.89-in) gun in service with 74 (Battleaxe Company) Battery, Royal Artillery in Germany in 1971. The M107 has a bulldozer blade mounted at the rear which is dug in to reduce the recoil forces when the gun is in action

Above: An M44 155-mm self-propelled howitzer based on the M24 tank chassis. Its turret gave the crew full protection under fire

GMC M53

With the postwar concern about fighting in a nuclear environment, exposed guns were no longer acceptable and turretted structures were developed—as with the M52 above. To replace the M40/43 series, the M53 155-mm (6.1-in) SP gun was designed in 1952-53. This used M48 tank parts and mounted the 155-mm gun M46 in a limited-traverse turret structure at the rear. Power operation was provided, together with mechanized ammunition handling and a chain rammer. Numerous defects appeared in this design and most were withdrawn, reworked and converted into M55s by changing the ordnance.

HMC M55

This was the same vehicle as the M53 but mounting the 8-in (203-mm) Howitzer M47. It appears to have been more reliable, probably due to lower recoil stress, but was retired from US service in the late 1960s. Some were still in use with Belgium and Italy in 1978.

GMC M56

Known as the 'Scorpion', this was a 90-mm (3.5-in) antitank gun mounted on a light airportable tracked chassis developed by Cadillac between 1953 and 1959. Used by US airborne divisions, they were withdrawn in the late 1960s. A small gun shield was the only protection for the crew.

HMC T92

This was stopped from reaching service by the sudden end of the war. It was the 240-mm (9.45-in) Howitzer M1 on a chassis built from T26 heavy tank components. Work began late in 1943, and 144 were authorized for procurement in April 1945. Five were completed and were awaiting shipment to the Pacific when the war ended. Production was cancelled, and the T92s were scrapped.

GMC T93

Partner to the T92 this was the same chassis with the 8-in (203-mm) Gun M1 mounted. Only two of the authorized 72 were built and they were scrapped after evaluation tests.

GMC M107

This is the 175-mm (6.9-in) Gun M113 mounted on a chassis specially designed for air-portable artillery use. Development began in the late 1950s and issues in the early 1960s. It was later adopted by the British and in 1978 was in use by the US, British, West German and several other armies. The hull is of aluminium and the crew are completely unprotected in the endeavour to save weight. Gun elevation and traverse, and ammunition handling and ramming are all power actuated. This equipment has never lived up to its promise; it is lively when fired, wears its barrel out quickly, and suffers from faulty ammunition design. It is expected to be phased out of service and replaced by the M110A1.

HMC M108

This was designed during 1953-55 to replace the M52 with a lighter weapon which could be air lifted and which had 360° of traverse. It mounts the 105-mm (4-in) Howitzer M103 in a closed turret at the rear of the vehicle, which is full tracked and diesel-engined. Aluminium armour is used throughout. In 1978 it served in the US, Brazil, Belgium and Spain.

HMC M109

Developed concurrently with the M108, this replaced the M44. It mounts the 155-mm (6.1-in) Howitzer M126 on the same basic chassis, but with the addition of twin recoil spades at the rear. The barrel is fitted with a large muzzle brake and a fume extractor. A later version, the M109A1, uses a longer barrel

Self-Propelled

A US Army M109 155-mm SP gun with its characteristic muzzle brake and fume extractor

and new ammunition to improve the range capability. This weapon is capable of firing a nuclear shell. By 1978 over 3000 had been built and were widely used throughout NATO and by many other armies. A German variant, the M109G has a different muzzle brake and a sliding block breech mechanism.

HMC M110

This is the partner piece to the M107, mounting the 8-in (203-mm) Howitzer M2A1E1 on the same tracked chassis. This also has nuclear capability and is used throughout NATO and by several other armies. It was due to be replaced in late 1978 by the M110A1 version which has a much longer barrel and uses improved ammunition to achieve an increase in range of about 30%.

COMPARATIVE DATA

Note: * indicates vertical range in the AA role.

Gun	Range (m/yards)	Elevation (degrees)	Traverse (degrees)	Weight (kg/tons)	Speed (km/h/mph)	(km/miles)	Crew
75-mm M3	9600/10 550	−10/+29	19L/21R	9071/8.9	72/45	320/200	5
37-mm M6	11 750/12 850	−10/+15	360	3334/3.3	88/55	290/180	4
105-mm M7	8500/9400	−5/+35½	15L/30R	22 967/22.6	40/25	185/115	7
75-mm M8	7175/8500	−20/+40	360	15 694/15.4	64/40	160/100	4
3-in M10	9375/10 250	−10/+19	360	29 950/29.5	48/30	320/200	5
155-mm M12	17 100/18 700	−5/+30	14L/14R	26 300/25.9	38/24	225/140	6
76-mm M18	11 900/13 000	−10/+19½	360	18 150/17.9	80/50	240/150	5
40-mm M19	4650/5100*	−5/+85	360	17 460/17.2	56/35	240/150	6
90-mm M36	17 900/19 600	−10/+20	360	28 120/27.7	48/30	240/150	5
105-mm M37	11 160/12 205	−10/+45	22½L/22½R	18 140/17.9	56/35	200/125	7
155-mm M40	23 500/25 700	−5/+45	18L/18R	36 290/35.7	38/24	172/107	6
155-mm M41	14 950/16 355	−5/+45	17L/20R	19 500/19.2	56/35	160/100	6
40-mm M42	4650/5100*	−3/+85	360	22 450/22.0	72/45	160/100	6
8-in M43	16 900/18 500	−5/+52	16L/18R	37 650/37.0	38/24	172/107	6
155-mm M44	14 950/16 350	−5/+65	30L/30R	28 350/27.9	56/35	120/75	5
57-mm T48	9375/10 250	−5/+15	27½L/27½R	8618/8.5	72/45	320/200	5
105-mm M50	3650/4000	−10/+20	40L/40R	8300/8.2	48/30	115/70	3
105-mm M52	11 270/12 325	−10/+65	60L/60R	24 050/23.7	56/35	160/100	5
155-mm M53	14 950/16 350	−5/+65	30L/30R	43 550/42.8	48/30	260/160	6
8-in M55	16 900/18 500	−5/+65	30L/30R	40 800/40.2	48/30	260/160	6
90-mm M56	13 250/14 500	−10/+15	30L/30R	7030/6.9	48/30	225/140	4
175-mm M107	32 800/35 850	−2/+65	30L/30R	28 170/27.7	56/35	725/450	5
105-mm M108	11 160/12 205	−4/+74	360	22 450/22.1	56/35	390/240	5
155-mm M109	14 700/16 075	−3/+75	360	23 790/23.4	56/35	390/240	6
8-in M110	16 900/18 500	−2/+65	30L/30R	26 550/26.1	56/35	725/450	5

At the turn of the century, the South African war showed British field artillery to be out of date. The standard field piece of the time was a 12-pdr breech-loader firing a bagged charge, on a carriage devoid of recoil control other than a cumbersome spring-loaded spade. By this time the French 75-mm (2.95-in) M1897 had shown what was possible in the way of light, fast-firing field guns with cased ammunition and on-carriage recoil systems, and various commercial gunmakers had put comparable weapons on the market. Some of these found their way into Boer hands, which brought the British weapons into rapid and unfavourable comparison.

Since it was unlikely that any British gunmaker could produce a new weapon quickly enough to have any effect on the war, the Director of Ordnance therefore went to a German firm, Erhardt of Dusseldorf (later to become Rheinmetall), and secretly bought 108 15-pdr guns with on-carriage recoil. These were the first 'quick-firing' guns to be adopted by the Royal Field Artillery. They had a cased charge and a hydro-spring recoil system which allowed the gun to recoil 48 in (122 cm) across the top of the carriage. The guns were said to be so steady that a coin on top of the wheel would remain there when the gun was fired.

Horse Artillery

As the South African war drew to its close, the Royal Artillery convened a 'Horse and Field Gun Committee' to draw up a specification for two new guns. This was then circulated to the principal gunmakers, who submitted designs. Prototypes were made and tested, and eventually a design incorporating an Armstrong wire-wound gun, a Vickers recoil system and a carriage designed by the Royal Carriage Department of Woolwich arsenal was put together. Two guns were developed, a 3-in (76-mm) or 13-pdr, and an 18-pdr of 3.3-in (83.8-mm) calibre. Trials of

An 18-pdr in action in Palestine against the Turks during the First World War. The 18-pdr was a versatile gun which gave excellent service during the war in all theatres

these guns were completed in 1903, and it was decided to adopt both weapons, the 13-pdr for the Royal Horse Artillery and the 18-pdr for the Royal Field Artillery. Both were similar in pattern, using pole trails, wooden wheels and with protective shields. Both were produced in large numbers from 1904 until the end of the First World War.

13-pdr

The 13-pdr remained unchanged, and, indeed, can still be seen today since it is the saluting gun used by the King's Troop, RHA, on ceremonial occasions. The 18-pdr, which became the backbone of British divisional artillery during the war, was gradually

improved. The original hydro-spring recoil system was replaced by a hydro-pneumatic one; a faster breech mechanism was adopted; and the carriage became a box-trail pattern to allow greater elevation and thus more range. After the war a split carriage was developed, as were pneumatic-tired carriages for high-speed towing behind motor vehicles, and the 18-pdr continued to serve until the latter part of the Second World War, albeit as a training and reserve gun.

18-pdr

The 18-pdr was a gun; that is to say, it fired a round with fixed propelling charge at high velocity on a flat trajectory. While this was

An 18-pdr during the battle of Lys in 1918. The fixed round is visible, ready for loading

admirable for many tasks, it was not well suited to lobbing explosive shells over intervening obstacles, and for this purpose a howitzer was developed in parallel with the two guns. Several designs were put forward, and the one selected was a 4.5-in (114.3-mm) howitzer from the Coventry Ordnance Works. This entered service in 1909 and also remained in use until the Second World War. The ordnance used a sliding block breech, the first to be seen in British field artillery, and the carriage was a box-trail type with shield.

In postwar years the carriage was modified by the addition of pneumatic tires and then by the adoption of a split-trail design, but the actual howitzer was never modified from its first pattern.

25-pdr

During the 1920s it was decided to try and develop a new weapon which would, as far as possible, incorporate the best features of both the 18-pdr and the 4.5-in (114.3-mm) howitzer. It was to have a heavier shell than the 18-pdr, longer range and higher velocity than the 4.5-in, and with a multiple charge system would be able to do both jobs. After much shuffling of designs, a 3.45-in (88-mm) gun-howitzer firing an 11-kg (25-lb) shell and using three propelling charges was approved in 1935. The first of these were made by removing the 18-pdr barrels from their carriages and inserting a new 3.45-in (87-mm) barrel and breech, which led to them being known as '18/25-pdrs', though the official name was the 'Ordnance 3.45-in'. In 1938

The 18-pdr Mk 1, development of which began before the First World War. During the war 8393 were built in Britain and 851 in the US, the latter able to accept French 75-mm ammunition

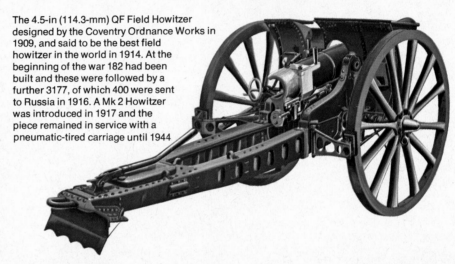

The 4.5-in (114.3-mm) QF Field Howitzer designed by the Coventry Ordnance Works in 1909, and said to be the best field howitzer in the world in 1914. At the beginning of the war 182 had been built and these were followed by a further 3177, of which 400 were sent to Russia in 1916. A Mk 2 Howitzer was introduced in 1917 and the piece remained in service with a pneumatic-tired carriage until 1944

During the battle of Arras in 1917 the crew of an 18-pdr move their gun into position in a gun-pit near Athies l'Abbayette, France

I V Hogg

Below: An RFA gun crew loading an 18-pdr near Meteren during the battle of Hazebrouck in France on April 13, 1918

Above: The working end of a Carriage, Field, QF 18-pdr, Mk 1 stowed for travelling

An 18-pdr QF on Mk IV Carriage with the No 4 Firing Platform stowed in the travelling position. This type of platform, which was also used in the 25-pdr Gun How has been reintroduced with the 105-mm Light Gun under trial in 1978

officialdom bowed to popular sentiment and the gun was officially called the '25-pdr'.

A new carriage to suit the new gun had also been designed, though the 18/25-pdr conversion was adopted as an economy measure in the first instance. The new carriage was to be a split-trail pattern, but comparative tests in 1938 showed that the users preferred a box-trail type with a firing platform which allowed the whole equipment to be rapidly traversed in any direction, and this pattern was put into production late in 1939. The campaign in France was fought with the 18/25-pdr, though a few of the complete 25-pdr equipments first saw action in Norway.

The 25-pdr was one of the best field guns of its day. While not firing so heavy a shell as the German and American 105-mm (4.1-in) weapons, it was far handier in action and had a better range. It was provided with an excellent antitank shot, which proved to be of immense value in the Western Desert when the 2-pdr antitank gun was outmatched by the German armour. In order to extract the utmost performance, a muzzle brake was fitted in 1942 and an extra propelling charge provided in order to obtain the highest muzzle velocity with the AP shot. A wide range of ammunition, including white and

The 18/25-pdr saw action in France and Norway in 1940; the carriage was introduced in 1938

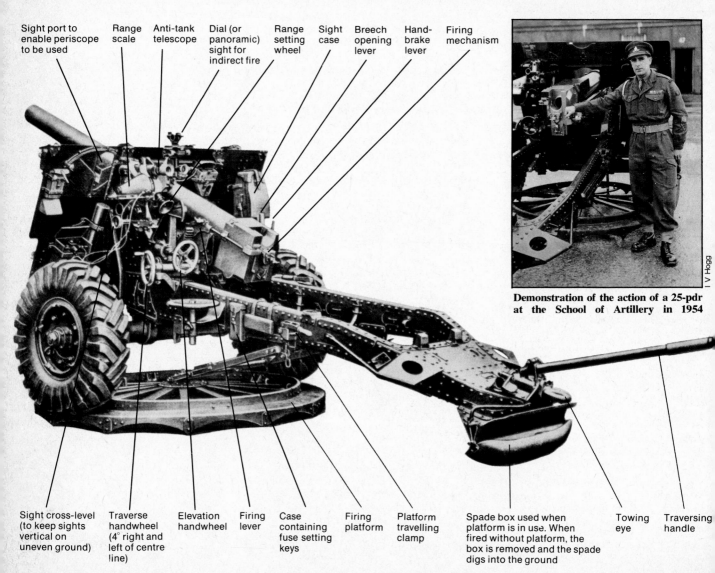

Demonstration of the action of a 25-pdr at the School of Artillery in 1954

Sight port to enable periscope to be used

Range scale

Anti-tank telescope

Dial (or panoramic) sight for indirect fire

Range setting wheel

Sight case

Breech opening lever

Hand-brake lever

Firing mechanism

Sight cross-level (to keep sights vertical on uneven ground)

Traverse handwheel (4° right and left of centre line)

Elevation handwheel

Firing lever

Case containing fuse setting keys

Firing platform

Platform travelling clamp

Spade box used when platform is in use. When fired without platform, the box is removed and the spade digs into the ground

Towing eye

Traversing handle

A Baluchi crewed 25-pdr in Oman in 1974. The gun is still widely used throughout the world

coloured smoke, flare, incendiary, propaganda, radar echo and squash-head shells were eventually provided; a hollow charge shell was developed but never issued. The 25-pdr remained in first-line service until the late 1960s, and in reserve until the early 1970s.

3.7-in Mountain Howitzer

During the First World War the Indian Army requested an up-to-date replacement for their elderly 2.75-in (70-mm) mountain guns. This was provided in the 3.7-in (94-mm) mountain howitzer, which used the same 'screw-gun' assembly of a two-piece barrel held together in the middle by a junction nut. This allowed the barrel to be split into two convenient pieces for mule carriage. The trail was a split type, a shield was provided and the whole equipment stripped into eight units for pack transport. It became the standard artillery piece on the North-West Frontier of India, and saw wide use in Italy and Burma during the Second World War. It was also adopted by airborne units and by the Royal Navy as a landing gun. Though not declared obsolete until 1960, it was rarely seen after 1945. A replacement, of 3.3-in (84-mm) calibre, was developed by the Canadian Army in the immediate postwar years, but was abandoned without entering service.

95-mm Infantry Howitzer

During the Second World War a proposal was put forward to develop a self-propelled 3.7-in (94-mm) howitzer; this calibre was chosen since barrels could be made from 3.7-in (94-mm) AA gun barrels, cut down and fitted with a 25-pdr breech mechanism. From this, the idea arose of a towed equipment, which became the 95-mm (3.74-in) Infantry Howitzer. This used the SP howitzer barrel and breech allied to a modified 6-pdr antitank gun recoil mechanism, all on top of a somewhat cumbersome trail welded up from sheet metal. In September 1943 the weapon was accepted for service by the Directory of Infantry, but there were some doubts about

Above: A 3.7-in (94-mm) mountain howitzer, it could be disassembled into eight parts for transport by pack animals. *Below:* The 3.7-in in action with an Indian crew in Burma. It was also used successfully in northwest Europe in a direct fire role against hardened targets

the whole idea. Infantry commanders, when asked, pointed out that they already had too much equipment and too few men. Nevertheless the howitzer went into production and several hundred were made before prolonged testing revealed serious defects in the recoil system. After much experimenting, it was realized that nothing short of a complete redesign would solve the problem, and by that time the war was almost over. Accordingly, in April 1945, the 95-mm (3.74-in) howitzer was declared obsolete.

Garrington Gun

After 1945 a great deal of work went into drawing up specifications for a new field gun to replace the 25-pdr and several designs were put forward. Eventually an 88-mm (3.46-in) calibre (1-mm larger than the 25-pdr) was developed and pilot models were built. This gun was designed by the Royal Armaments Research & Development Establishment and was built by Garringtons, and was hence always called the 'Garrington Gun'. It had an unusual carriage in which the trail looped high in the air and passed over the gun detachment's heads. The looped trail was covered with a thick glass-fibre shield which gave protection from splinters and also from nuclear fallout. The weapon had a number of ingenious features and fired a more lethal shell than had the 25-pdr. Just as it was about to be approved, however, a NATO agreement was reached which laid down that the future field gun would be of 105-mm (4.1-in) calibre. Since no amount of faking could turn the Garrington Gun into a 105-mm (4.1-in) weapon, the design was dropped. At much the same time it was decided to make the next field gun a self-propelled weapon. As an interim measure the Italian OTO-Melara 105-mm (4.1-in) pack howitzer was adopted until such time as the 105-mm (4.1-in) Abbot SP gun was ready for service.

A 95-mm (3.74-in) Infantry Howitzer, evaluated during the war but shelved in 1945

A 105-mm (4.1-in) Pack Howitzer kicks up dust during a shoot on a Salisbury Plain range. The weapon was superseded by the Abbot SP gun

FIELD ARTILLERY DATA

Gun	Calibre	Shell Weight (kg/lb)	Maximum Velocity (m/sec/ft/sec)	Maximum Range (m/yards)	Weight in action (kg/lb)	Elevation (degrees)	Traverse (degrees, left and right)
15-pdr Erhardt	76-mm	6.4/14	510/1675	5850/6400	1030/2270	−5/+15	3
13-pdr QF	76-mm	5.7/12.5	510/1675	5390/5900	1014/2235	−5/+15	4
18-pdr QF Mk 1	84-mm	8.4/18.5	492/1615	5966/6525	1279/2820	−5/+16	4
18-pdr QF Mk 4	84-mm	8.4/18.5	495/1625	10 150/11 100	1413/3116	−5/+30	4
3.71-in Mtn Howitzer	94-mm	9.1/20	297/975	5395/5900	730/1610	−5/+40	20
4.5-in Howitzer	114-mm	15.9/35	308/1010	6675/7300	1365/3010	−5/+45	3
18/25-pdr	87-mm	11.3/25	442/1450	11 700/12 800	1625/3584	−5/+37½	4
25-pdr Gun	87-mm	11.3/25	518/1700	12 250/13 400	1800/3968	−5/+40	4
95-mm Howitzer	94-mm	11.3/25	330/1080	5486/6000	955/2105	−5/+30	4
105-mm Light Gun	105-mm	16/35.4	617/2025	17 000/18 600	1814/4000	−5/+70	5

Note: The traverse figures given are those 'on carriage'; in all cases, the carriage could be easily moved to give any desired switch, and in the 25-pdr and 95-mm, 18/25-pdr and 105-mm Light, the incorporation of a traversing platform virtually guarantees 360 degree traverse. Note also that the actual calibre of the 95-mm Howitzer was 94-mm or 3.7-in; it acquired the name '95 mm' solely in order to distinguish it from other 3.7-in weapons.

105-mm Light Gun

When Abbot was adopted, there was still a place for a towed equipment which could be air-lifted, and work began on the '105-mm Light Gun'. This entered service in October 1974, and is expected to attract overseas sales as well. The barrel accepts the same ammunition as the Abbot, but a replacement barrel can quickly be fitted which allows the use of the standard US pattern 105-mm (4.1-in) ammunition so that whatever is available in a particular theatre can be used. The trail is an unusual tubular structure, and a firing platform, similar to that of the 25-pdr, is provided. The wheels are attached via a torsion-bar suspension system, and the barrel is rotated 180° to clamp to the trail for towing.
See also Abbot.

A 105-mm Light Gun at Larkhill. Its semi-fixed ammunition is stacked to the left of the gun

Medium Artillery

The first gun to be classed as a 'medium' field artillery weapon in British service was the breech-loading 5-in (127-mm) howitzer, which first saw action in the Nile campaigns of 1897-98. This used a simple box trail and carried the gun barrel in a ring cradle with hydro-spring recoil system, but in such a manner that the barrel could not be traversed and the whole gun had to be slewed for any changes in direction of firing. They had been superseded in 1896 by the 6-in (152-mm) 30-cwt howitzer which was little more than a scale-up and required a special 'siege platform' to reach its full elevation. Few were built, but two achieved some sort of fame when they were sited near the Royal Navy's powder magazines in 1912 as the first antiaircraft defence.

6-in 26-cwt Howitzer

Late in 1915 a totally new design appeared, the 6-in (152-mm) 26-cwt howitzer. This gun used a new type of hydro-pneumatic recoil system, could elevate to 45°, could traverse, and was a much better weapon in every respect. By the end of the First World War over 3600 had been made, and they stayed in service until the latter part of the Second World War, seeing action in Libya, Eritrea and Burma.

60-pdr Guns

The object of howitzers was to drop heavy shells at moderate ranges over intervening obstacles, but the First World War showed that there was also a need for a medium gun which could fire similar shells to greater ranges in order to upset the enemy's rear areas. Heavy artillery did this, of course, but what was wanted was a gun under command of the division, given the particular task of delivering counter-bombardment fire on to enemy gun batteries. The idea had actually occurred before the war broke out, although the counter-battery task had not been widely appreciated, and in 1904 the 60-pdr gun was introduced. This was a cumbersome weapon with box trail and traction-engine wheels, and in order to distribute the load behind the horse team, it was designed so that the gun could be uncoupled from the recoil system

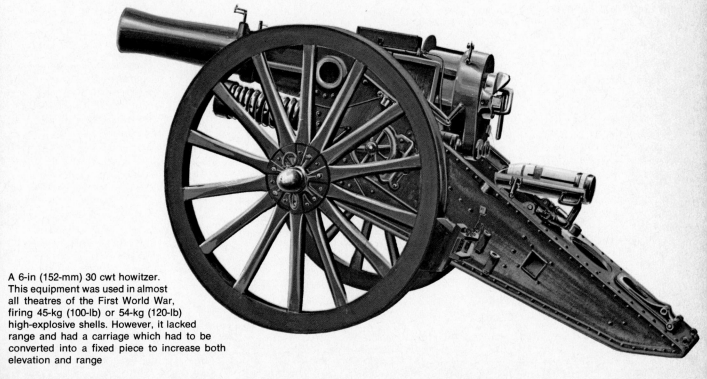

A 6-in (152-mm) 30 cwt howitzer. This equipment was used in almost all theatres of the First World War, firing 45-kg (100-lb) or 54-kg (120-lb) high-explosive shells. However, it lacked range and had a carriage which had to be converted into a fixed piece to increase both elevation and range

and pulled back across the trail before moving off. The trail end was supported by a two-wheeled limber, so that the equipment became a four-wheeled load of just over four tons. By 1914, 41 of these had been made and issued.

On the outbreak of war the design was hastily reworked to make it easier to manufacture, and the 'running-back' feature was designed out. Other simplifications resulted in putting the weight up by over a ton, and since the towed weight was no longer well spread over the wheels, it was necessary to abandon the use of horses whenever possible and adopt the Holt tracked tractor in their place.

While this was satisfactory as an interim measure, it was a retrograde step and work began on a totally new design, the Mk 2 gun and Mk 4 carriage. This appeared in 1918 and was a much cleaner design. The recoil system was now in a cradle under the barrel instead of being spread around the barrel in several cylinders. The running-back idea was revived in a simpler form, the breech mechanism was improved, and the barrel was made longer so as to obtain better performance. This entirely replaced the earlier models and was to remain in service until 1944. It was in action in Africa until 1941 and thereafter was used as a training weapon.

6-in Guns

During the South African war, Captain Percy Scott, the great naval gunnery advocate, mounted some 4.7-in (120-mm) and 6-in (152-

I V Hogg

A 60-pdr Mk 1 Field Gun on Mk 2 carriage, replaced by the Mk 2 on Mk 4 carriage in 1918

mm) ship's guns on to improvized two-wheeled wooden carriages and sent them to the front, accompanied by parties of sailors. In the 1900s, the War Department began to experiment with better-designed mountings for these guns, and two of the improved equipments were in existence when the First World War broke out. They were sent to France early in 1915, proved to be useful weapons, and more were made as the '6-in Mk 7' gun. The weapon was, in fact, the standard coast defence gun, while the carriage was of a simple box trail pattern with no provision for traverse. It was extremely heavy and difficult to move, and in 1916 it

began to be replaced by a new design, the 6-in Mk 19. In order to speed up production, a new gun had been designed so that it could be dropped straight on to the carriage of the 8-in (203-mm) howitzer, which was already in production and which thus did away with the need to design a new carriage. This allowed a maximum elevation of 38°, allowed a sufficient amount of traverse and, best of all, was ten tons lighter than the previous model. A small number of 6-in (152-mm) were retained after the war. In 1939, 12 were sent to France but were abandoned there in 1940, after which the 6-in (152-mm) was no longer a service weapon.

A battery of 60-pdr Mk I field guns moving through shell-gutted St Venant on August 22, 1918, during the British advance on Flanders

MOD

A 6-in BL Mk 7 Field Gun on a Percy Scott carriage in action during the First World War. It was extremely heavy and difficult to move

4.5-in and 5.5-in Guns

During the interwar years the provision of a new medium gun was at a low priority, and eventually, in 1933, it was decided to modify the existing 60-pdr guns by relining the barrels to 4.5-in (114-mm) calibre. This allowed the use of a more modern shell and improved the range without seriously affecting the deadliness at the target end. In 1937 the first conversion was tested and gave a range of 18 290 m (20 000 yards)—a sizeable improvement on the 60-pdr—and the conversion was approved for service. But it was then found that there were only 76 60-pdr guns available for conversion, which was not enough to equip an expanding army. So in 1938 the Director of Artillery authorized the design for a new gun which would fit the carriage of the new 5.5-in (140-mm) gun then being developed. This new equipment, the 4.5-in (114-mm) Mk 2 gun, was approved in August 1939 but production did not begin until late in 1940, and guns were not issued until 1941.

In every respect except calibre and barrel length, the 4.5-in (114-mm) was the same as the 5.5-in (140-mm) described below. The guns were issued to Medium Regiments Royal Artillery, one battery usually being given 4.5-in (114-mm) and the other battery 5.5-in (140-mm). Due to the 4.5's longer range the battery was usually called the 'long-range snipers' of the regiment. But the extra range did not entirely compensate for the lighter shell and the 4.5 was never as popular as the 5.5.

The 5.5-in (140-mm) gun was developed in

A BL 6-in 26 cwt Mk 1 on travelling carriage

A 6-in 26 cwt howitzer. During the First World War in France and Flanders they fired a staggering total of 22 400 000 rounds

Medium Artillery

COMPARATIVE DATA—MEDIUM ARTILLERY

Gun	Calibre (mm)	Shell weight (kg/lb)	Muzzle velocity (m/sec/ft/sec)	Maximum range (m/yards)	Weight in action (kg/lb)	Elevation (degrees)	Traverse (degrees) left and right
5-in BL Howitzer	127	22.6/50	240/788	4390/4800	1212/2673	−5/+45	0
60-pdr Mk 1	127	27.2/60	634/2080	11 250/12 300	4470/9856	−5/+21½	4
60-pdr Mk 2	127	27.2/60	650/2130	14 175/15 000	5465/12 048	−4/+35	4
6-in 26-cwt Howitzer	152	45.4/100	376/1234	8685/9500	3693/8142	0/+45	4
6-in Mk 7 Gun	152	45.4/100	770/2525	12 525/13 700	25 630/56 500	−5/+22	0
6-in Mk 19 Gun	152	45.4/100	716/2350	17 145/18 750	10 338/22 800	0/+38	4
4.5-in Gun Mk 2	114	24.9/55	686/2250	18 745/20 000	5842/12 880	−5/+45	30
5.5-in Gun Mk 3	140	45.4/100	510/1675	14 815/16 200	6190/13 646	−5/+45	30
5.5-in Gun Mk 3	140	36.3/80	594/1950	16 550/18 100	6190/13 646	−5/+45	30

the early 1930s as a replacement for both the 6-in (152-mm) guns and the 6-in (152-mm) howitzers. No effort was spared in order to produce the best possible design, but the designers went a little too far. The gun was conventional enough but was given a very complicated breech and firing mechanism, based on a naval design, which gave endless trouble and eventually had to be scrapped and replaced by a simpler design. The split trail carriage mounted the gun in a cradle with a 'quick-loading gear' which allowed the gun to be uncoupled from the elevating mechanism and sights and swung down to the loading position, while the gunlayer continued to set sights and elevation. After loading, the gun was swung back and locked into engagement with the sights and elevating gear ready for firing. In order to balance the barrel mass, two hydro-pneumatic balancing presses were fitted, vertically alongside the barrel, giving the appearance of two horns. This, too, gave trouble during development and was eventually discarded and replaced by a simpler spring apparatus. Due to these difficulties and to problems in organizing production, it was not until May 1942 that the first 5.5-in (140-mm) guns went into action in the Western Desert. They were highly successful and well liked, but during the Italian campaign a sudden rash of premature detonations of the shells inside the barrel gave the gun a bad reputation which took some time to live down. Once the causes had been identified and remedied, the 5.5 lived out its remaining years without complaint.

It was originally provided with a 100-lb (45-kg) shell, but demands for more range led to the adoption of an 82-lb (37-kg) shell in 1943, and in postwar years this almost completely supplanted the 100-lb (45-kg) model. The 5.5 remained the standard medium gun after the war and was gradually replaced in first-line service by the 155-mm (6.1-in) howitzer.

Baluchi gunners with a 5.5-in Gun Mk 3 in Oman in the 1970s

The 'Five Five' which entered service in 1942 with the 8th Army in North Africa. It remained the standard medium gun after the war but was gradually phased out of front-line service by the 155-mm howitzer

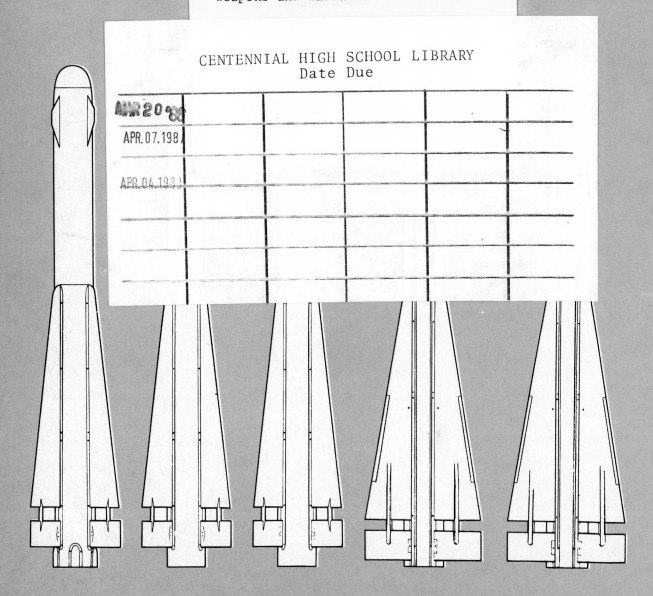